CW00584652

The Birds of Blakeney Point

Andy Stoddart and Steve Joyner

wren
publishing

Previous page illustration – Whinchat by James McCallum.
Cover illustration – Red-spotted Bluethroat by Robert Gillmor.

ISBN 0-9542545-2-X
First published 2005 by Wren Publishing, 4, Heath Road, Sheringham, Norfolk, NR26 8JH.
Design by Nik Taylor.
Printed in Great Britain by Crowes Complete Print of Norwich, Norfolk.

'September 12th. Wind E., turning to N. by noon, and becoming very gusty… The day was passed at the sandhills, and a most prolific haunt they proved. Bluethroats were present in extraordinary numbers, for we reckoned those seen at from eighty to one hundred.'

From Ornithological Notes at Cley and Blakeney, September 3rd to 19th 1884, *Transactions of the Norfolk and Norwich Naturalists' Society*, 4 (1), 36-43.

'The long, narrow strip of shingle beach running west from Cley to Blakeney Point, dotted here and there with clumps of suaeda bushes, and separated from the main-land by Blakeney Channel, Cley Channel and the mouth of the River Glaven has long been famous as the landing stage of countless tired bird-travellers which have crossed the North Sea during the autumn migration.

It is probably a fact that more rare migrants have been obtained by collectors with-in this area than in any other of equal extent in England, or, with the exception of Fair Isle, in Great Britain, and how rich this ornithological harvest has been may be gath-ered from the fact that it includes four species never before obtained in England – namely Pallas's Willow Warbler, Eversmann's Warbler, Yellow-breasted Bunting and Indian Stonechat…'

From B.B. Riviere's Foreword to H.N. Pashley's *Notes on the Birds of Cley, Norfolk*, 1925.

'A narrow strip of shingle turning in at the finish, hook-shaped, towards the Morston-Stiffkey shore; upon this a short sand dune, crowned with marram grass; the silver sand of the dunes, the golden sands left by the receding tide upon which the seals bask, on the far side of the channel; the stir and whisper of the breeze through the grey-green marrams; the ceaseless murmur of the sea against the far sands; white wings against a deep blue sky; the harsh cries of the wheeling terns… this is the Bird Sanctuary on Blakeney Point.'

From Reginald Gaze's *Bird Sanctuary*, 1947.

Contents

Introduction

Few places in Britain, or indeed anywhere, have as long an ornithological history as Blakeney Point. The Point has always been known for its colony of Common Terns but was 'discovered' in the 1880s as a haunt of autumn Bluethroats and subsequently acquired a reputation as a rich hunting ground for bird collectors. Early rarity credits from this era include the first British Pallas's Warbler and Yellow-breasted Bunting and the first English Arctic Warbler.

The tern colonies and breeding waders have always been of national importance and benefited from some of the country's earliest and most enlightened conservation efforts, continued today through the work of the National Trust. Between the 1950s and the 1970s Blakeney Point was renowned as a place to observe 'falls' of continental migrants and was at the forefront of the bird observatory movement. Today the Point continues to cast its spell, with such exciting birds as Snowy Owl and Pallas's Grasshopper Warbler now added to its growing list.

Blakeney Point ranks as one of only a tiny handful of places, alongside the likes of Fair Isle and Heligoland, where birds and their migration have been studied for well over a century. Unlike these and other famous migration sites, however, the Point has never hosted a long-term bird observatory. Its birds have never been recorded systematically in the observatory manner and, with the exception of Rowan and White's short checklists first published in 1918 and 1969 respectively, no fully detailed account of its avifauna exists in one place. The sources of information on the Point's birds are many and varied but are well scattered.

This book therefore attempts to bring together for the first time a complete account of Blakeney Point's long history of birds. It includes a description of its topography and wider natural history, a history of its ornithology, an account of migration and the influence of weather through the year, an overview of its breeding birds, tales of some 'great days' and a full Systematic List.

We have tried throughout the book to reflect modern ornithological concerns, for example in respect of taxonomy and today's welcome renewed interest in bird 'forms'. We have also attempted to recognise the contribution made by the many people who have helped to give the Point such a fascinating avian (and human) history. Much of their story is told in the 'Ornithological History' chapter and their often eloquent observations are also scattered throughout the Systematic List.

The Point has a short list of breeding species, though some of these are of great conservation significance, and most of its birds are mere transient visitors travelling to and from places far away. We have therefore made a particular effort to relate this wider context to their brief appearances here. We have also tried to convey something of typical encounters with each species on the Point and give a flavour of how they find a temporary niche in this unique habitat.

However, as well as the purely 'scientific' recording, we also hope to communicate through the text, photographs and artwork something more intangible – the 'feel' of this special place and its capacity to delight and inspire. Standing on the furthest spits one can still feel a real sense of isolation in one of north Norfolk's few remaining areas of true wilderness. Thanks to the benign stewardship of the National Trust, we can confidently expect that this unique experience will be available for generations to come.

Andy Stoddart
Steve Joyner
May 2005

Acknowledgements

This book would not, of course, have been possible without the help of many people.

Aaron Boughtflower, Ken Bunch, Giles Dunmore, James McCallum, Richard Porter, Joe Reed, Moss Taylor and David Wood kindly read drafts of the text and provided many useful suggestions and contributions. In particular, David Wood provided the chapter on breeding birds and Richard Porter also provided much useful information on the breeding birds as well as the text on the Point's plants and butterflies.

Moss Taylor and Giles Dunmore also provided considerable assistance in tracing literature or photographs and offered much advice during the book's preparation.

Dr. Tony Irwin at Norwich Castle Museum provided extracts from the Norfolk and Norwich Naturalists' Society archive, arranged access to a number of specimens referred to in the text and offered much assistance in taking the biometrics of the 1923 Marsh Warbler.

Michael Cant kindly provided many records and reminiscences from his time on the Point, particularly from the period 1960 to 1969. Dr. John Lines provided extracts from some of Bob Pinchen's diaries, Dr. Roger Riddington provided some early *British Birds* references and John Williamson assisted with information and discussion on the 1953 and 1954 Gyr Falcon records. Percy Trett gave permission to reproduce an extract from his *Eastern Daily Press* article on the 1905 Yellow-breasted Bunting.

We are particularly grateful to Ian Wallace, for many a true birdwatching hero, for providing his distinctive reminiscences of the unprecedented September 1965 'fall'.

Very special thanks are also due to James McCallum for allowing the use of his evocative illustrations and also his own 'great day' account. It is a particular pleasure to see his vibrant artwork enliven these pages.

We are also extremely grateful to Robert Gillmor for the use of his specially created study of a Bluethroat. Robert needs no introduction, having been one of Britain's foremost bird artists for over forty years, and it is a great privilege to have an example of his work grace the cover of this book.

Particular thanks are due to Julian Bhalerao, Robin Chittenden, Barry Jarvis, Tim Loseby, Dave Nye, Mike Page and Richard Porter for allowing the use of their excellent photographs.

Thanks are also due to Sarah Jackson of the British Trust for Ornithology for the provision of Wetland Bird Survey (WeBS) data. WeBS is a joint scheme of the British Trust for Ornithology, The Wildfowl and Wetlands Trust, Royal Society for the Protection of Birds and Joint Nature Conservation Committee (the last on behalf of the Countryside Council for Wales, Department of the Environment Northern Ireland, English Nature and Scottish Natural Heritage).

We are also grateful to the Meteorological Office in Bracknell for the provision of isobar charts on which the weather maps in the 'Weather and Migration' chapter are based.

In addition, Mark Cavanagh, Graeme Cresswell, Richard Drew, Giles Dunmore, Mark Eldridge, Pete Feekes, Steve Holloway, Tony Marr, James McCallum, Richard Porter, Alan Vittery, Chris Wheeler and Norman Williams have all at various times been good companions in the field and finders of many of the birds described in this book.

A special recognition should, of course, be made of the support given over many years by the National Trust Wardens Joe and Janet Reed, David Wood and a succession of enthusiastic summer Wardens, notably Aaron Boughtflower, James McCallum and Stefan McElwee.

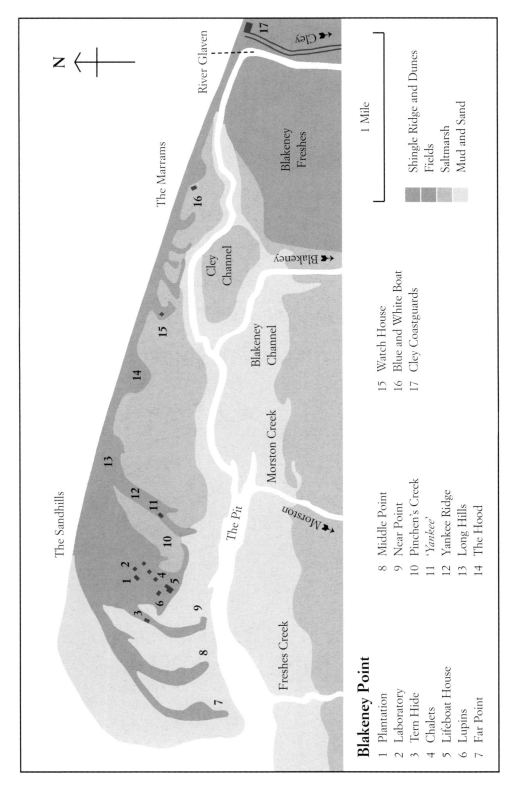

Blakeney Point

N

The Sandhills

The Marrams

River Glaven

Cley ➤➤

17

Blakeney Freshes

16

Cley Channel

Blakeney ➤➤

15

14

Blakeney Channel

13

12
11

10

Morston Creek

1 2
4
5
6
3

9

The Pit

Morston ➤➤

8

Freshes Creek

7

1   Plantation
2   Laboratory
3   Tern Hide
4   Chalets
5   Lifeboat House
6   Lupins
7   Far Point

8   Middle Point
9   Near Point
10 Pinchen's Creek
11 'Yankee'
12 Yankee Ridge
13 Long Hills
14 The Hood

15 Watch House
16 Blue and White Boat
17 Cley Coastguards

Shingle Ridge and Dunes
Fields
Saltmarsh
Mud and Sand

1 Mile

An Introduction to Blakeney Point

Physical Geography

Blakeney Point is perhaps the most conspicuous geographical feature on the north Norfolk coast, stretching its fingers westwards for four miles from the small village of Cley-next-the-Sea and enclosing the large estuary of Blakeney Harbour. In his 1935 book *Sea Swallows*, R.J. (Robert) Pinchen, the Point's first Watcher, describes it as follows:-

> 'For the benefit of those unacquainted with Blakeney Point I will briefly describe its position and topography. The Point lies between Sheringham and Wells on the north Norfolk coast. It is a spit of beach and dune running roughly east and west. At the eastern end it is joined to the mainland and it stretches westward at a slight angle to the shore so that the head of the Point is about a mile from the mainland. The nearest village which can be reached without a boat is Cley, a four-mile walk along the crunching pebbles.
>
> If you walk westward towards the head along the spit from Cley you will travel at first along a strip of beach climbing steeply to the sea. On the landward side are salt-marshes threaded by creeks. Presently sand dunes tufted with the characteristic coarse and spiky marram grass begin to appear and finally the narrow spit broadens out into a wide expanse of dunes.
>
> As a demonstration of the complete dependence of topography and relief upon the play of physical forces, steadied by the plant covering, Blakeney Point is unrivalled. From its wonderful setting, combined with its delicate sensitiveness to change in lighting, it is a place of penetrating beauty.'

A full description of the forces responsible for the growth and evolution of the Point is beyond the scope of this book. In summary, however, it has been demonstrated that the movement of the shingle is an ongoing process caused by wave action, a phenomenon particularly pronounced in periods of strong onshore winds. Although waves from the northwest may move the shingle to the east, the greater distance travelled and therefore force of waves from between east and north have more effect and, over time, spread the shingle inexorably to the west. Daily tidal currents largely affect the lower sandy reaches of the beach below the shingle deposition and have little or no role in long-term shingle displacement.

Each of the lateral shingle 'recurves', for example those in the Marrams, at the Watch House, the Hood and Yankee Ridge, formed at one time the end of the Point. Periods of consolidation of the shingle ridge with slower lateral movement allowed dune systems to develop, created by blown sand from the extensive foreshore lying to the west. Eventually, however, further westward exten-sions of the shingle ridge isolated these growing dunes from their source of new sand and in turn created new outer spits on which the dune formation process started once again.

Very early maps, such as those displayed in the National Trust visitor centre, therefore show a much shorter peninsula, whilst as recently as the early years of the twentieth century the Point terminated in a single spit just beyond the Lifeboat House (today's 'Near Point'). The Point of today reaches as far west as Stiffkey and continues to stretch out fingers towards Wells. A full and fascinating account of these processes can be found in Steers (1934).

Other forces at play include an occasional rolling back of the main shingle ridge due to extreme combinations of wind and tide. On such occasions, most notably of course in the infamous storm surge of January 1953, the ridge is over-topped by the sea, with only the high dunes remaining above water. This phenomenon was repeated in 1996 when, during the night of 19th – 20th February, the sea moved the shingle back several metres, flattening the profile of the ridge, removing beach-top vegetation and burying a number of stretches of *Suaeda*. Such events have moved the shingle inland at the rate of about 100 metres per century but, compared with the damage caused to the artificially banked-up shingle ridge to the east, the natural profile of Blakeney Point has proved remarkably resilient.

The Birds of Blakeney Point

The wide variety of habitats described by Pinchen at least partly explains the Point's attractiveness to birds and their watchers. Its prominence as the most northerly point of the north Norfolk coast provides good opportunities to watch birds at sea, whilst to the south Blakeney Harbour (actually the estuary of the Rivers Glaven and Stiffkey) contains extensive areas of saltmarsh, creeks, inter-tidal mud and sandbanks. The Point itself with its shingle spine, *Suaeda* belts, sand dunes and isolated bushes provides temporary shelter to the migrant birds for which it has become famous. For its size the Point therefore boasts an impressively long and varied bird list.

This diverse avifauna is completely dominated by the phenomenon of migration. Only around twenty species can be said to be regular breeders but even amongst these are some of the world's great wanderers. These include the Barn Swallow, with its winter quarters in southern Africa, and the Arctic Tern, which exchanges long summer days on Blakeney Point for equally long days in the southern summer around the Antarctic pack-ice.

Amongst the many regular wintering species are birds from distant corners of the globe. For example, the Russian Arctic is 'home' for the wintering Dark-bellied Brent Geese and a host of waders including Grey Plover and Bar-tailed Godwit. By contrast, other Arctic breeders such as Pink-footed Goose, Knot, Turnstone and Snow Bunting originate largely from the northwest, in Iceland, Greenland or even Arctic Canada.

Amongst the many migrants in spring or autumn are summer visitors to Scandinavia, including regular species such as Common Redstart, Willow Warbler and Pied Flycatcher as well as scarcer species such as Dotterel, Long-tailed Skua and Bluethroat. Further source areas for the Point's migrant birds include central Europe, home to sought-after scarce species such as Barred Warbler, Icterine Warbler and Red-breasted Flycatcher, and the Mediterranean, haunt of the rarer Short-toed Lark and Subalpine Warbler. From much further afield come regular Richard's Pipits and Yellow-browed Warblers from Siberia and Sooty Shearwaters from the southern oceans.

Nor is Blakeney Point the final destination of these, and other, seasonal migrants, for most are bound for wintering grounds as far afield as southern Asia, the Middle East, sub-Saharan Africa and the waters off South America.

In addition to these more regular visitors can also be found occasional vagrants from, for example, the High Arctic (Ross's Gull and Snowy Owl), far eastern Asia (Oriental Pratincole) or North America (Laughing Gull). Birdwatching on the Point is therefore to witness bird movements on a truly global scale!

By contrast, the Point lies away from the main routes taken by British-breeding migrants entering or leaving the country which are so obvious around the Irish Sea and along the south coast. The weather conditions associated with arrivals on the Point consistently indicate that the overwhelming majority of birds recorded are continental in origin. In this respect the Point demonstrates some of the characteristics of an island.

Despite the relative proximity of the 'mainland' (Morston Quay is but a mile from the end of Yankee Ridge), the rarity of some species common across the water is striking and further reinforces the feeling of 'island-effect'. Many locally-common breeding species such as Blackbird, Song Thrush, Robin and Chaffinch are hardly known as wanderers from the 'mainland', appearing on the Point almost entirely as immigrants from the continent.

The Point is a very sensitive barometer of these bird movements, its isolated location and sparse cover making new arrivals relatively easy to detect. These factors make it an ideal location for the student of bird migration as even the smallest fluctuation in numbers can easily be monitored.

The responses of these newly-arrived migrants to the Point's new and unfamiliar environment are of particular interest. Far from being random, these show constant patterns which are both fascinating in themselves but also of great assistance in predicting the locations and behaviours of those which will follow in their footsteps.

Newly-arrived passerine migrants clearly do not see the landscape in precisely the same way as humans. This is most obvious in examining the occurrence of birds in the Plantation. This small stand of trees is, to most birdwatchers, the most famous landmark on the Point and has the appearance of a classic 'bird magnet'. In fact its track record of attracting migrants, and in particular producing rare birds, is relatively poor, with many birds, and the vast majority of rarities, generally found elsewhere along the Point.

At both seasons small migrants tend to congregate in the *Suaeda* at the tips of the south-facing spits, to which they work their way following an arrival from the seaward side of the Point, often banding together in loose mixed-species groups. Perhaps surprisingly, the most northerly bushes are not as a rule the best places to find these small migrants and in both spring and autumn it is also common to find no birds in the apparently identical stretches of *Suaeda* in between these favoured locations. This suggests that birds are keen to move on but, on arrival at the tip of a spit, feel discouraged from taking the final leap to the 'mainland', normally clearly visible a mile away. This is a negligible distance compared with a crossing of the North Sea and one which they could easily cover in a couple of minutes.

It is interesting to speculate on what extent of unsuitable habitat is necessary to deter a bird from resuming its flight but experience at the Point suggests that it may be quite short and certainly less than a mile. This unwillingness to continue towards what must be obvious as more attractive habitat is presumably a consequence of the birds' tiredness and their desire to seize the first opportunity to rest, feed and re-orientate. It may also reflect their reluctance to cross open water or mud and so be vulnerable to predators. The state of tide appears to have little effect on this phenomenon, open mud seeming to be as much of a barrier as a body of water.

A further important factor influencing the behaviour of small migrants on the Point is the time of year. In spring and early to mid-autumn the Point provides attractive feeding opportunities which encourage birds to linger whilst, after September, it becomes progressively more bleak and hostile with many fewer insects available to small birds. At this time more birds stay only briefly or overfly the Point altogether.

The status of the scarcer *Phylloscopus* warblers provides a good illustration of this phenomenon. In the county as a whole the commonest of the scarce leaf warblers are Yellow-browed Warbler and Pallas's Warbler, both arboreal specialists, typically arriving in September/October and October/November respectively. Neither species occurs on the Point as frequently as would be expected by comparison with nearby sites, notably the trees of Holkham Meals, and this can only be due to the absence of good feeding on the Point in late autumn. Good evidence for this is provided by a Yellow-browed Warbler which was once observed flying in across the beach within a few feet of the observer before continuing at high speed across the Harbour towards Blakeney! If, however, we examine the status of the Greenish Warbler, typically arriving in August and early September, a different picture emerges. Greenish Warbler is as much an arboreal species as its smaller congeners yet the Point is one of its most reliable sites in the whole country, with at least 16 records to date. This may largely be attributable to the more attractive feeding opportunities available in early autumn. There are important lessons here for those seeking small migrants in Norfolk later in the season.

These examples illustrate birds' expertise at selecting suitable habitat for themselves, even migrants and vagrants in unfamiliar surroundings. This must account for Blakeney Point's pre-eminence in Norfolk for Red-throated Pipit and Short-toed Lark, for which the short grass and shingle must closely resemble their tundra and desert breeding grounds respectively. Similarly, the now regular Subalpine Warblers must find the *Suaeda* an acceptable substitute for their preferred Mediterranean scrub.

North Norfolk is noted for the scale and variety of its 'visible passage' of diurnal migrants, noticeable as near as Sheringham and Weybourne to the east and, perhaps most impressively, at Hunstanton to the west. It may therefore come as a surprise to note that these passages are significantly reduced at Blakeney Point. Westerly diurnal passages in both spring and autumn become more diffuse west of Weybourne and much of the flow passes along the inland side of Blakeney Harbour. Small diurnal migrants must therefore either be at a sufficient height to see that the Point is a 'dead-end' or otherwise must intuitively feel that the inland side of the Harbour presents a more attractive or less hazardous 'leading line'. This is not to say that diurnal migration does not occur on the Point, for hirundines, pipits and Starlings, for example, can on occasion be numerous, but their numbers are but a fraction of what one would expect by extrapolation from neighbouring sites. Similarly, the Point offers little attraction to large diurnal migrants, such as birds of prey, which presumably regard it as a somewhat difficult physical feature with little capacity for generating thermals.

The Point's topography, particularly its constant state of change, also has, of course, a profound effect on the distribution of the breeding birds. The terns and Black-headed Gulls favour the isolation of the outermost ridges of shingle and sand, though changing their preferred location from year to year. In return, their presence has a modifying effect on the landscape, most noticeable in the vigorous growth of *Suaeda*, assisted by accumulations of 'fertiliser' from the colonies. The *Suaeda* has in some places now reached a height and density which precludes further nesting by gulls and terns.

The *Suaeda* is, however, important as a nesting habitat for passerines, notably Linnets and Reed Buntings, whilst the grassy areas hold good numbers of breeding Sky Larks and Meadow Pipits. The breeding density of these four passerines is amongst the highest in Norfolk.

Flora and Non-avian Fauna

There is, however, much more to Blakeney Point's natural history than birds, for the area also has unique botanical interest. It hosts a typical variety of shingle vegetation which includes pioneer species on the exposed ridge and more complex grassland communities on the sheltered 'recurves'. The Point displays some of the best examples in the country of the transition between shingle and saltmarsh, with a number of species more typical of the Mediterranean, and supports a wide range of coastal plant communities with many nationally-important species.

Nearly 200 species of flowering plants have been recorded on the Point and a walk along its entire length will lead through a great variety of plant communities. Starting from Cley, the shingle ridge is host to cushions of Sea Campion, Sea Sandwort and Biting Stonecrop with a scattering of Curled Dock, Birdsfoot Trefoil and an abundance of Yellow Horned-poppy.

On the Harbour side to the south the shingle is flanked by Shrubby Sea-blite or *Suaeda*, dense in places, with patches of Annual Sea-blite, Sea Beet and several species of Orache along the strand-line. The mudflats themselves are densely covered with Sea Purslane, Common Cord-grass, Sea Aster (sadly lacking here the purple ray florets), various species of Glasswort (the famous Samphire) and Common Sea-lavender – in full bloom in late summer.

On the 'recurves' at the Marrams, the Watch House, the Hood and Yankee Ridge the vegetation is denser with several grasses and pink displays of Thrift in early summer, mixed with Sheep's Sorrel and the rare Sea-heath.

On reaching the Sandhills one is aware of a major change in the plant communities. Here the shingle gives way to sand and the hillocks are dominated by Marram Grass. On the older dunes, consolidated by time, Grey Hair-grass, a national rarity, Sand Sedge, mosses and lichens form the vegetation base and, in places, a colourful array of Common Dog Violet, Sea Bindweed and large patches of Rosebay Willowherb delights the eye. There are also stands of Bramble and the low, creeping Dewberry.

In the large hollow in the dunes, known as 'Great Sandy Low', late summer sees a fine carpet of Matted Sea-lavender and Rock Sea-lavender, the former being one of the Point's botanical specialities and a 'Red Data' species. Surprisingly, there are no orchids.

In the area around the Lifeboat House, particularly its garden (the Lupins) and the Plantation, there are several clumps of Elder and a few introduced trees, most of which were planted over 90 years ago and which provide useful cover for migrant birds. These include Sycamore, White Poplar, Silver Birch, a lone Tamarisk and a Black Pine along with Tree Lupins and Yuccas.

The vegetation is of course in a state of constant change. New dune grasses continue to form on the outer spits and the *Suaeda* is rapidly colonising the newly-forming shingle ridges and hollows. At the same time, the once-prominent Lupin growth in the Sandhills is now a pale shadow of its former self due to infestation by aphids. The lushness of the dune grasses in the Sandhills is largely governed by the state of the Rabbit population. With Rabbits now at a low ebb, the vegetation appears increasingly thick but this is partly offset by the threat to the high mature dunes posed by wind 'blow-outs' and human trampling.

The Point also has considerable butterfly interest. At least 22 species have been recorded, of which 13 have bred or have probably done so. Of these the Small Copper and Grayling are the most numerous and widespread. The Gatekeeper, Common Blue and Brown Argus have good but localised populations, whilst Wall Browns occur in isolated pockets in the dunes. In some years migrant Painted Ladies can be very numerous, and may breed, and there is at least one record of the rare Camberwell Beauty.

The Point's most well-known natural attraction, however, is undoubtedly its colony of Common and Atlantic Grey Seals, but other mammals include a population of Rabbits, subject to significant fluctuations due to myxomatosis, and an increasing number of Brown Hares. Some mammals, for example Red Fox, Common Rat and Stoat are significant predators of ground-nesting birds. A wide variety of other mammals has been recorded including Otter and, perhaps surprisingly, wandering individuals of several species of deer. The rarest mammal recorded is the Harp

Seal found dead in late March 1988.

Blakeney Point falls within an Area of Outstanding Natural Beauty (AONB) and, in recognition of its significant natural history importance, has Site of Special Scientific Interest (SSSI) status. It is also designated as a National Nature Reserve (NNR), is a Special Protection Area (SPA) under the EEC Birds Directive, comprises part of a 'Ramsar' wetland site and a Marine Special Area of Conservation (SAC) and is included in the UNESCO list of Biosphere Reserves.

Access to the Point

Access to the Point is on foot from Cley Coastguards – a four mile trudge each way along the shingle. At low tide faint paths along the *Suaeda* edge can be followed, although these can be very muddy or, alternatively, firm sand can be sought along the lower edge of the outer beach. At high tide, however, these areas are inundated and in extreme conditions the ridge itself may be over-topped by the sea. On such occasions a visit to the Point would be extremely dangerous. There is strictly no vehicular or other wheeled access.

As an alternative, seal-boat trips leave Blakeney and Morston quays all year round over the high tide period (weather permitting) and can sometimes land visitors at Pinchen's Creek for a short stay of around an hour.

Particular care should be taken during the spring and summer to minimise disturbance to the breeding birds, and the roped-off areas in the Marrams and on the far spits should be avoided altogether. Dogs should always be kept on a lead. Visitors should also avoid excessive trampling of the fragile dunes and take care not to run or jump on the areas of exposed sand and 'blow-outs' as this hastens erosion. Other common sense restrictions apply to littering, camping and lighting fires.

The Point is wardened full-time by the National Trust between March and September and on a visiting basis during the winter. There are no longer any refreshments available at the Lifeboat House and the only facilities for visitors are an information display and public toilets. It should be noted that the Tern Hide, reached via the boardwalk over the dunes from the Lifeboat House, no longer overlooks the tern colony, whilst a sea-watching hide was destroyed by a series of gales in spring 2005.

Common Shelduck. (*James McCallum*)

Ornithological History

The Nineteenth Century – 'What's Hit is History...'

'Gunners' or 'gentlemen collectors' began hunting bird specimens in north Norfolk during the nineteenth century (as they did also in neighbouring Suffolk, Lincolnshire and Yorkshire) and by the 1880s the *Suaeda* bushes along Blakeney Point had become renowned for the appearance of small migrants (and attendant rarities) in autumn with an east or northeast wind. The credit for this recognition goes to F.D. (Fred) and G.E. (George) Power, both London doctors, who in 1884 shot the Point's (and Norfolk's) first Barred Warbler. They also discovered the occurrence of Bluethroats on the Point, recording at least 80 at a time when only a tiny handful of previous records existed for the whole country. Their *Ornithological Notes at Cley and Blakeney, September 3rd to 19th 1884* appear amongst the early *Transactions of the Norfolk and Norwich Naturalists' Society* and describe the 'Blue-throated Warbler' as the commonest small migrant recorded during their visit!

An article by C.J. (Clifford) Borrer of Cley, last (and most tenacious!) of the generation of 'gentlemen collectors', in *The Shooting Times & Country Magazine* of September 16th 1955 was recently re-published (*Birding World* 13: 126-127). It provides a fascinating insight into these far-off days when naturalists indulged in 'bush-shooting' to secure specimens of uncommon and rare birds. A flavour of the activity may be gained from the following extract from Borrer's article:-

> 'Every sort of device was tried to induce the birds to show themselves, including the dragging of chains and ropes through the bushes. But the only effective method was the use of a suitable dog... what was needed was a close-ranging animal which would move from side to side in front of the guns, causing the birds to flutter forward above the shrubs or to fly out on the flanks affording the wing-gunners a clear shot.'

Their persistence is well illustrated by the following extract from E.C. Arnold's *Memories of Cley*:-

> '... a warbler, darker and greener, as I thought, than Chiffchaff. It seemed to possess a charmed life, for I pursued it till my barrels were red hot and my No. 8 cartridges gave out. I was then reduced to shooting at it with No. 4 after which it soared wildly up with hanging legs and finally dropped in thick bush, where I was never able to find it!'

Arnold, a former headmaster of Eastbourne College, has been described as the most successful and most scientifically-minded of the gunners. He visited Cley every September for over fifty years and is now largely remembered in connection with 'Arnold's Marsh' at Salthouse, of which he was temporarily the owner.

The toll of migrants taken by the Blakeney Point 'gentlemen gunners' and the local wildfowlers whom they commandeered to the task must have been considerable. Arnold is quoted as reckoning that one bird in five hundred may be 'a desirable specimen', whilst others estimated the ratio as nearer one in a thousand.

Amongst the other notable gunners of the time were J.H. Gurney and F.I. (Frank) Richards, whilst R.J. (Bob) Pinchen, at first a wildfowler, later became an important figure in the Point's history as the first official 'Watcher'. He was aided in his task by his dog 'Prince' whose grave can be found to this day in the Plantation. Special mention must also be made of local wildfowler Ted Ramm, to whose dog 'Duchess' falls the credit for finding Britain's first 'Pallas's Barred Willow Warbler' (now known simply as Pallas's Warbler) on the sea-wall at the base of the Point in October 1896.

It was, however, not just the migrant birds which suffered. The Point had always harboured a small colony of Common and Little Terns (fluctuating but approximately 140 and 60 pairs respectively) but their breeding success had traditionally been poor as their eggs had been taken for food by local people. They had also been targeted by the gunners. H.N. (Nash) Pashley, the celebrated taxidermist of Cley and father-in-law of Ted Ramm, recounts the following in August 1893:-

> 'A party of gentlemen from Norwich, who generally put in an appearance the night before the 1st so as to be on the estuary by daybreak, got as usual a large bag, 156 of all sorts and ages, from full-grown Tern to birds that could scarcely rise from the ground. I was told by a gentleman who went to the Point on the 3rd and 4th that he did not see a Common Tern at all during the two days.'

Many of the gunners' avian victims passed through Pashley's hands. His book *Notes on the Birds of Cley, Norfolk*, published in 1925, contains notes of the major bird movements and most important sightings of the period 1887 to 1924, as seen through the specimens brought to him by the gunners and others. His book therefore documents the Pallas's Sandgrouse invasion of 1888, Norfolk's first Yellow-browed Warbler in 1894 and the 1896 Pallas's Warbler, as well as noting regular 'falls' of birds whose composition would be familiar today – warblers, chats and flycatchers in September, followed by thrushes and Goldcrests in October. His book also provides fascinating recollections of the wildfowlers, boatmen and collectors of the area.

Pashley's notes provide a surprising insight into the changing fortunes of the area's birds. At the turn of the century the Sandwich Tern was a rare visitor and Pashley did not see a Black-tailed Godwit pass through his hands until 1917. Of the Carrion Crow he wrote:-

> 'I have never yet seen this bird in the flesh nor known it to have been ever seen or taken in the neighbourhood'.

Conversely, his diaries record large passages of Hooded Crows and note that over the same period he was brought 33 Pallas's Sandgrouse, many of them from the Point!

Although Pashley's work details birds brought to him throughout the year, it is interesting to note that 'bush-shooting' was regarded as an exclusively autumnal activity with what he terms the 'vernal migration' not watched at all.

By the end of the century the first examples of what would today be a familiar list of regular scarce birds had been secured. These included the 1884 Bluethroats, with Barred Warbler and Ortolan Bunting the same year, Red-breasted Flycatcher in 1890, Balearic Shearwater in 1891, Yellow-browed Warbler in 1894, Aquatic Warbler and Pallas's Warbler in 1896 and Icterine

Warbler in 1899. Pinchen shot a Broad-billed Sandpiper in 1895, with Arnold securing a Buff-breasted Sandpiper in 1899. Nine Common Cranes also occurred that autumn and a Eurasian Nuthatch in October of the same year closed the century.

1900 – 1949 – Conservation

The 'sport' of 'bush-shooting' continued into the early years of the new century, with Pashley documenting Arnold's shooting of Britain's first Yellow-breasted Bunting at the Watch House in 1905 (with another on the Hood in 1913) and an 'Eversmann's Warbler' (now known as Arctic Warbler) in 1922. M.A. Catling of Cley obtained the first Norfolk Desert Wheatear in 1907 and Frank Richards shot the Point's first Tawny Pipit in 1910. Other notable records from the time include Norfolk's first Water Pipit in 1905, Little Bunting in 1908, Firecrest in 1913 and Marsh Warbler in 1923.

It was not only the small birds which came in for the gunners' attentions. Pashley again notes:-

> 'In the early morning (of 17th February 1901), just as day was breaking, Geo. Long and his son and T. Cringle of Wells with their gun punts drew up to a flock of Knot, computed at between four and five thousand. They fired simultaneously at about 80 yards distance and the result was 603 Knot, 9 Redshanks and 6 Dunlins. It took them till 10.30 to collect the dead and wounded… GL told me that the noise of their wings attracted his attention before he saw them - he took it to be a train running into Wells Station'.

It was therefore an event of great importance when in 1901 the Point came under formal protection as a bird sanctuary and Bob Pinchen, former gunner and wildfowler, was appointed as the first breeding season Watcher under the auspices of the Blakeney and Cley Wild Bird Protection Society. His book *Sea Swallows*, published in 1935, recounts the event:-

> 'Charles Hammond of Twyford Hall first mooted the idea of a bird sanctuary. He spoke to me on the subject and asked if I would like to become the Watcher. There being other aspirants, however, a meeting was held at Cley at which I was appointed to act for ten weeks of each nesting season at the weekly wage of 15 Shillings.'

Pinchen's initial accommodation was in a houseboat named *'The Ark'* but he later moved to the houseboat *'Britannia'*, moored off what is now known as 'Pinchen's Creek', where he was to live for around twenty years. Under his protection Oystercatchers started to breed in 1906 and the size and success of the tern colonies increased markedly, rapidly quadrupling in size. Sandwich Terns, now considered almost an emblem of the Point, only started breeding for the first time in 1920, although nests had been suspected in the 1890s.

In 1911 the Point was acquired by A. Crundall (along with other Norfolk property) on the death of its previous owner, Lord Calthorpe, and in 1912 the Point was purchased by the National Trust. This purchase was facilitated by the enlightened efforts of Prof. F.W. (Francis) Oliver, a keen field ecologist and Professor of Botany at University College London, and followed a public appeal which led to the funds being committed by Charles Rothschild. As a consequence the Point became the first bird sanctuary in Norfolk to be safeguarded by freehold purchase. By 1913 permission had been given for University College London to construct the Laboratory building which stands to this day near the Plantation.

Bob Pinchen was employed as Warden by the new National Trust Executive Committee during the breeding seasons until 1921 when he became full-time. He recounts the following:-

> 'I was offered a wholetime engagement but having at that time a wife and eight children dependent on me I had to refuse owing to the inadequacy of the remuneration. This, however, was increased to my satisfaction and I was duly installed in my work at Blakeney Point.'

In 1922 the National Trust purchased the Lifeboat House to provide accommodation for the Watcher and a tea-room for the increasing number of visitors ferried in from Blakeney and Morston. The Watch House was purchased by the National Trust in 1930 and was subsequently leased to the Girl Guides Association. It is now operated by an independent local trust.

'Bush-shooting' was restricted by the Point's closure during the 1914-1918 war and by the stationing of soldiers, and by 1925 the gunners' heyday had well and truly passed. New wild bird protection legislation had been introduced and the practice of taxidermy went into decline as birdwatching became ever more fashionable.

Reports from Blakeney Point, focusing on the fortunes of the breeding birds, appeared regularly from 1910 in the Norfolk Wild Birds Protection Committee's (latterly the Norfolk Naturalists Trust's) annual publication *Wild Bird Protection in Norfolk* until this evolved into the *Norfolk Bird Report* in 1953. In particular, William Rowan conducted some early research into the nesting terns in the summers of 1913 and 1914 which was subsequently published in *British Birds*.

The first complete account of the Point's birds was Rowan's *Annotated List of the Birds of Blakeney Point*, published in the *Transactions of the Norfolk and Norwich Naturalists' Society* for 1918 and also in *British Birds*. This draws heavily on his contact with Arnold, Gurney, Pinchen, Ramm and Richards and details the occurrence of 210 species up to and including 1917. He concludes that:-

> 'There are probably few places with such a limited area on the British coast that could produce a longer or more interesting list of birds.'

The introduction to Rowan's list also gives a fascinating insight into the prevailing attitudes of the day:-

> 'However expert a man may be at identifying birds on the wing, many of his records are bound to be received with scepticism by other ornithologists. Many closely-related birds are so alike, particularly in winter plumage, that an element of doubt must always creep in. In short, the use of the gun, while it does little conceivable harm during the legitimate season, renders a great service to ornithological knowledge. Without it, such a list as the following would be a mere farce.'

Further published contributions included Katherine Watson's 1921 *The Tern Colony on Blakeney Point* (based on a University College London study of Common Tern nests in 1920) and *The Birds of Blakeney Point – A Visit in the Breeding Season* published in 1923 by the celebrated Cheshire ornithologist T.A. Coward. The production of both these papers was assisted by Prof. Oliver, and both appear in the *Transactions*, along with over twenty wider natural history contributions by Oliver and his colleagues, including work on dune systems and shingle ridges, the Rabbit population and the shingle and saltmarsh plants.

The 1920s saw significant improvements in the fortunes of the Point's breeding birds, with

Sandwich Tern nesting from 1920, Arctic Tern from 1922 and Black-headed Gull from 1925. Ringing of tern chicks commenced in 1925 and continued until the outbreak of the 1939-1945 war, yielding recoveries of Sandwich Terns from Angola and Ivory Coast.

During his tenure as Watcher, Pinchen's ornithological highlights included a Eurasian Scops Owl which he saw in October 1922 and a dead Little Shearwater which he picked up from the beach in May 1929. He retired in 1931 and in 1935 published *Sea Swallows – Reminiscences of a Bird Watcher*, an account of his years on the Point priced at one shilling. The ornithological highlight of that year was Norfolk's first Sooty Tern. Pinchen was replaced as Watcher by Bill Eales who wardened the Point until 1938 when, on his sudden death, his son Ted was appointed. Ted spent the war years of 1939-1945 in the Navy, during which time the Point was taken over by the Admiralty and became 'out of bounds'. On his return he resumed his position as Watcher, overseeing the visits of thousands of Norfolk schoolchildren under the National Trust's educational programme.

Reginald Gaze was a seasonal warden in the summers before the 1939-1945 war and when Ted Eales took up the Watcher's post in 1946, he became his assistant. He was a keen (and pioneering) photographer and published, amongst other works, *Bird Sanctuary* in 1947 as a vehicle for his photographs of the Point's breeding terns and waders. His photograph of a Blakeney Point Roseate Tern chick appears in the 1939 edition of *Wild Bird Protection in Norfolk*. His photographs also document the breeding attempt of Kittiwakes in the Sandwich Tern colony in 1958 in that year's edition of the *Norfolk Bird Report*.

Bird Sanctuary shows him to have been a real Blakeney Point enthusiast with a poetic turn of phrase:-

> 'Blakeney days and Blakeney nights! When does one see the Point at its best? In summer when the skies are blue and terns scream, dive, fight and play overhead and seals bask in the sunshine on the sandbanks; or when skies are grey and lowering in a bitter north-easter with strings of geese honking overhead, and the frosts have turned the tips of the suaeda bushes, reds and golds and russets.
>
> To know Blakeney Point, one must live with her in all her moods and know that like a fickle maiden she is never twice the same, but always lovable.
>
> The harvest moon has risen in a great golden ball above the channel, shedding a path of glory athwart the waters. There is no sound save the gurgling of the water past the hull and the hum and whine of the wind in the rigging; driving before the wind the little sailing craft fairly hurtles through the phosphorescent water leaving a sparkling wake of iridescent fire leading straight into fairyland. This is Blakeney Point.'

In 1949 R.A. (Richard) Richardson established Cley Bird Observatory, although its boundaries did not initially include Blakeney Point. This exciting new development helped to rescue local ornithology from what he aptly described as 'the doldrums in which it had lain becalmed during the 1930s and 1940s'. A further Little Bunting occurred in 1945 whilst a young White-tailed Eagle which spent much of December 1949 and January 1950 on the Point neatly marked the century's mid-point and ended two decades which had seen little in the way of significant bird recording.

1950 – 1970 – Ringing and Migration

Ted Eales remained as Watcher throughout this period until his retirement in 1979. An anecdote-filled account of his years on the Point can be found in his *Countryman's Memoirs – A Warden's Life on Blakeney Point*, published in 1986.

Two Broad-billed Sandpipers were seen in 1950 but the discovery in September 1951 of a Greenish Warbler amongst migrant Willow Warblers in the Plantation and an Arctic Warbler in the *Suaeda* signalled a new interest in seeking (but not shooting!) rare passerines. This was to become a dominant feature of the Point's ornithology in the decades to come. October 1951 also saw the famous 'Robin Rush', an event which was to inspire a new generation of migration students. November 1952 saw an astonishing gathering of 15 Glaucous Gulls whilst at least one grey Gyr Falcon lingered in the area from late 1953 into 1954.

Cley Bird Observatory erected heligoland traps on the beach at Cley in order to trap migrants but these were destroyed by the infamous gale and flood of 31st January 1953, which also caused considerable damage to the Watch House. Subsequently, however, National Trust permission was gained to ring birds on the Point (with the exception of the breeding species) and a wooden hut was erected at the Hood, with two small heligoland traps in use here by the end of April 1954. The boundaries of the ringing area were the outer southern limits of the *Suaeda* bushes and the crown of the shingle ridge. The running of the ringing station was largely dependent on visiting ringers who stayed there at a cost of four shillings per day, the basic accommodation (lacking both electricity and water) being sufficient to take two 'men students'.

Amongst the operation's early successes was the trapping of the Point's first spring Bluethroat on 2nd June 1954, whose enchanting photograph, held alongside the appropriate volume of the 'Witherby Handbook', appears in the 1954 *Norfolk Bird Report*. Barred and Aquatic Warblers were also trapped in the August of that year. News of such rarities was communicated to those at Cley by means of a tea-towel tied to the top of a pole by the ringing hut! A further Gyr Falcon was reported in October 1954.

A variety of trapping methods was employed on the Point in 1955 in order to extend operations beyond the Hood. These included a mobile hoop net and, the following year, a simplified Fair Isle 'yeoman net', a small wooden trap, meal-baited spring nets and the then newly-available and revolutionary Japanese mist nets. 1955 saw the capture of an Icterine Warbler and, on 29th September, Britain's second Subalpine Warbler, a species destined to become a regular spring visitor in the late 1980s and 1990s.

A feature of the late 1950s was a series of September 'falls'. That of 1956 included up to seven Bluethroats and eight Ortolan Buntings in a day and a Red-breasted Flycatcher was trapped and ringed. In early September 1958 there were up to 12 Wrynecks, 6 Bluethroats and 6 Ortolan Buntings amongst 150 Common Redstarts, 150 Northern Wheatears and 200 Willow Warblers. Between these years, 1957 had seen an extraordinary irruption of continental tits, with Blue, Great and Coal Tits all recorded during the late autumn of that year.

The hut was totally destroyed by a gale on 4th November 1957 and thereafter Cley Bird Observatory activities focused largely on Walsey Hills, Cley. Mist netting on the Point, however, continued in 1958 and was responsible for the trapping of a Rustic Bunting in the Plantation in the September of that year. A Red-footed Falcon was seen in May 1959 and, amazingly, another dead Little Shearwater was found along the tideline in May 1960, a month which also featured a Woodchat Shrike and the Point's second Subalpine Warbler.

B.R. (Barry) Spence, a regular visitor since 1951 and later to become Warden of Spurn Bird Observatory, trapped on 3rd October 1961 one of Blakeney Point's more notable contributions to British ornithology – the country's second ever Radde's Warbler, mist-netted on the Hood. The bird was taken back to Cley and kept in Richard Richardson's outdoor aviary in order to be inspected by Kenneth Williamson who travelled overnight to see it! This record was documented fully in the pages of *British Birds*. This and the following winter saw further White-tailed Eagles whilst 1962 saw the Point's only record of Alpine Swift and, on the Hood, the first Norfolk Yellow-browed Warbler for 43 years!

Less ringing took place in 1962, a year more noted for a large 'wreck' of Fulmars, and the Bird Observatory was finally dissolved at the end of 1963. Annual reports from Cley Bird Observatory, detailing its activities on Blakeney Point, appear in *Wild Bird Protection in Norfolk* from 1949-1952 and in its successor *Norfolk Bird Report* from 1953-1963. More details of the activities of Cley Bird Observatory can be found in Moss Taylor's biography of Richard Richardson, *Guardian Spirit of the East Bank*, published in 2002. 1963 was also notable for another large early September 'fall' of migrants, featuring good numbers of Common Redstarts, Garden Warblers and Pied Flycatchers.

R.G.H. (Michael) Cant, however, obtained permission from the National Trust to ring in 1964 and did so until 1969, normally staying on the Point for two weeks in the spring and autumn, supplemented by occasional weekend visits. He ringed 3,000 birds during this period, including 127 Common Redstarts, 105 Pied Flycatchers, 168 Goldcrests and 627 Linnets as well as 12 Wrynecks, a Yellow-browed Warbler, three Red-breasted Flycatchers, three Great Grey Shrikes and a Little Bunting. He still retains fond memories of the Point, including the following thoughts in a letter to the authors:-

> 'In my early teens the Point was to me a magical place. Seventy years later the feeling has not diminished. Whether searching Yankee Ridge for Bluethroats, swimming surrounded by seals whilst hundreds of Gannets dived for mackerel over the Bar or watching skein after skein against a winter's sunset – it has it all.'

1964 saw the Point's first record of Mediterranean Gull, and Common Gull bred for the first time. 1965, however, has become famous for the events of 3rd September, when an avalanche of Common Redstarts and other migrants cascaded into East Anglia. The main focus of the event was in northeast Suffolk but massive numbers of birds also arrived on the Point, with 25-30 Wrynecks and a dozen Bluethroats recorded along the shingle ridge between Salthouse and the furthest spits. A diary of this exciting 'fall' by Ian Wallace can be found elsewhere in this book and a full account is contained in *British Birds* 59: 353-376.

1966 was notable for a Woodchat Shrike and for a further Sooty Tern, commuting between the Blakeney Point and Scolt Head terneries, whilst 1969 saw the Point's only record of Two-barred Crossbill.

The National Trust booklet *Blakeney Point and Scolt Head Island* was first published in 1952, edited by Professor J.A. Steers of the University of Cambridge. This was rewritten in 1964 and new editions with further minor amendments were published in 1971 and 1976, with a brand new edition produced in 1989, edited by Hilary Allison and John Morley. It contains an excellent chapter by Michael Seago on the birds of Blakeney Point and Scolt Head.

The next summary of the Point's birds was *An Annotated Checklist of the Birds of Blakeney Point, Norfolk*, published in 1969 by Dr. D.J.B. White of the Department of Botany, University College London, thereby continuing the long association between the Point and the University. Dr. White chaired the advisory committee overseeing the programme of school educational visits and contributed the botany and plant ecology section to Professor Steers' National Trust booklet as well as producing his own *An Annotated List of the Flowering Plants and Ferns on Blakeney Point, Norfolk* in 1967. White's 1969 checklist showed that the Point's bird list had risen from 210 in Rowan's day to a new total of 256.

1970 – 2004 – Modern Birdwatching

Ted Eales continued as National Trust Warden throughout the 1970s. Joe Reed took over in 1980 until he too retired in 2003. Active conservation of the tern colonies continued, with further contributions published in the bulletins of the Norfolk Bird Club. These included Richard Gilbert's *Predation on Blakeney Point's Tern Colonies* and Dougal McNeil's *Tern Research on Blakeney Point* and *Sandwich Terns on Blakeney Point*.

The bird observatory era spawned a new generation of birdwatchers, enthusiastic about finding and observing migrants and increasingly familiar with scarce and rare birds.

Although regular ringing did not persist on the Point into the 1970s a revival took place of the old habit of 'bush-bashing', only now with the aim of finding, identifying and observing migrants, particularly scarce and rare ones. For a time the Point became a popular gathering ground, particularly in August and September, and observers from this era still retain a sense of nostalgia for the tea-room and its cases of stuffed bird specimens.

Other more recent habits have been an increasing focus on looking for migrants in the spring (particularly since the mid-1980s), more time spent sea-watching, more effort devoted to wildfowl and wader counting and greater attention paid to large gulls.

These new habits have been fuelled by better quality optics, more widespread use of telescopes, more and better identification literature and, through foreign travel, an increasing familiarity with a wider range of species. These developments have also led to the now dominant phenomenon of 'twitching' which has taken widespread enjoyment of birdwatching in a new direction from that pioneered by the observatory movement in the 1950s and 1960s.

Given the Point's former popularity, it is surprising that the number of visiting observers has fallen in recent years. This decline is no doubt attributable to these changes in birdwatching styles and more particularly to the introduction of pager information services. Most coverage of the Point is now carried out by a small number of individuals undertaking regular, systematic observations.

A second updated edition of White's *An Annotated Checklist of the Birds of Blakeney Point, Norfolk* was published in 1981, correcting a number of earlier errors and documenting seven further additions to the Point's bird list, giving a new total of 263. This remains until the present work the most complete record of Blakeney Point's birds.

The last thirty years have seen an explosion of new records for the Point:-

1973 Common Rosefinch.
1975 Arctic Redpoll, Dusky Warbler.
1977 Golden Oriole.
1978 Magpie.
1983 Lesser Crested Tern, Rose-coloured Starling.
1984 Pale-bellied Brent Goose, Ross's Gull, Cory's Shearwater, Siberian Stonechat.
1985 Greater Sand Plover, White-billed Diver.
1986 Dartford Warbler.
1987 Slender-billed Gull, Olive-backed Pipit, Siberian Chiffchaff, Red-breasted Goose.
1988 Grey-headed Wagtail, Western Bonelli's Warbler, Thrush Nightingale, Red-throated Pipit, European Bee-eater, Short-toed Lark, Pied Wheatear.
1989 Rose-ringed Parakeet, Black-headed Bunting, Little Egret.
1990 Red Kite, Yellow-legged Gull.
1991 Snowy Owl, Purple Heron, Egyptian Goose.
1992 Great Spotted Cuckoo.

1993 Asian Desert Warbler, Oriental Pratincole, Caspian Tern.
1995 Laughing Gull, Collared Pratincole.
1996 European Serin.
1997 Eurasian Jay, Fea's Petrel, Great Shearwater.
2000 White Stork, Ruddy Shelduck, Isabelline Wheatear.
2001 Black Brant, Caspian Gull, Pallas's Grasshopper Warbler, Surf Scoter.
2003 Common Pheasant, Pallid Harrier.
2004 Bullfinch, Pallid Swift.

Since 1970 a number of rarities have proved to be of regular and predictable occurrence, most notably Short-toed Lark, Red-throated Pipit and Subalpine Warbler in spring and Siberian Stonechat and Greenish Warbler in autumn. Red-throated Pipit, for example, was only recorded for the first time in 1988 but has now proven to be near-annual, with a total of at least 14 records. To what extent this is due to increased coverage and to what extent a real change in status has occurred is impossible to judge, though both factors are likely to be at work. The Point's greatest rarities at the beginning of the twenty-first century are three species unrecorded since the nineteenth – Buff-breasted Sandpiper and Eurasian Nuthatch, last seen in 1899, and, now absent since 1888, Pallas's Sandgrouse.

In addition to these sightings of individual rarities, a number of significant avian events have also entered the Point's record books. The choice is necessarily arbitrary but amongst the most significant events since 1970 have been:-

1972 The first breeding record for the Point (and Norfolk) of Herring Gull.
1974 The sole breeding record for the Point of Common Kestrel.
1975 A year of unprecedented arrivals in October, featuring a Dusky Warbler and a Rustic Bunting.
1977 An astonishing influx of around 22 Icterine Warblers in August, with eight birds present on two well-separated days.
1978 The first breeding record for the Point (and Norfolk) of Lesser Black-backed Gull and a summering Magpie which built a nest in 1979.
1983 A large February 'wreck' of auks and attempted breeding by a pair of Kentish Plovers.
1985 The first large spring Bluethroat 'fall', with an absolute minimum of 16 birds present in May, and a record movement of Pomarine Skuas in early November.
1986 A record September movement of Sooty Shearwaters and the unprecedented arrival of a wintering flock of ten Black-necked Grebes, remaining into 1987.
1987 A further spring Bluethroat 'fall', featuring a minimum of 11 birds, and a massive August 'fall' producing multiple Greenish Warblers, many Wrynecks and a Great Snipe.
1988 One of the largest ever 'falls' of thrushes, accompanied by the first Radde's Warbler since the bird of 1961 and the Point's first, and only, Pied Wheatear.
1990 Another massive October 'crash' of thrushes, accompanied by an Olive-backed Pipit and three Arctic Redpolls.
1991 A memorable complex late September 'fall' producing a Red-throated Pipit and up to five Siberian Stonechats.
1992 A 'classic' spring, with multiple Red-footed Falcons and Red-throated Pipits, Thrush Nightingale, Woodchat Shrike and the first spring Greenish Warbler as highlights, followed by the first breeding record of Mediterranean Gull.
1993 A territory-holding and nest-building Asian Desert Warbler.

1995 A huge September 'fall' of Common Redstarts, the largest since the 'great fall' of 1965.

1998 An enormous early October 'fall' of Robins, the largest since the 1951 'Robin Rush', followed by a notable influx of Great Grey Shrikes and a record winter for Shore Larks.

1999 A summering Laughing Gull in the Black-headed Gull colony.

2000 A single Honey Buzzard noted as part of that September's record influx into Britain.

2001 A huge January movement of Guillemots and a memorable and protracted September 'fall' featuring a host of 'semi-rarities', several Great Spotted Woodpeckers and Radde's and Pallas's Grasshopper Warblers. The year closed with an enormous gathering of Common Scoters off the Marrams.

2002 The first proven breeding record of Wren and an unprecedented October influx of Firecrests.

2003 A Short-toed Lark holding territory for over two weeks, a prospecting Common Pheasant and the first breeding records of Greylag Goose and Woodpigeon.

2004 A February 'wreck' of Fulmars featuring a high percentage of 'blue' birds and a mid-October irruption of Waxwings and Northern Bullfinches.

2005 A significant late March 'fall' of thrushes and other northbound passerine migrants.

Like all coastal migration watchpoints, the Point is a highly sensitive indicator of bird movements, both from day to day during a season and also across the years, when fascinating trends in occurrence emerge. These can be important conservation indicators although a degree of caution should be exercised in their interpretation as patterns of observation have generally been neither consistent nor systematic. It should also be remembered that the Point's changing bird fortunes are as much a reflection of the vagaries of climate change, trends in weather patterns and the health of continental bird populations as they are of the fate of British birds. Many short-term fluctuations are documented in the Systematic List but some of the most obvious long-term changes are set out below.

Increasing

- Bewick's Swan, formerly very rare but since the 1950s a regular autumn migrant en route to new Fenland wintering grounds.
- Pink-footed Goose, formerly much scarcer but now regularly seen due to the record numbers currently wintering in the county taking advantage of stubble, sugar beet top and grassland feeding opportunities close to secure roost sites.
- Greylag and Canada Geese, both increasingly recorded following historical introductions.
- Dark-bellied Brent Goose, formerly present in hundreds, now wintering in thousands with new cereal and grassland feeding habits assisting winter survival.
- Black Brant and Pale-bellied Brent Goose, unrecorded in the older literature but now regular amongst the Dark-bellied Brent Geese.
- Common Shelduck, scarce in Rowan's day but increasing during the twentieth century, particularly between 1920 and 1950, in line with wider national trends but also benefiting from conservation measures on the Point.
- Common Eider, scarce until the late 1950s but subsequently much more regular.
- A number of northern seabirds, notably Fulmar, Northern Gannet and Great Skua, all of which have spread into British waters with the assistance of the general climatic amelioration between 1850 and 1950, commercial fishing activity and reduced persecution at the breeding colonies.

- Great Cormorant, increasing significantly during the twentieth century as the form *sinensis* has spread across northwest Europe.
- Little Egret, first recorded in 1989 and now present in small numbers throughout the year as a consequence of its astonishing spread into southern Britain – perhaps the most obvious symbol of current climate change.
- Eurasian Spoonbill, formerly scarce but much more regular since the 1980s as a consequence of its increase in the Netherlands.
- All birds of prey, formerly rare and persecuted but now benefiting from legislation and active conservation measures across Europe. All are now much more regularly recorded, most notably Hen Harrier, Peregrine, Osprey, Hobby, Marsh Harrier, Common Buzzard and Sparrowhawk, the latter four increasing as local breeders.
- Common Crane, traditionally a vagrant from the continent but, since the 1980s, a regular wanderer from the slowly-increasing Broadland population.
- Oystercatcher as a breeding species, absent as a breeder in Rowan's day but increasing thereafter as part of a nationwide increase and now nesting in significant numbers assisted by conservation measures on the Point.
- Icelandic Black-tailed Godwit, formerly very rare but now regularly present in numbers in the Harbour on passage.
- Mediterranean Gull, with only two records before the 1980s and now a semi-regular breeding species as a consequence of its dramatic spread into northwest Europe.
- Little Gull, rare and irregular until the 1970s, since when it has become much more frequent with some large movements noted – a consequence of its range extension in northern Europe.
- Black-headed Gull, a threatened species in Pashley's day but now a regular breeding bird, albeit in varying numbers, thanks to a dramatic nationwide increase during the twentieth century assisted by conservation measures on the Point.
- Common Gull as a breeding species, only recorded nesting for the first time in 1964 but now a regular breeder in small numbers.
- Yellow-legged Gull, unknown before the 1990s and now present almost daily in summer as the species increasingly migrates north to Britain from the Mediterranean after the breeding season – a further witness to current climate change.
- Kittiwake, scarce in Rowan's day but recorded more regularly from the middle of the twentieth century as part of a nationwide increase.
- Sandwich Tern, scarce until the 1920s but now present throughout the summer and a regular breeding species, albeit in varying numbers, due to nationwide increases assisted by conservation measures on the Point.
- Arctic Tern as a breeding species, formerly absent but with a small colony established since the 1920s due to a more widespread increase assisted by conservation measures on the Point.
- Shore Lark, not noted wintering prior to the 1880s but now a regular feature of many winters following the extension of its breeding range into Scandinavia.
- Richard's Pipit and Yellow-browed Warbler, both recorded much more regularly since the 1960s though much of this is no doubt due to increased observations.
- Dunnock as a breeding species, only nesting for the first time in 1961 but now with a significant breeding population.
- Bluethroat in spring, with only one record, in 1954, before a series of remarkable 'falls' in the 1980s (although now unrecorded at this season since 1996).
- Blackcap in autumn, much more regular since the 1950s due to increasing numbers of con-

tinental birds now wintering in Britain.
- Greenish Warbler, unrecorded before 1951 but now more of a scarce migrant than a true rarity in late August and early September.
- A number of Siberian *Phylloscopus* warblers (Pallas's, Radde's and Dusky Warblers and Siberian Chiffchaff), now increasingly expected features of late autumn.
- Firecrest, increasingly recorded in both spring and autumn since the 1960s as the species expanded into northwest Europe.
- A number of continental rarities and 'semi-rarities' in spring (Red-footed Falcon, Dotterel, Wryneck, Short-toed Lark, Red-throated Pipit, Grey-headed Wagtail, Thrush Nightingale, Icterine Warbler, Subalpine Warbler, Red-breasted Flycatcher, Red-backed Shrike, Common Rosefinch and Ortolan Bunting), previously unrecorded at this season but now regularly noted since the mid-1980s. Of these, Icterine Warbler and Common Rosefinch have recently expanded their breeding range to the north and west and this no doubt partly accounts for their increasing occurrences on the Point. Conversely, Red-backed Shrike and Ortolan Bunting are declining in northwest Europe and the apparent increase is probably more due to increased observer activity.
- Carrion Crow, not listed by either Rowan or Pashley, but now commonly recorded in small numbers as its range has expanded northwards in northern Europe.
- Goldfinch and Siskin, both very rare in Rowan's day but much more regular today.

Decreasing

- Ringed Plover as a breeding species, not always abundant but with 180 pairs in 1972 now reduced to around 15 as a consequence of disturbance and predation.
- Northern Lapwing, formerly an abundant late autumn immigrant, now in much reduced numbers following widespread declines across northern Europe linked to changing agricultural practices.
- Common Tern as a breeding species, formerly present in significant numbers but now much reduced.
- Turtle Dove, presumably more common historically (though this cannot be judged from the available literature), but with only one record since 2000 – a reflection of the combination of wintering habitat degradation, continued hunting in the Mediterranean and changing agricultural practices in northern Europe.
- Sky Lark, formerly an abundant late autumn immigrant, now in much reduced numbers at this season following widespread declines across northern Europe linked to changing agricultural practices. It is, however, still one of the commonest breeding passerines.
- Bluethroat in autumn, regular in small numbers until the 1970s but subsequently very rare. The reasons for this decline are, however, not obvious although Sahel droughts have been implicated.
- Aquatic Warbler, formerly semi-regular but with only one record since the 1970s, reflecting this species' decline in its threatened eastern European wetland habitats.
- A number of 'common' passerine migrants. Although definitive evidence is lacking, some species, notably Willow Warbler and Spotted Flycatcher, appear to be less common than formerly.
- Rook, formerly a common autumn immigrant but now rare at this season due to the changing migratory habits of Scandinavian birds.
- Hooded Crow, formerly abundant, with flocks of hundreds arriving in late autumn, subsequently decreasing rapidly and now unrecorded since 1995 probably due to a combi-

nation of displacement by the Carrion Crow and the changing migratory habits of Scandinavian birds.

- Twite, not always abundant but recently regularly present in the low hundreds in winter and now only an occasional visitor following declines in the Pennine breeding population.
- Ortolan Bunting in autumn, regular in August and September until the 1960s but now much more erratic in its occurrences due to its increasing scarcity in northwest Europe.

2005 and Beyond — What Next?

In terms of bird recording, fascinating short and long-term trends continue to emerge and the Point's bird list has now risen to around 309 (depending on taxonomic preference), surely one of the best lists in Britain for a place of its size, and fully confirming Rowan's assertion of 1918.

Furthermore, the Point's list still has much potential to grow, with five species in particular (Great White Egret, White-rumped Sandpiper, Lanceolated Warbler, Booted Warbler and Sardinian Warbler) perhaps poised for an early appearance.

To date no fewer than 17 species have been added to the Norfolk List from Blakeney Point, from the 1884 Barred Warbler to the 1997 Fea's Petrel. The other Norfolk 'firsts' recorded during this 120-year period are White-billed Diver, Balearic Shearwater, Lesser Crested Tern, Sooty Tern, Water Pipit, Desert Wheatear, Aquatic Warbler, Marsh Warbler, Asian Desert Warbler, Greenish Warbler, Yellow-browed Warbler, Radde's Warbler, Red-breasted Flycatcher, Rustic Bunting and Little Bunting. In addition, three other Norfolk 'firsts' (Oriental Pratincole, Slender-billed Gull and Ross's Gull) have also been observed on the Point after first being found elsewhere in the county.

In terms of conservation and the breeding birds, the future of the Point and its birds appears secure under the stewardship of the National Trust and its new Warden, David Wood, in post since 2003. The Trust continues to provide a full wardening presence from April until the end of September and great effort is expended throughout the year to control both tern colony predators and human visitors.

Prof. Oliver's legacy also lives on and the Lifeboat House and Laboratory are still used to this day for field trips by students from the University College London Department of Biology.

The number of day visitors ferried from Morston and Blakeney, however, may be reducing, with many mid-summer seal boat trips no longer calling at the Point. The provision of refreshments at the Lifeboat House has also been discontinued.

In addition to this slight reduction in human pressure the early years of the new century have seen vigorous vegetation growth thanks to the ravages of myxomatosis on the Rabbit population.

The Point therefore provides to this day a unique year-round birdwatching experience. For both migrant and breeding birds the Point remains as productive as ever and, thanks to its continued protection, it can still offer the same excitements which first drew bird enthusiasts over 120 years ago.

In the words of White, in the introduction to his 1981 Checklist:-

'That the birds have prospered is due in great measure to the devoted work of the Warden and to the cooperation he receives from the visiting public. Long may it continue!'

Autumn Bluethroat. A characteristic view of this formerly regular autumn migrant. (*James McCallum*)

Weather and Migration – the Blakeney Point Year

The birdwatcher's year on Blakeney Point is totally dominated by the phenomenon of migration – both regular movements driven by the changing seasons and more irregular wanderings triggered by hard weather or food shortages.

For countries in the world's temperate mid-latitudes there are marked seasonal variations in climate. Day-to-day weather systems are also highly mobile, bringing rapid changes in air masses and therefore temperature and wind speed and direction. These forces both initiate and influence great movements of birds. Though their scale is vast they are often only fully visible under certain conditions and at favoured locations such as islands or coastal promontories. In this context, Blakeney Point's topography places it in an enviable position for the recording and study of migratory birds.

A big arrival day on the Point can provide some of the most rewarding and enjoyable bird-watching to be found anywhere. Even the most inveterate 'twitcher' cannot fail to be moved by the sight of tired migrants struggling to reach the shore after the long and hazardous journey across the North Sea, finally having to run the gauntlet of a marauding Merlin or Great Black-backed Gull. For many, observing migration is the most fascinating form of birdwatching. However, predicting when a large 'fall' or a smaller arrival will occur is not always straightforward, being something of an art as well as a science, but an attempt to 'read' the weather will certainly assist the visitor in making the most of the Point's potential.

The account which follows takes a season-by-season view of the ebb and flow of the Point's bird movements. It describes those events which can be regarded as typical of most years, whilst making reference to particular days which most clearly illustrate the vectors which can produce both common and scarce species. The great rarities have been less predictable and are not generally mentioned here unless their occurrence serves further to illustrate a particularly productive weather pattern.

Winter

The winter months between late November and late February are generally quiet periods with little real migration, though on occasion late arrivals of winter thrushes can be a feature well into December, when their departure from the breeding grounds is delayed to exploit heavy crops of berries in Scandinavia. Moderate numbers of Goldeneye and Red-breasted Mergansers winter in the Harbour, joined in some years by a few Eiders, a Great Northern Diver or a Slavonian Grebe. Red-throated Divers and auks are present offshore, occasionally in large numbers, and significant 'passages' can occur at this time. Mobile flocks of Snow Buntings can usually be found on the beach, elusive Rock Pipits inhabit the saltmarsh creeks and a small party of Shore Larks is often present. The Harbour muds host flocks of wintering estuarine waders, with Oystercatcher and Dunlin being the most numerous. A variety of wildfowl also frequents the mudflats, notably Dark-bellied Brent Geese, always worth searching through carefully for a Pale-bellied Brent Goose or a Black Brant, both now regular visitors to the area. Common Shelduck and noisy flocks of Eurasian Wigeon are also prominent, whilst flocks of Pink-footed Geese shuttle along the coast and Hen Harriers and Merlins hunt in and around the Point and the Harbour. In the evenings huge numbers of gulls roost in the Harbour.

During cold spells, when local inland waters freeze over, the Harbour can be a refuge to larger numbers of wildfowl, grebes and, on occasion, Coots. Plummeting temperatures and cold easterly winds or heavy snow on the near-continent also force wintering birds to flee across the North Sea in search of more clement conditions. Typically these hard weather movements involve Golden Plover, Northern Lapwings, Woodcock, gulls, Sky Larks and thrushes but if the Dutch wetlands or western parts of the Baltic freeze over, wildfowl and grebes also move west seeking open water. On these occasions Goosanders can sometimes be seen passing west at sea and the very occasional Smew can be sought in the Harbour.

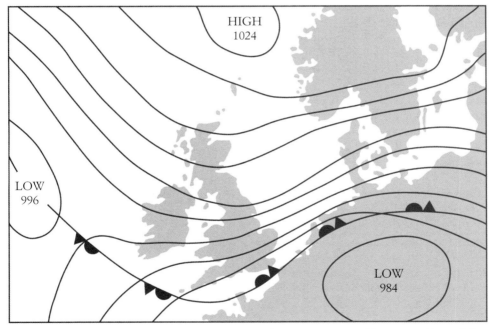

Fig. 1. Chart for 14th February 1979. Conditions initiating cold weather movements generated by a strong, cold, easterly flow on the southern side of a high pressure area centred to the north of Britain.

Spring

Typically, the rapidly-lengthening days of late February and early March see signs of spring, with the first tentative movements of Meadow Pipits, Pied Wagtails and Linnets pushing into any mild westerly or southwesterly breezes.

After the middle of March mild spells signal the arrival of the first real summer migrants in the form of Northern Wheatears and Common Chiffchaffs and the occasional Black Redstart, European Stonechat or Firecrest. The most favourable conditions are those which produce brief rises in temperature, typically found in the warm sectors of low pressure areas or in the southeasterly winds to the west of anticyclones over the near-continent. In colder, more easterly conditions there may be evidence of northbound Robins, thrushes, Dunnocks, Goldcrests or Chaffinches 'stalled' at the coast prior to a crossing of the North Sea or displaced from the near-continent.

A regular feature of early spring is a strong passage of gulls, particularly Common and Lesser Black-backed Gulls. March is a good month for Glaucous Gull and the year's first prospecting adult Mediterranean Gulls are usually also seen at this time, as are the first passage Icelandic Black-tailed Godwits. Parties of noisy Common Shelducks roam the dunes and vocal Oystercatchers are hard to miss whilst all along the Point the songs of the breeding Sky Larks, Meadow Pipits, Dunnocks, Linnets and Reed Buntings start to build, providing a delightful backdrop to a day in the field.

During the first two weeks of April the number and variety of migrants slowly increase. Although there are rarely any large 'falls' of grounded birds, the movements of Meadow Pipits, Pied Wagtails and Linnets are at their strongest whenever the wind swings into the southwest or west and are increasingly joined by White Wagtails and Goldfinches. At this time hirundines also start to appear, Sand Martins preceding Swallows and House Martins, and small corvid movements may also be noted. If the wind shifts into the southeast a Black Redstart or a Firecrest may still be found whilst Northern Wheatears remain prominent and Willow Warblers increasingly replace the earlier Common Chiffchaffs. As the end of April approaches, mild conditions can produce large numbers of Yellow Wagtails (with the occasional Blue-headed Wagtail) and Northern Wheatears, now comprising larger, browner birds bound for Greenland, whilst in two recent Aprils the Point has hosted a Richard's Pipit. Late April is also the best time to look (or listen) for Grasshopper Warbler.

Easterly winds in early spring are often cold and birdless but such conditions at the end of the month may drift across the North Sea scarcer species such as Wryneck, Ring Ouzel or Pied Flycatcher – all amongst the earliest of the summer migrants to return to central and northern Europe.

April is most notable, however, for the arrival of the breeding Black-headed and Common Gulls and terns, first the raucous Sandwich Terns followed by the Common, Arctic and Little Terns, and an increasing variety of waders in the Harbour including noisy Whimbrels and Common Sandpipers and increasing numbers of colourful Icelandic Black-tailed Godwits.

Whilst April can be rather predictable, May often holds surprises and rarely fails to provide at least one real highlight. Commoner species such as Common Redstart, Whinchat, Northern Wheatear, Lesser Whitethroat, Common Whitethroat and Willow Warbler can be prominent in the first half of the month and this is also the best time to look for Common Nightingale and Wood Warbler. In easterly or southeasterly winds, which from early May are increasingly productive, the occasional Wryneck or Pied Flycatcher might now be joined by an early Bluethroat, Red-backed Shrike or Ortolan Bunting. The Point's three most regular spring rarities - Short-toed Lark, Red-throated Pipit and Subalpine Warbler - have also all been seen in these conditions in the first half of the month.

In May the remaining waders in the Harbour become increasingly restless as they prepare to leave for northern breeding grounds. Small groups can be seen making noisy trial flights out over the sea before returning to the sanctuary of the Harbour. At the end of the month the sometimes large flocks of Dunlin often contain numbers of *tundrae* Ringed Plovers, whilst sudden panics amongst the waders are good indicators of a passing raptor, usually a Marsh Harrier, but Ospreys are also increasingly recorded. This is also the time to look out for wandering Common Cranes from the Broadland population, typically heading high to the west on bright, sunny days. Very occasionally, warm southeasterly winds in early May can prompt displacements of Black Terns from the continent and on these rare but exciting occasions large numbers of birds can be seen passing east through the Harbour. For the adventurous, beach-walking in early May might be productive as two tideline Little Shearwaters have occurred at this time!

Mid to late May has an impressive track record for scarce and rare birds though numbers of common migrants decline rapidly after mid-month. The range of species in a particular year is, however, heavily dependent on the prevailing weather patterns. Westerly or southwesterly winds at this late stage of the season invariably lead to quiet days with very few grounded migrants, though strong passages of hirundines can be obvious. However, when an anticyclone is centred to the west of Ireland, giving cold northwesterly or northerly winds, even these movements grind to a halt.

By contrast, eagerly-anticipated warm winds from the southeast signal much more exciting possibilities. Such conditions encourage birds migrating into or through southern Europe to 'over-shoot' north and west of their normal range. Red-footed Falcon, Short-toed Lark, Tawny Pipit, Red-throated Pipit, Subalpine Warbler and Woodchat Shrike are the scarce or rare species particularly prone to these warm weather displacements and usually occur on bright, clear days. On such occasions hardly any migrants may be present on the Point but the percentage of these scarce or rare species may be extremely high. The productivity of such conditions first became obvious in May 1988 with the first of the modern run of Red-throated Pipits and Subalpine Warblers and also a Western Bonelli's Warbler. The most memorable year for such 'overshoots', however, was 1992, which saw unusually persistent hot southeasterly conditions, producing 'mini-invasions' of Red-footed Falcons and Red-throated Pipits along with Short-toed Lark, Tawny Pipit and Woodchat Shrike – see Figure 2.

Such conditions occurred again in 1995, when no fewer than two Red-throated Pipits and three Subalpine Warblers were recorded during the month, and 2002, when a Red-footed Falcon, a Red-throated Pipit and a Subalpine Warbler occurred on the same day. The same conditions in 2003 produced a Short-toed Lark and a Red-throated Pipit within a few hundred yards of each other.

Given the Point's northerly aspect, the occurrence of these 'overshoots' from the southeast is perhaps surprising and it is interesting to speculate on the route by which they arrive. The Red-footed Falcons possibly approach from the south, halting when they reach the coast and being forced to travel either west or east. The route taken by the other species is, however, less obvious.

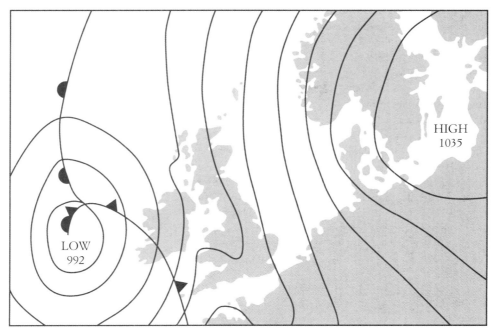

Fig. 2. Chart for 14th May 1992. Hot, long range southeasterly winds produced a Montagu's Harrier, two Red-footed Falcons and a Red-throated Pipit in perfect 'overshooting' conditions with, the following day, a Woodchat Shrike also present.

If the wind moves further into the east or northeast there is frequently a colder edge to the breeze and if the winds are light sea frets are a regular feature. Whereas early in the season these conditions are poor for birds, after mid-May more and more migrants are heading north or north-west into Scandinavia and the Baltic region. If the airflow originates in this area birds may be drifted westwards across the North Sea and, as the month progresses, winds between east and north may become as productive as southeasterlies. On such occasions there might only be a tiny sprinkling of common migrants but there will be an increasing chance of a wider range of more northerly-breeding scarce or rare species. Wrynecks, Red-throated Pipits and Pied Flycatchers can still feature at this time but might now also be joined by Dotterel, Grey-headed Wagtail, Thrush Nightingale, Bluethroat, Icterine Warbler, Greenish Warbler, Red-breasted Flycatcher, Red-backed Shrike or Common Rosefinch. Most of these species have been heard singing on the Point, lending a touch of the exotic and, with closed eyes, transporting the listener to an eastern European woodland or the Scandinavian tundra.

Illustrated below are the very different weather patterns which produced memorable 'falls' of Bluethroats in 1985 and 1987. In the following decade, late May 1992 continued its earlier promise with an outstanding run of Icterine Warblers and the Point's first spring Greenish Warbler, whilst Figure 5 illustrates the memorable 'fall' of 27th May 1993.

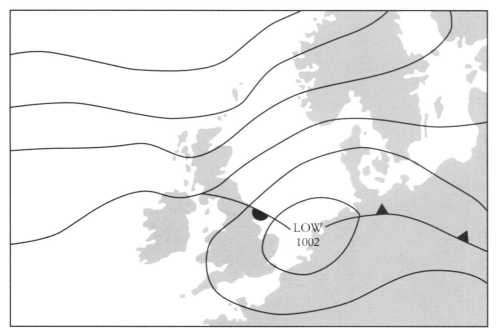

Fig. 3. Chart for 14th May 1985. An arrival in easterly conditions on the northern edge of a low pressure area. Species recorded included two Wrynecks, an exceptional 14 Bluethroats and four Pied Flycatchers.

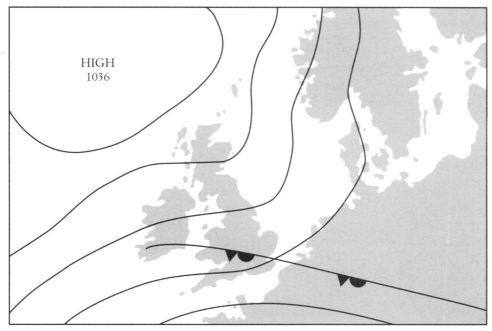

Fig. 4. Chart for 23rd May 1987. A Wryneck and 11 Bluethroats were seen in easterly winds on the southeastern flank of a high pressure area centred to the northwest of Scotland.

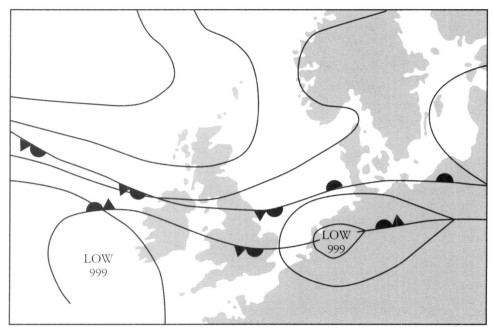

Fig. 5. Chart for 27th May 1993. This 'classic' combination of a low pressure area situated over the Netherlands and heavy frontal rain produced two Icterine Warblers, an Asian Desert Warbler and a Common Rosefinch.

Even in the first half of June migrants can still be found. Movements of Common Swifts are sometimes noted whilst easterly or northeasterly airflows out of Scandinavia have produced very small but varied arrivals of late migrants, with Spotted Flycatchers often prominent at this time. These conditions have also produced many of the scarce or rare species more associated with May with, to date, Short-toed Lark, Grey-headed Wagtail, Thrush Nightingale, Bluethroat, Icterine Warbler, Red-breasted Flycatcher, Red-backed Shrike and Common Rosefinch all noted in the first few days of the month. However, whilst these spring migrants are still arriving in northern Europe the first 'autumn' Northern Lapwings have already started to appear in the Harbour.

Summer

During the summer, between mid-June and late July, there is virtually no passerine migration but, perversely, some of the rarest species on the Blakeney Point list have been recorded during this period! Mid-summer can be a rewarding time, with the tern colonies to enjoy and rapidly-increasing numbers of a variety of waders in the Harbour, particularly Golden Plover, *schinzii* Dunlin and Eurasian Curlew. To add rarity interest, Greater Sand Plover and Broad-billed Sandpiper have each occurred more than once in the Harbour at this time. As the first waders appear from the continent and pass west offshore, the breeding Common Shelducks flight out to the east, on moult migration to northern Germany. At sea, the first stirrings of autumn can also be visible, with Manx Shearwaters possible offshore in windy conditions and Arctic Skuas, initially adults, increasingly visible harassing the terns. Other characteristic features of mid-summer are large flocks of young Starlings roaming the *Suaeda*, increasingly regular Yellow-legged Gulls amongst the large gulls loafing in the Harbour, an occasional Roseate Tern or a sudden visitation by a Hobby. July traditionally closes with the occasional very young-looking Northern Wheatear or Willow Warbler.

Autumn

August signals the start of concerted autumn migration. Waders continue to fill the Harbour and Greenshank, Whimbrel and Common Sandpipers can frequently be seen or heard calling amongst the increasing numbers of commoner species, as can more rarely Little Stints and Curlew Sandpipers. Waders also increasingly pass west offshore, as do the first autumn flocks of immigrant Eurasian Teal. Late summer and early autumn traditionally see a build-up of what are presumably largely locally-bred Sand Martins and Yellow and Pied Wagtails, all of which can gather on the Point in significant numbers.

Autumn 'falls' of continental passerine migrants are, however, largely responsible for Blakeney Point's fame in the ornithological world. Radar evidence has shown that there is a regular autumn passage of night-migrants, mainly chats, warblers and flycatchers, heading south-southwest from Scandinavia across the North Sea. This movement peaks at the end of August and the beginning of September and is at its most intense when areas of high pressure settle over Scandinavia and the Baltic region, producing light winds, clear or light cloud conditions and falling temperatures. The western flank of this movement generally passes near or over the Norfolk coast but in fine conditions birds pass over high and few come to ground on the Point.

However, if the easterly wind-flow along the southern fringe of the high pressure area strengthens, birds may be drifted to the west, not only from the western fringe of the movement but also from further east. In this respect, experience has shown that areas of high pressure building from the east are more productive than those moving in from the Atlantic. If an area of low pressure encroaches from the south, ideally positioning itself over the Dutch coast, the easterly flow will strengthen further and displace large numbers of migrants west across the North Sea. On such occasions birds become disorientated in the associated frontal cloud and rain and seek landfall at the first opportunity, arriving at coastal locations such as the Point. Occasionally these 'falls' have been spectacular, with particularly memorable arrivals occurring in the first few days of September in 1956, 1958, 1963 and 1965 and again in August 1987. On 3rd September 1965 an estimated half a million birds made landfall along 24 miles of the northeast Suffolk coast and very large numbers of birds were also seen on Blakeney Point including up to 25 Wrynecks, a dozen Bluethroats and an Aquatic Warbler – see Figure 6.

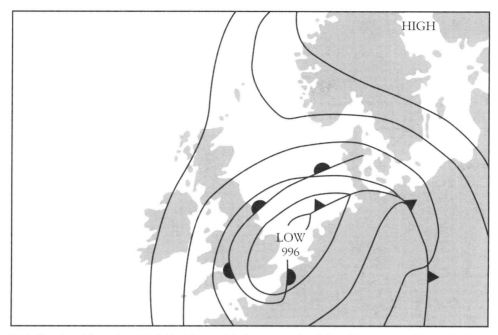

Fig. 6. Chart for 3rd September 1965. A 'classic' map with high pressure and settled conditions over Scandinavia and a north-ward-moving rain belt associated with a low pressure area moving into the southern North Sea. At midday large numbers of migrants were arriving from Suffolk north to Yorkshire as the front reached the coast, accompanied by a shift of wind direction to the southeast.

Such very large 'falls' are, however, relatively rare events, although more 'marginal' weather patterns regularly produce smaller arrivals. As Blakeney Point has a north-facing aspect any wind with a northerly component, even a northwesterly behind a departing low pressure area, may precipitate an arrival, particularly when associated with easterly winds in the northern sector of the North Sea. Calm, anticyclonic conditions associated with a high pressure area over the southern North Sea can also prompt small arrivals, particularly of *Phylloscopus* warblers. Conversely, if the wind is westerly or southwesterly it is generally best to ignore the bushes altogether, although 'visible migrants' such as hirundines may be more obvious. Highlighted here are several examples of conditions initiating these moderate 'falls'. Interestingly, these more 'marginal' conditions can often produce scarcer or rarer species whereas, perhaps surprisingly, rarities are not necessarily a feature of the very largest 'falls'. For example, in September 1965 hardly any rarities were found amongst the hundreds of thousands of birds in East Anglia and none occurred on the Point – a phenomenon repeated in the massive Common Redstart 'fall' of 18th September 1995.

The first two weeks of August mark the real start of this autumn passerine migration and small 'falls' are regular in suitable conditions. Pristine young Northern Wheatears and Willow Warblers usually outnumber other migrants but Pied Flycatchers can also be prominent at the beginning of the month. Aquatic, Wood and Greenish Warblers have all occurred before the middle of August, though Icterine Warblers are the most regular highlight at this early stage of the season, most notably in 1977 when over 20 were recorded – see Figure 7.

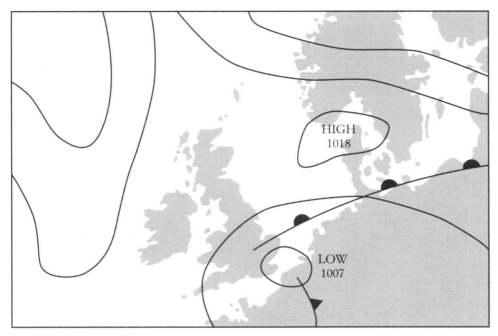

Fig. 7. Chart for 7th August 1977. Not an ideal weather pattern, with a high pressure area centred further south than normal, giving westerly winds over Norway and Sweden. However, with easterly winds off Denmark and light northeasterlies accompanied by rain over the Norfolk coast, there was a small arrival of commoner migrants, predominantly Willow Warblers, but also featuring no fewer than eight Icterine Warblers.

During the second half of August and the first half of September migration moves into full swing and favourable conditions initiate further arrivals of birds from Scandinavia and northern Europe. These typically involve Common Redstarts, Whinchats, Northern Wheatears, Garden and Willow Warblers and Pied Flycatchers and also scarcer species such as Tree Pipit, Fieldfare, Grasshopper Warbler, Lesser Whitethroat, Common Whitethroat, Wood Warbler and Spotted Flycatcher. However, most attention is focused on the regular 'semi-rarities' – Dotterel, Wryneck, Barred Warbler, Icterine Warbler, Red-backed Shrike and, increasingly likely as August turns to September, Tawny Pipit and Red-breasted Flycatcher. Although now rarer than formerly, occasional Ortolan Buntings can also still be encountered at this time though Bluethroats are increasingly a memory.

The traditional rarity in early autumn is Greenish Warbler, the Point having a particularly impressive record for this species in the second half of August and the first week of September. They typically arrive with only very small numbers of Willow Warblers or Pied Flycatchers but may also occasionally be swept up in larger 'falls'. Like their late autumn Siberian congeners they often arrive in bright, clear conditions with very light easterly winds associated with anticyclones positioned over the southern North Sea or the Baltic - conditions which do not generally trigger larger 'falls'. Other rarities found on more than one occasion in late August or early September include Great Snipe and Arctic Warbler.

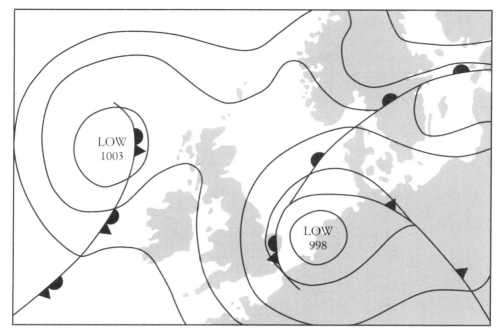

Fig. 8. Chart for 25th August 1987. Easterly winds along the southern Baltic combined with an onshore northeast wind at Blakeney Point produced a large 'fall' of migrants including several Wrynecks and Icterine Warblers and two Greenish Warblers, together with an obliging Great Snipe.

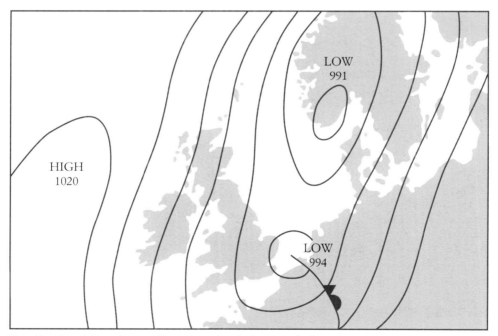

Fig. 9. Chart for 14th September 1975 showing a very disturbed pattern with a low pressure area crossing the southern North Sea giving overnight easterly winds out of the Netherlands, followed the next morning by strong northerly winds down the North Sea. Only a small number of migrants was seen but these included a Wryneck, two Bluethroats, two Barred Warblers, three Red-breasted Flycatchers and a Red-backed Shrike.

However, no two autumns are the same and in years with a regular procession of depressions tracking west to east to the north of East Anglia the winds will be predominantly westerly, giving days or even weeks with hardly a small migrant to be seen. On such occasions consolation may be found in sea-watching, especially if the wind swings into the north. Shearwaters, both Manx and Sooty, pass offshore in strong winds, as do Fulmars, Northern Gannets and Kittiwakes, and all four skua species can occur, Long-tailed Skuas peaking in mid-September, together with the very occasional Cory's or Balearic Shearwater or Sabine's Gull. Arctic Skuas can pass in particularly large numbers and often linger off the Point to be seen in aggressive pursuit of the feeding terns.

From mid-September there is a noticeably different 'feel' as the days shorten and nights become cooler. On the Point this is potentially the most exciting time of all - the variety of species is at its highest, with summer visitors still moving south out of northern Europe and winter visitors now starting to arrive. The congregations of hirundines and wagtails and the early autumn chats, warblers and flycatchers have by now largely faded away and are increasingly replaced by the first continental Robins, Song Thrushes, Blackcaps, Common Chiffchaffs and Goldcrests. The first autumn Rock Pipits and Snow and Lapland Buntings are usually seen by the middle of the month and loose parties of migrant Meadow Pipits typically frequent the high dunes. Later in the month come Fieldfares, Redwings and Bramblings. Amongst the scarcer species, Red-breasted Flycatchers from Europe and Richard's Pipits and Yellow-browed Warblers from Siberia are the most regularly seen.

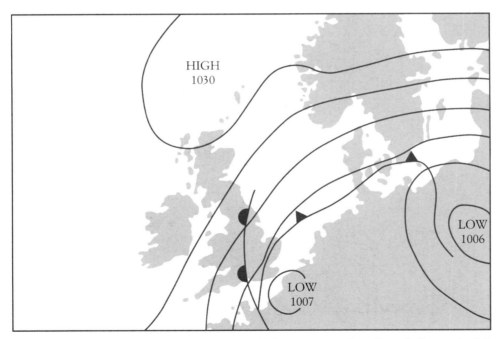

Fig. 10. Between 18th and 23rd September 2001 a large area of high pressure persisted over Russia, feeding easterly winds from southern Siberia into Scandinavia. Under the influence of a low pressure area moving slowly from northern France to Denmark, the wind in the southern North Sea remained in the north for several days. This chart is for 18th September 2001.

Even rarer Siberian species can also be sought, perhaps particularly when there is a northerly component to winds over the southern North Sea linked to an easterly flow out of Scandinavia and the Baltic region. Such conditions prevailed for a number of days during the third week of September 2001 and, even though the total number of migrants was modest, the variety was excellent. Along with Hoopoe, four Northern Great Spotted Woodpeckers, two Bluethroats (a real taste of days gone by!), Barred Warbler, Yellow-browed Warbler, Red-breasted Flycatcher and Ortolan Bunting came Pallas's Grasshopper and Radde's Warblers, the latter one of two now recorded in late September – see Figure 10.

Unfortunately, such a sustained weather pattern is relatively unusual. Easterly winds in September are normally more transient, occurring north of relatively fast-moving depressions passing to the south of East Anglia. The chart for 29th September 1991 (Figure 11) demonstrates these conditions, with a low pressure area centred to the south of Britain feeding light northeasterly winds into Norfolk. Although there was only a brief 'window of opportunity', an exciting day ensued with good numbers of commoner migrants including 50 Common Redstarts and 35 Blackcaps, whilst rarer species included Wryneck, an adult Red-throated Pipit in full summer plumage, an Icterine Warbler and up to five Siberian Stonechats. More surprisingly, the day also produced an excellent sea-watch, featuring ten Leach's Storm-petrels, an adult Sabine's Gull and a number of Pomarine Skuas trailing long lines of Kittiwakes.

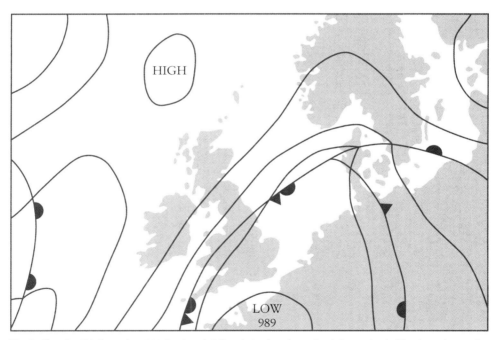

Fig. 11. Chart for 29th September 1991 showing a brief interlude of northeasterly winds associated with a depression moving quickly to the south of Britain.

Nevertheless, despite such occasional excitements, September can be, and often is, a most frustrating month if the wind stays relentlessly in the west. Then perhaps only an occasional Lapland Bunting or, at sea, a Red-necked Grebe can relieve an otherwise quiet month.

Of all months, October is arguably the most dominated by migration. The onset of winter becomes suddenly obvious, temperatures plunge over northern Europe and Russia, the days shorten rapidly and the weather conditions over western Europe become progressively more hazardous to migrant birds. In most years the lazy days and balmy nights of August seem far behind and a real sense of urgency dictates movements as birds are seized by the imperative to reach suitable wintering areas.

October sees a further change in the species mix. Large 'falls' of Robins can be a feature early in the month, as in 1951 and again in 1998, whilst large arrivals of Goldcrests become more likely as the month progresses and Wrens and Dunnocks become more obvious. High-flying flocks of winter thrushes and small numbers of Bramblings can be heard passing over and although a few linger in the *Suaeda* bushes the majority hurry off inland. Diurnal migrants include arriving or coasting flocks of Northern Lapwings, Sky Larks and Starlings. The very occasional Great Grey Shrike may be seen harrying small migrants and the first winter Shore Lark is also usually recorded at this time. Hen Harriers and Merlins quarter the dunes and saltings hunting small birds whilst usually secretive immigrants, for example Water Rail, Jack Snipe, Woodcock and Long-eared and Short-eared Owls, may occasionally be flushed from the edges of the *Suaeda*.

When there is a strong onshore wind, sea-watchers may be rewarded with close views of Leach's Storm-petrels or Pomarine and Great Skuas and Little Gulls or, if really lucky, a European Storm Petrel, Grey Phalarope or Sabine's Gull. An increasing number and variety of wildfowl, divers and grebes are also an exciting feature of this period as they pass west offshore, notably returning Dark-bellied Brent Geese, Common Shelduck, Eurasian Wigeon and Common Scoter. Flocks of the latter, with the occasional Velvet Scoter, may also build up temporarily off the Marrams but rarely linger into the winter.

October is generally regarded as the best month for Siberian birds. The loud *'schreep'* of a Richard's Pipit can still occasionally be heard, announcing the usually brief presence of this excitable and evocative species. Early October in Norfolk also sees the arrival of further small waves of Yellow-browed Warblers, though usually only single birds are seen on the Point. Arrivals of both these species typically take place in settled anticyclonic conditions, usually with light southeasterly winds.

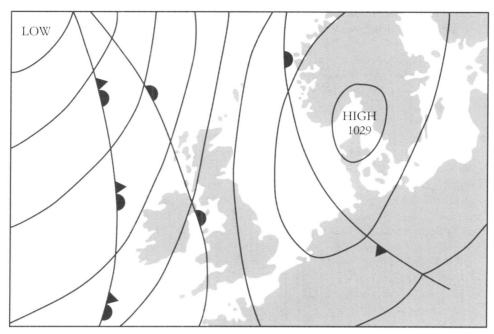

Fig. 12. Chart for 1st October 1979. A Yellow-browed Warbler arrived on Blakeney Point in typical conditions with light southeasterly winds across the southern North Sea. The same conditions often also favour the arrival of Red-breasted Flycatchers.

As well as Richard's Pipits and Yellow-browed Warblers, rarer relatives such as Olive-backed Pipit, Siberian Stonechat, Pallas's, Radde's and Dusky Warblers and Siberian Chiffchaff have all been encountered on two or more occasions on the Point in October. These species have a standard autumn migration route east and then south from Siberian breeding grounds to wintering grounds in southeast Asia or, in the case of Siberian Chiffchaff, the Indian subcontinent. Why some individuals migrate in the opposite direction to arrive in northwest Europe has long been the subject of speculation. 'Reverse migration' has been suggested as a possible mechanism, though the apparent track, initially west into the Baltic region and then progressively southwest through Britain, suggests that the explanation may be more complex than a simple 'mirror image' of the standard route. We may, for example, be witnessing random attempts by populations of these species to establish more westerly wintering ranges, perhaps re-adopting routes lost to the last Ice Age.

However, it is also possible that post-fledging dispersal from Siberian breeding ranges is taking place randomly to all points of the compass. The odds will, of course, be severely stacked against those individuals heading north or south, where their largely unobserved flights will be cut short by mountains, deserts or Arctic ice. Those travelling west, however, which successfully break through to western Europe before winter 'closes the door' not only stand a slim chance of survival but are likely to pass through areas such as Norfolk where birdwatchers may notice them.

Weather patterns also favour this western route for it has long been noted that easterly or southeasterly winds to the south of large anticyclones over European Russia and Siberia facilitate arrivals of these species and that the numbers of such migrants are greatest when these areas of high pressure are strongest or most persistent. Once in the Baltic region, these Siberian birds continue their journey in a more southwesterly direction under the influence of western Europe's more volatile and maritime climate, sometimes arriving on their own, but often also becoming swept up in 'falls' of more local northern European species. Whatever the reasons for the occurrence of these Siberian wanderers, it is clear that the weather in the North Sea merely influences the final stages of a process initially driven by other forces.

As in early and mid-autumn, large 'falls' are relatively rare in October, though two of the more memorable were those of 16th October 1988 and 18th October 1990. Interestingly, these occurred in very different circumstances. In 1988 a large anticyclone was centred over Sweden, dominating all of northern Europe, pulling in cold air from Russia and giving light easterly winds and dull overcast conditions on the north Norfolk coast – see Figure 13. Amongst the large numbers of thrushes and other migrants, the highlights were a Pied Wheatear and a Radde's Warbler. As with many of the larger 'falls', birds were seen arriving from early morning right through until dusk, whereas on days when only a few birds are seen they tend to arrive mainly before the middle of the day.

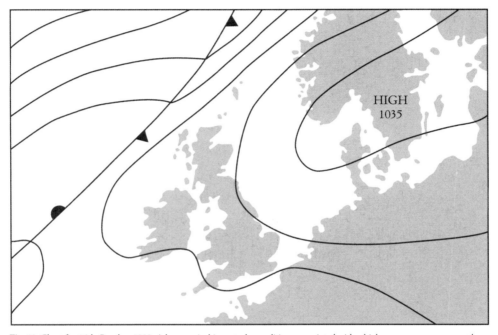

Fig. 13. Chart for 16th October 1988. A large arrival in easterly conditions associated with a high pressure area over southern Scandinavia.

The conditions on 18th October 1990 were exceptional, and unique in the authors' experience. Thick fog persisted for most of the day and the visibility was so poor that the Harbour was completely invisible. This must account for the numbers of birds seen on the ground, particularly the thrushes which carpeted the entire length of the shingle bank in their thousands. Unexpected finds included two 'finger-tame' Arctic Redpolls (with another two days later) and an Olive-backed Pipit which uncharacteristically frequented the saltings, clearly unaware of the more hospitable terrain just across the Harbour – see Figure 14.

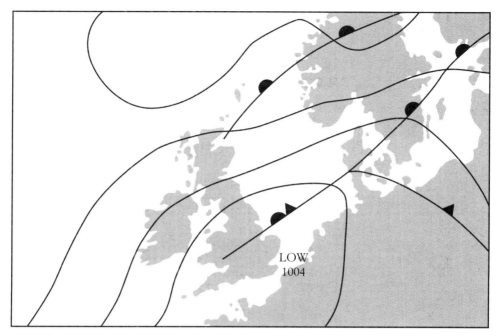

Fig. 14. Chart for 18th October 1990. A huge 'fall' in poor visibility associated with slack northeasterly winds and the northward passage of an occluded front.

Warblers are scarce by late October, comprising typically only Blackcaps and Common Chiffchaffs, but other passerines can include late Robins and Goldcrests and, particularly in southeasterly conditions, the occasional Black Redstart, European Stonechat, Ring Ouzel or Firecrest. Arboreal species find the Point particularly inhospitable at this time of the year, probably because the relatively exposed location and cooler temperatures afford few feeding opportunities. Many birds that do land are only transient visitors, dallying briefly before tripping across the Harbour in search of more favourable cover.

Despite the habitat and feeding limitations, however, October has produced a respectable list of regularly-occurring rarities. This list is dominated by the Siberian wanderers but other 'regulars' include Desert Wheatears from the deserts of Central Asia and Arctic Redpolls and Little Buntings from the Scandinavian tundra and birch zone.

Irruptive or nomadic species, driven from their continental home ranges by high population levels or failures of their normal food supply, can also be a feature of October, though their appearances are by their very nature erratic. Amongst those to have occurred on the Point at this time are Rough-legged Buzzard, Northern Great Spotted Woodpecker, Continental Blue, Great and Coal Tits, Waxwing, Common and Arctic Redpolls, Northern Bullfinch and Common Crossbill, though years can go by between arrivals of any of these species. From closer to home come more local irruptions of Bearded Tits. These species can provide some incongruous moments, for example Great Spotted Woodpeckers clinging to *Suaeda* fronds, high-flying Bearded Tits or ridiculously tame redpolls or Common Crossbills.

As October turns to November the westerly passage of Dark-bellied Brent Geese, ducks, divers and grebes continues, with Great Northern and Black-throated Divers often a particular feature. Strong onshore winds at this time can still produce heavy sea movements, particularly of

Kittiwakes and auks and, in some years, high numbers of Pomarine Skuas and Little Auks can be seen, displaced into the North Sea by rough conditions further north. Little Auks are notable for often occurring in near-calm conditions, invariably giving splendid views as they hurtle rapidly west through the breaking surf. Coasting flocks of Bewick's Swans, en route to the Fens, are also an evocative sight at this time and some days are characterised by a steady westward procession of *argentatus* Herring Gulls.

Winter visitors continue to arrive into November, mainly thrushes, together with smaller numbers of Northern Lapwings, Sky Larks and Starlings, and the wintering Snow Bunting flock starts to gather along the beach. Large arrivals of Blackbirds are a regular feature of this time, gathering in large groups at the tips of the spits and in the Lupins before continuing to the 'mainland'. The day-long passages of Hooded Crows, however, are now but a distant memory.

In some years November has produced unusually late migrants including Tree Pipit, Common Nightingale, Bluethroat, Common Redstart, Reed Warbler and Willow Warbler. In terms of rarities, November continues the theme set by October and has contributed further examples of Desert Wheatear, Pallas's Warbler, Dusky Warbler, Siberian Chiffchaff, Arctic Redpoll and Little Bunting. Light southeasterly winds and unseasonally high temperatures are often the best conditions in which to look for these late stragglers.

The close of the season is usually marked by the sight of parties of Starlings flying in from the sea and hurrying away inland - a sure sign of the winter months to come.

Small migrants on the Plantation fence. A typical sight in autumn 'fall' conditions. (*James McCallum*)

Oystercatchers and Common Gull. Common Gulls are significant predators of the eggs and chicks of Oystercatchers and other ground-nesting birds. (*James McCallum*)

Great Days

4th - 5th September 1965

Ian Wallace

I'd like to pretend that my share of the famous 'bird avalanche' of early September 1965 came from study of synoptic charts and an inspired dash to north Norfolk. In fact my diary does note an unusual weather situation for the night of 2nd – 3rd, illustrated with a sketched chart, but the only bird that I enjoyed on the 3rd was my first British Pied-billed Grebe at Chew Valley Lake. As I ticked off another Yank I had no idea of what was simultaneously pouring onto East Anglia, and it was mainly the lure of a cock Black-eared Wheatear, present at Salthouse since 31st August, that drew my wife Karin and me north from Epping Forest at 0630 on the 4th.

About halfway between Swaffham and Fakenham the weather 'lowered' into clammy scudding clouds. When Wheatears started to appear along the road just north of Fakenham and hirundines also became prominent, I sensed an unusual 'fall' (a term learnt from the Americans in the '50s). As we turned east through Cley and drove along the marsh road, the first species to strike the eye was Whinchat. They popped about in all directions and, disembarking at Salthouse, we stepped straight out onto a carpet of night migrants and under a heavy coasting passage of waders. Joining up with 'the Selsey Bill men', we learnt that on the previous day the arrival had been more than a 'fall'… a 'crash' at least. As we pushed out into the east Salthouse marsh there were birds everywhere on the ground, on its fence posts, in its pools, in the sky. Sitting on its appointed stake, the rare wheatear was splendid but there was so much going on that we were soon on our way, hoping for a rarity find of our own.

Suaeda bush-bashing (a term of James Ferguson-Lees) along the Point had to be the best option but we didn't have to go that far for 'first strike'. Near the hillock one of the Pieds (Flycatchers) was particularly tame and I gave it a closer look. Yes, it was paler/greyer. Yes, it did have a full wing-bar (extending onto the primaries) and a faint collar effect. Incredibly it had to be a Collared and, after half an hour with it, as close as 20 feet, we were sure (but not later the Ten Rare Men!).

With *embarras de richesse* now a definite problem and our three hours half-gone we decided that a dash along Blakeney Point was still the best last ploy. Back to the car (Morris Minor), park at the Coastguard, out along to the Watch House cover we piled. Even from the sparsest clump Redstarts could be flushed and when we got into real *Suaeda* the full spectrum of the crash, nay avalanche, became apparent. Lesser Whitethroats and Garden Warblers outnumbered Common Whitethroats three-to-one and Redstarts were simply everywhere, with glimpses of Bluethroats thrown in at ground level. On any patch of grass Wrynecks appeared and, at one, a Red-backed Shrike was encircled by Willow Warblers and the odd Chiffchaff. On the shingle Wheatears and Whinchats held sway.

We crossed to the last big *Suaeda* belt before the Watch House and immediately were amongst streaked *Acrocephali*. I put one up from my feet and, with the sun at last almost fully through the dispersing clouds, I was dazzled by its plumage tone. Surely no Sedge? I paused and, true to form, it took a look back. It was a superb Aquatic Warbler, about the best-marked I'd ever seen. It played well for those following in our tracks. What would be next? Alas, nothing for us. It was time to go home to 'Pipit' (nickname of our first daughter).

By 2200 I had plans to return with Bob Emmett on the 'morrow.

Opinions on the second day of the aftermath vary. To my eyes there were actually more birds at Salthouse, with Whinchats now spread into the cornfields and early Siskins on the move. Following up on a Bluethroat took us down the main ditch on the inner side of the marsh track. As we came to the bend a weakly flitting thing got up and dived into cover. 'Crake?' asked Bob. 'Why not?' I replied. Sure enough, a gentle thrash produced splendid views of a Spotted Crake.

So once again to the Point. It was quickly obvious that four out of five of yesterday's birds had gone but there were still moments of magic, as with a large dark, streaked pipit (never identified), a Nightingale in the Lupins and three Wrynecks in the same pine tree. In an appropriate 'final event' we shepherded two Bluethroats – one a fine drake Red-spotted – from bush to bush for at least half a mile, enjoying splendid views in close flight and very occasionally on the ground.

My diary closed with the note that Cley had lived up to its reputation at long last. Richard Richardson had never seen anything like it. A schedule shows that I looked closely at 1,038 night migrants. How many I just walked through is not recorded.

Over the 38 years since what was actually a Suffolk avalanche and a Norfolk overspill, the birds that have taken the best memory slot are the Bluethroats. On the 4th we saw 16 between Salthouse and the Watch House and the two shepherded on the 5th had to be well west of any of the 16. The minimum of 18 birds on two autumn days would be unthinkable now but it does not compete with the 80 seen in September 1884. If only one could be born again in the past when there were so many more birds!

10th October 1975

Steve Joyner

'Great Days on Blakeney Point' will for many be a contradiction in terms as it conjures up memories of eight-mile walks along soft shingle, poor views of common migrants and vows never to visit again. However, as every patch-worker knows, perseverance is the watchword, and for the persistent there will eventually be the never-to-be-forgotten day.

It may be the excitement of a spectacular arrival of migrants, the buzz from finding a really rare bird or the personal satisfaction from identifying a particularly difficult species in testing conditions. There is even a perverse pleasure in seeing a 'good bird for the patch' no matter how common elsewhere. A recent Coot on the Point was, for instance, greeted with great enthusiasm!

The vintage October of 1975 was one of those special times. The weather was ideal, the synoptic charts showed isobars flowing horizontally due west out of Russia and curving south over the North Sea, like tramlines carrying Siberian migrants straight onto the north Norfolk coast. Amazingly, the favourable conditions prevailed for twelve days.

The first few days were characterised by large movements of passerines and arrivals of hordes of thrushes overnight. The fields and hedgerows near the coast were thronged with newly-arrived visitors. The numbers gradually subsided, only to be replaced by an amazing procession of eastern vagrants. The Holkham Woods rarity list was unprecedented, including a Yellow-browed Bunting (the first for Britain) and a Black-throated Thrush (fifth for Britain). October 1975 was for many of us our first taste of several rarities only previously known by their short entry as 'accidentals' in the back of Peterson's Field Guide.

Blakeney Point's contribution to the rarities list was more meagre, with a single Dusky Warbler and Rustic Bunting. However, despite the exotics found elsewhere, one of the abiding memories of that autumn was arriving at the Cley Coastguards car park on 10th October with Norman Williams and immediately being aware that something special was happening. Lines of Brent Geese and ducks were streaming by over the sea and as we walked along the Point continuous flocks of coasting Lapwings, Sky Larks and Starlings worked their way westwards along the shoreline. Overhead the characteristic calls of thrushes could be heard. Hundreds of Redwings, Blackbirds and Song Thrushes were tumbling out of the sky and swooping low over the beach, the more tired individuals landing immediately, whilst others continued inland low over the fields and the harbour. Exhausted Goldcrests were skimming low over the waves and across the shingle and diving into the first available cover.

The sheer volume of birds reinforced the feeling that we were within touching distance of a rarity. However, the only unusual bird seen was an evocative Great Grey Shrike flying westwards over the saltings amongst a flock of Starlings. As the spectacular movements gradually reduced we rushed back to the car and made a dash to Holkham hoping to make the most of the remaining hours of daylight. Sufficient time remained for us to search the Dell and be rewarded with views of a Yellow- browed Warbler and the discovery of the first British autumn mainland record of Olive-backed Pipit.

Even these finds have not eclipsed the memories of the huge movement on this exciting and spectacular day.

27th May 1992

Andy Stoddart

During May the ears of migration students are tuned constantly to the weather forecasts. Whilst most Mays are characterised by long spells of cool weather and only occasional arrivals of birds on warm zephyrs from the continent, 1992 was to be different.

In the early days of the month a Short-toed Lark had quickened pulses, but on 14th May the wind swung firmly into the southeast and temperatures soared. This perfect combination of conditions produced in the space of a couple of hours a Red-throated Pipit in the Marrams, a female Red-footed Falcon at the Hood, a male Red-footed Falcon at the Long Hills and a Montagu's Harrier over the Lifeboat House, followed the next day by a superb Woodchat Shrike in the Plantation.

After a temporary lull, the long-range southeasterly vector reasserted itself on 25th and a new Red-throated Pipit promptly appeared in the Long Hills – unusually a female with no red on the throat.

Work intruded on 26th but, as conditions remained settled on 27th, an afternoon was spared. In the bright crystal clear conditions and high temperatures, working the *Suaeda* was hard work and by the time the Watch House had been reached no birds had presented themselves. Indeed it was at this point that Graeme Cresswell and I met another birdwatcher returning from the end of the Point with the rather disappointing news that there appeared to be no birds there either.

Nevertheless we trudged on, covering the Hood, again with no result. On rounding the corner onto the base of Yankee Ridge, however, a slim, pale shape caught the eye, slinking unobtrusively in the *Suaeda*. A close approach revealed the day's first migrant - a fine Icterine Warbler complete with long bill and wings, staring face and silver wing-panel and only the fifth ever spring Icterine on the Point. With spirits raised, a few more steps produced a shockingly bright male Grey-headed

Wagtail, bound for Scandinavian forest clearings, striding around on the ridge's central gravel area. Perhaps there were birds after all!

Tradition demands seeking Red-throated Pipits alongside Grey-headed Wagtails and, so as not to disappoint, a superb fully-saturated male Red-throated Pipit immediately leapt into view within yards of the wagtail and perched perfectly on a *Suaeda* sprig. It promptly launched itself into the air, hovering and fluttering in song-flight as though over a tundra territory, filling the afternoon with its soft, liquid cadences. Just delightful! Scandinavia-bound, all these birds had clearly ridden the persistent warm vector and found themselves far out over the North Sea before making a welcome landfall on the Point.

Having gorged on this fine trio of birds we headed eagerly across the saltmarsh towards the Sandhills. On crossing the shallow creek a small bird flew out from our feet and called the unmistakable loud, ringing *'psseeeeeeh'* of a Red-throated Pipit. Surely we had just left it on the ridge? A quick bit of manoeuvring brought it into view – a much duller individual with a pale orange watercolour wash confined to the throat and more heavily-streaked below. A second bird, doubtless a female, and the third in three days!

Flushed with success, the walk to the Plantation hardly seemed to register. On arrival, a pale shape doing its best to remain unseen in the dark shadows of the pine became another Icterine Warbler, thereby producing the first multiple spring arrival for the Point.

A quick search around the Point as afternoon turned to evening produced a few common migrants but in the Sandhills a Red-throated Pipit passed over calling. We put it down as one of the other two birds but the day had still not played its last card for, on arrival at the Watch House *Suaeda*, we were confronted with an indisputable third Icterine Warbler, thereby making a spring day-total record not only for the Point but for Norfolk as well.

Such miraculous days are of course rare but are all the more enjoyable when they materialise from such inauspicious beginnings. With subsequent days also producing Greenish Warbler, Thrush Nightingale, Common Rosefinch and Red-backed Shrike, spring 1992 will live long in the memory and has still not been surpassed for its run of scarce and rare birds.

16th May 2003

James McCallum

Friday 16th May started dull and grey with a little light drizzle in the air. Aaron Boughtflower and myself began with a look at the brambles and elders of the Lupins – our garden! A hen Blackbird skimmed low over us to land in the highest brambles - a good start but morale dropped when it appeared to be the only migrant here. Next, the Plantation was empty but a look in the Tamarisk behind the Laboratory lifted spirits with a female Blackcap and a Willow Warbler. Despite the poor start we were hopeful of a good day.

Around mid-morning, now joined by fellow Warden David Wood, we set out once more. Within minutes a passerine came bounding in high over the dunes. It was clearly a pipit, but looked stocky and long in both tail and body. I called to my companions to look at it and fortunately it dropped down, perching on the top of a small elder, confirming suspicions of Tawny Pipit. It was quite flighty but by carefully moving through the dunes and not breaking the skyline, we were rewarded with good views. Richard Porter appeared nearby and we waved him over, but the bird flipped over the next dune ridge, landing somewhere near the Lifeboat House. This enabled us to grab our 'scopes and, having relocated it, we got some fantastic views. It was a smart, clean-cut bird with only a light sprinkle of streaks on the sides of its breast.

After a while we headed off towards the Plantation and the Tamarisk once again. The Blackcap and Willow Warbler had been joined by a further Willow Warbler and a Chiffchaff, while several Wheatears flew up to land on the chimney of the Laboratory and roofs of the wooden huts. Working back through the grey dunes we headed towards the tern hide, passing through a bay of low *Suaeda* on the way. Continuing to the very last bush a larger stockier bird flew from my feet. It flipped over the marrams out of my view. Dave and Aaron got a brief flash of red, suggesting a Redstart. It was, however, clearly bigger and as it suddenly dived into a nearby bramble its silhouette showed it to be a nightingale - to work out which species we would need better views. We waited by the bramble then re-checked the area, but couldn't re-find it, so we decided to have a look at another area then return later. Richard Porter joined us in this further search, which again proved fruitless.

Walking up the boardwalk Aaron said 'raptor' as a bird of prey flicked above the dune ridge. It was clearly a small, slim-winged harrier, and it was heading diagonally towards us. Raising my binoculars I was totally shocked to be looking at a Pallid Harrier. It was a magical, almost unbelievable moment as it passed only forty yards from us. In many ways it was a blueprint of the bird that had wintered at Warham. It was still in full juvenile dress with rich sandy unstreaked underparts, superb head and neck markings and blackish secondaries. The harrier now passed high over the bay and out over the Harbour, then over the same stretch of coast where its predecessor had wintered.

We met Steve Joyner, Andy Stoddart and Giles Dunmore at the beginning of the boardwalk and told them our news. Quickly putting the disappointment of missing the harrier behind them, they became very interested in the nightingale. They soon re-found the bird, pencilling in Thrush Nightingale on the first few flight views. Although only in flight, the views were very good and we were now able to make a rational identification. The upperparts were dull dingy grey-brown and the underparts were clearly dull and smudged with brown-grey, the overall colouration being reminiscent of an outsized young Black Redstart.

We decided that we would gain nothing further by repeated flushing so, as it had moved into a patchwork of small, isolated *Suaeda* clumps, we would wait in the hope of getting some views on the ground. The nightingale, however, had other ideas and flipped over the nearby dunes and, despite searching, none of us could find it.

By late afternoon everyone had left and, although drizzle persisted, the sun had come out. We decided to have a quick look for the nightingale. To our amazement it flew up at our feet once again from the very same spot where we first saw it. This was clearly its favourite spot, but some new tactics were needed if we were going to get some good views on the ground.

Tucking up in the bushes, keeping as dry as possible, we waited quietly. After half an hour we got our first view – a high-speed run across the narrow paths, followed ten minutes later by another dash. Over the next couple of hours the bird became more relaxed, the dashing runs turning to hops and bounds. Bit by bit we were able to piece together its features and subtle colours and markings. Finally it hopped out a couple of times and froze in the middle of the path, giving some super views through the telescope. Although much more dingy than its more familiar counterpart, it shared many of the behavioural and structural features. However, the subtle, delicate grey markings on the face and breast combined with the large, dark pale-rimmed eye rendered it quite attractive.

Later that evening heavy rain set in once more so it was no surprise when the nightingale appeared on the path once more at 0630 the following morning. It seemed much more relaxed but I was surprised when it flew to a nearby bramble and, following a few loud croaks, broke into its full, loud, rich, fluid song. Nearby a Corn Bunting landed and it was ironic to note that in present times one is as likely to see a Thrush Nightingale as a Corn Bunting on Blakeney Point!

(This account is a slightly shortened version of 'A Memorable Spring Fall on Blakeney Point' which first appeared in Norfolk Bird Club Bulletin No. 51).

Pallid Harrier. (*James McCallum*)

Systematic List of Birds

Recording Area

For the purposes of this book the birds of Blakeney Point are defined as those recorded anywhere along the shingle ridge west of the Cley beach road, including the tidal sands and muds of Blakeney Harbour, the sandbars at the Harbour mouth and the open sea visible from land. The area therefore does not include the fields at Blakeney Fresh Marsh or the saltmarshes at Blakeney, Morston and Stiffkey. This treatment corresponds with that of Rowan (1918).

A particular problem is posed by birds which have been seen at Cley passing along the coast and which therefore must also have entered the Blakeney Point area. This is especially true of course of seabirds where sea-watching is carried out far more regularly from Cley than it is from the Point itself. A pragmatic decision has been taken to exclude all such records, including Cley sea-watching records, unless the observer was known to be stationed to the west of Cley Coastguards. Although this will result in some 'lost' records, this treatment will not unduly affect the status descriptions in the Systematic List. The only exception to this policy is the inclusion of a record of a Great Shearwater which would otherwise be missing from the list entirely.

All locations referred to in the species accounts can be found on the map before the 'Introduction to Blakeney Point' chapter.

Period Covered

Records are included up to the end of May 2005.

Sources and Attributions

Records are included from a wide range of sources, both published and non-published. All published sources are listed in the bibliography, but the key references are:-

Issues of *Wild Bird Protection in Norfolk* to 1952.
Issues of the *Norfolk Bird and Mammal Report* 1953 to 2003.
Gantlett, S.J.M. 1995. *The Birds of Cley* (5th edn.).
Pashley, H.N. 1925. *Notes on the Birds of Cley, Norfolk*.
Richardson, R.A. 1962. *Checklist of the Birds of Cley and Neighbouring Norfolk Parishes*.
Rowan, W. 1918. Annotated List of the Birds of Blakeney Point, Norfolk. *British Birds* 8: 11

and *Transactions of the Norfolk and Norwich Naturalists' Society* 10 (30): 256-279.

Seago, M.J. 1977. *Birds of Norfolk* (2nd edn.).

Taylor, M., Seago, M., Allard P. and Dorling, D. 1999. *The Birds of Norfolk*.

White, D.J.B. 1969 and 1981. *An Annotated Checklist of the Birds of Blakeney Point, Norfolk*.

WeBS count data (wildfowl from 1982 and waders from 1993).

The other main source is the authors' and others' personal notes, notably those of R.G.H. Cant. Pinchen's hand-written diaries for 1922, 1926, 1927 and 1929 have recently come to light and these are also drawn on as appropriate. These local sources are generally cited in respect of individual records but in an attempt to assist the flow of the narrative broader statements on species' identification, taxonomy, status, distribution and movements are not generally referenced. Sources for these statements are listed in the Bibliography, though particular mention should be made of *The Migration Atlas: movements of the birds of Britain and Ireland* (Wernham *et al.* 2002) which has been drawn on extensively.

Despite an attempt to trace as many records as possible, there will nevertheless be some which have been overlooked across a period of over 120 years of bird recording. These are most likely to involve those species which are scarce or rare on the Point but which are common elsewhere and so would have received little or no mention in the pages of county-wide reports and avifaunas. The recording of species scarce or rare in the county as a whole is likely to be much more complete. All omissions and errors are of course the responsibility of the authors who would welcome details of any missing records. It is nevertheless hoped that the records assembled here are more than sufficient to give an accurate indication of each species' status.

A particular problem applies in much of the older literature where the precise location of records is often unclear. References to the *Suaeda* bushes along the shingle ridge, and therefore relating to Blakeney Point, are often just attributed to 'Cley', 'Blakeney' or 'the beach'. The best judgement on the location of these records has been made from the available information and, where there appears to be some doubt, this is always clearly stated. The published literature contains many references to birds recorded at 'Blakeney' but these have not been taken to refer to the Point unless there is good evidence that this is the case.

There is also some ambiguity about a number of records in Rowan, Pashley and White, with contradictions both between themselves and with other sources. It should be noted in particular that in his introduction to Pashley's *Notes on the Birds of Cley, Norfolk*, Riviere makes specific reference to Pashley's unreliability over dates. A number of date errors are also scattered through White's list. Such cases of ambiguity are highlighted and the best judgements are proposed in the light of information published elsewhere. It is also worth noting that, although White's work was clearly based on Rowan's earlier list, he seems to have made little or no use of the information contained in Pashley's diaries and they are not listed in his bibliography.

A number of old records now seem somewhat surprising in view of modern experience. However, it would be inappropriate to undertake a wholesale review of records prior to the creation of local and national records committees. In many cases the status of some species will have changed significantly over the course of over a century and it would be an error to 'rewrite history' and so lose potentially valuable information. Potentially contentious old records contained in the literature are therefore retained, albeit sometimes with an explanatory note. Other species whose identification is questioned in the literature or whose appearance is otherwise unproven are included in an appendix. It is worth stating here that the authors have scrupulously avoided acting as a local 'records committee' and that no published records have been 'reviewed out' in the preparation of this book.

Since the creation of local and national records committees, the compilation task has become much easier. Nevertheless, as knowledge advances, older records which were not submitted at the time, but which would now probably gain acceptance were they to be submitted, have been referred to in order to portray a more accurate picture of the species' status. The same approach has also been taken with a few records known to be genuine but which have, for whatever reason, never been submitted. Such 'unofficial' records are, however, always clearly identified in the text. Unless otherwise indicated, all rarity records listed here have been submitted to and accepted by the relevant local or national committee. Throughout the text the *British Birds* Rarities Committee is referred to as 'BBRC' and the British Ornithologists' Union Records Committee as 'BOURC'.

Records of scarce or rare species prior to modern times are, where known, generally attributed to an observer (or, more likely, a shooter!) as this has a degree of historical interest. With the recent exponential growth in the number of such records, however, it would now be onerous to attempt to list all the finders and identifiers involved. These details are largely published elsewhere and are, in any case, of secondary importance.

Species Accounts

In drafting the species accounts we have tried to maintain a consistent approach to their content and structure without being over-formulaic. We have for each species attempted to review, as far as is possible from the available sources, its historical status, establish its recent and current status, provide some context for, and interpretation of, its pattern of occurrences and, wherever appropriate, give a flavour of typical encounters.

Taxonomy

The taxonomic status of the bird forms occurring in Britain is becoming increasingly fluid, with no definitive list now reflecting the views of all interested parties. We have therefore chosen to adopt taxonomic judgements in the light of the most up to date and reliable information as we see it, much of which is driven by the production of evidence to support the separate treatment of taxa under the Phylogenetic Species Concept (PSC). Such an approach therefore deviates from the BOURC and *British Birds* lists in a small handful of instances. This stance should not be construed as criticism of BOURC or of *British Birds* but we hope that it will more accurately reflect an emerging consensus and avoid a premature dating of the book's content. It should be pointed out that the authors are not taxonomists and that the species list presented here makes no claim to be definitive.

The few such deviations from the BOURC and *British Birds* lists are clearly identified. We have in all cases attempted to deal in the currency of bird forms or taxa and we have tried to make it clear in all cases which form is under discussion should future work result in an alternative taxonomy. As a rule-of-thumb, all well-differentiated (i.e. diagnosable in the field) non-clinal taxa are accorded separate treatment, irrespective of their current specific or subspecific status.

All recent (as at December 2004) BOURC recommendations regarding species placement within genera have been adopted, most notably those affecting Great Skua (now included in *Stercorarius*), Snowy Owl (now included in *Bubo*) and Corn Bunting (now included in *Emberiza*).

Species Order

In July 2003 the BOURC adopted the recommendations of its Taxonomic Subcommittee and placed the wildfowl and gamebirds at the beginning of the Systematic List. This new, although as yet unfamiliar, approach is followed here in the expectation that this revised version of the traditional Voous order will become generally accepted, as it has already been by *British Birds* and the *Norfolk Bird Report*. The BOURC December 2003 recommendations on species order within the genus *Sylvia* have also been adopted.

Terminology

Terminology is also in something of a state of flux. Other than in a few cases where the taxonomy adopted here differs from that recognised by BOURC and *British Birds* we have adopted the names proposed by *British Birds* in January 2004 (as amended in April 2005) . However, in order to secure the maximum possible clarity over which species or form is being discussed we have also listed any alternative English names known to be in use, including those previously proposed by *British Birds* and those used in the BOURC list. We have also listed names in general use for a number of subspecies. Ultimate clarity is hopefully provided by the use of scientific names, with trinomials being used in all appropriate cases. Shorter, more familiar versions of the full name are usually used within the species text to assist the flow of the narrative.

In the case of scientific names we have attempted to maintain nomenclatural accuracy and grammatical correctness and have incorporated all such BOURC announcements to December 2004.

The Systematic List

All relevant species categorised by BOURC as A, B or C and which are not proven or near-proven escapes are included in the main list. Those categorised as D or E and records of birds in A, B or C deemed to be proven or near-proven escapes are treated in an appendix.

Status Descriptors

The following general status descriptors are used:-

Very Rare	Fewer than 10 records in total.
Rare	Less than annual in occurrence.
Scarce	1-20 records per year.
Common	More than 20 records per year.
Very Common	Present almost daily at the appropriate season.

These descriptors are, of course, not rigid categories and are designed only to give a broad indication of status. In reality the diversity of occurrence patterns does not lend itself to simple categorisation and detailed reference to the species account will normally be necessary.

Photographs

An attempt has been made to identify all rarity records supported by photographs, particularly those published in the local or national literature. Where possible, published photographs taken on the Point are referenced to allow examination.

Mute Swan
Cygnus olor

Rowan and White list this largely sedentary introduced species as occasional in small numbers, chiefly in winter, but sometimes in summer and autumn. A flock now often frequents the outflow of the River Stiffkey on the south side of the Harbour at the edge of our area. A few birds are, however, also regularly seen in the Glaven Channel. Only very rarely do birds venture over the shingle ridge to the seaward side. Mean WeBS counts are around four to five birds, with a recorded maximum of 18.

Bewick's Swan (Tundra Swan)
Cygnus columbianus bewickii

Rowan records only one bird which had been shot 'many years ago' and two or three other sightings, always in winter. Pinchen's diaries note herds of eight and ten 'swans' (possibly this species) west on 6th November 1922 and specifically note a Bewick's on 22nd November of that year.

White, however, records it as a fairly regular visitor from the 1950s on passage to newly-established Fenland wintering grounds. This movement takes birds from their breeding grounds in Arctic Siberia through the Baltic and along North Sea coasts to Britain.

Birds are still usually recorded passing west in small family groups in late October and November, with a peak count of 43 on 27th October 1989. The earliest autumn record involves a herd of eight on 5th October 1989. The soft bugling of these Siberian swans from a grey sky is always a particularly evocative feature of late autumn on the Point.

Records outside this period are rare, though 'herds of over 50' were in the Harbour during a period of severe frost in early 1956, up to 24 were in the Harbour in January 1968 and 20 flew east over the Harbour on 17th December 2000. The largest number recorded, however, is 70 on 30th December 1964.

There are to our knowledge no records of birds on return spring passage as most leave the Fens in an easterly direction to pass through the centre of the county, often being seen in February and March over Norwich and Great Yarmouth.

Whooper Swan
Cygnus cygnus

Rowan lists the species as rare, having occurred several times passing over high in severe weather. Pinchen's diaries contain notes of herds of four and 60-70 on 22nd November 1922, 50 on 26th November 1922 and a further five on 27th October 1926. Given current understandings of swan movements and an acknowledgement of the still real difficulties in separating the two 'wild swans' at range, however, it is perhaps best to retain an open mind over the identity of some of these earlier records.

In modern times, birds passing westwards in autumn have been almost exclusively Bewick's Swans. This reflects the fact that the majority of the Whooper Swans wintering on the Fens are Icelandic in origin, although some continental birds have also been shown to reach Britain.

White lists the species as a scarce winter visitor, with an unprecedented herd of about 100 east on 26th December 1954, and notes that the appearance of this swan is said to foretell a thaw after a long cold spell.

The species is nowadays better described as rare. The only recent records are as follows:-

5 on 28th October 1984.
5 on 1st January 1985.
5th November 1989.

7 on 7th November 1999.
4 on 4th November 2000.
22 on 6th November 2003.
14th November 2004.

The concentration of records in late October and early November is striking.

Tundra/Taiga Bean Goose
Anser serrirostris rossicus/A. fabalis fabalis
Although not currently 'split' by BOURC, the two forms of Bean Goose occurring in Britain are increasingly recognised as specifically distinct – a large, long-necked and long-billed Russian and Scandinavian taiga-breeding form and a smaller, shorter-necked and shorter-billed Russian tundra-breeding form.

Bean Geese of any form are very rare on the Point. The following are the only records but in none of them is the form involved clear. Given the current patterns of Bean Geese occurrence, however, it is likely that most of these records refer to Tundra Bean Geese:-

7 on 25th October 1952 in the Harbour, two birds being shot.
1st October 1954.
2 west on 8th November 1987.
7 west on 17th February 1991.

Pink-footed Goose
Anser brachyrhynchus
Rowan records the species as a regular winter visitor, often seen crossing the Point in considerable numbers, usually 'en route for the Holkham Marshes'.

Its appearances on the Point subsequently became more infrequent for White lists it as 'regular, though now in small numbers'. 'A small party' was noted on 5th October 1947, with 'some' on 18th October 1948 and 15-20 fed on the 'Beachway Marsh' (east of the Lifeboat House) in the hard weather of January and February 1963.

This reflects the rapid decline of the Holkham population after 1938 as a consequence of firing range activity at Stiffkey and subsequent wartime ploughing of the adjacent fresh marshes.

Since the early to mid-1980s, however, the Holkham wintering population (breeding in Iceland and Greenland) has become re-established and grown significantly. Pink-footed Geese are once again regular winter visitors to the Point, with flocks into the low hundreds often seen flying over, though almost never on the ground. The Point lies away from the main flightlines between the Warham roost and inland feeding areas and so the huge numbers now present only a few miles away are not generally recorded in the area although they can be seen in the distance shuttling to and fro. Birds passing over the Point are presumably commuting to and from feeding areas in east Norfolk, as significant numbers now take this route. Small flocks of birds arriving from the sea are also sometimes noted from the third week in September onwards.

A lone bird which flew west with 37 Canada Geese on 1st June 2003 is likely to have been either a feral or an injured bird.

On rare occasions Pink-footed Geese attempting to return to the Warham roost from inland feeding areas can become disorientated in foggy conditions. At such times numbers of birds can be grounded on the Point overnight to be flushed from the dunes the following morning. Storms present further dangers for in *Sea Swallows* Pinchen recounts a notable event involving this species:-

'Geese in hundreds careered over and around the '*Britannia*'. They were all in a very distressed and agitated condition. Some came to the ground and a great number seemed to be maimed. A fork of terrific lightning had caught them and created havoc in their ranks. Feathers and wings and even limbs were singed and burnt and a great many wounded birds were picked up over a wide area.'

White-fronted Goose (Greater White-fronted Goose)

Anser albifrons albifrons (European White-fronted Goose, Russian White-fronted Goose)
Rowan lists the species as having been 'secured' but provides no details. By the time of White's checklist it was described as 'very rare, not often recorded'.

Although a few hundred individuals of this Siberian goose winter as close as Holkham, the only records specifically traced from the Point are:-

27th November 1950.
26 on 15th February 1977, amongst Brent Geese.
7 on 1st November 1983.
2 on 12th November 1983.
2 on 16th January 1988.

Greylag Goose

Anser anser anser
Rowan lists one taken in the Channel on 14th October 1901 by Frank Richards. White describes the species as 'occasionally recorded'.

Introductions of this species in Norfolk took place between the 1930s and the 1960s and there are now large numbers present as close as Cley and Stiffkey. Flocks can often be seen moving between these sites along the south side of the Harbour. Despite this, the species remains surprisingly scarce on the Point itself. Interestingly, a high proportion of those recorded actually on the Point has been in mid-October, hinting at a possible continental origin for at least some birds. A lone bird on 12th October 1985, for example, was seen arriving from the sea with Dark-bellied Brent Geese.

In 2003 the species bred for the first time on the Point, with two pairs present in the Sandhills. They were, however, extremely elusive, as is typical with breeding Greylags. Both nests were predated and, although one pair relaid, this attempt was also unsuccessful. A pair also held territory for a short period in 2004 but no breeding was noted.

Canada Goose (Greater Canada Goose)

Branta canadensis canadensis (Atlantic Canada Goose)
The species is not listed by Rowan but White describes it as occasionally seen in the Channel.

Introductions of this species in Norfolk had taken place by the nineteenth century and birds are now resident as close as the Glaven Valley and Blakeney Fresh Marsh. Despite this, the species remains scarce on the Point, with traced recent records as follows:-

2 on 10th March 1990.
3 on 9th April 1994.
30th March 2002.
37 west on 1st June 2003.
89 on 5th June 2003.
2 on 10th June 2004, with 31 Barnacle Geese.
35 on 11th June 2004.

Although other records presumably exist it is striking that all these traced records are in spring. The flocks in June 2003 and 2004 reflect a recent spate of records of birds passing along the north Norfolk coast in the first half of June. Might these be connected with the well-documented moult migration to the Beauly Firth or are they headed to some other location?

In an interesting parallel to the previous species, a pair of Canada Geese frequented the Point on a number of occasions in the spring of 2004 and appeared to be prospecting.

Barnacle Goose
Branta leucopsis

Rowan lists the species as taken once but possibly observed on one or two other occasions. White lists one on 16th September 1955, with three tired birds on the 'Beachway' on 13th November 1965. Cant's notes, however, give the date of this record as 14th November.

Recent records are as follows:-

4 east on 12th November 1983.
12th October 1985.
16 west on 14th October 1990.
1 west on 4th November 1990.
1 west on 27th September 1997.
16 west on 15th October 1997.
6 on 21st April 1999.
20 on 13th June 2001.
6 on 15th April 2003.
2 on 16th May 2003.
31 on 10th June 2004, with two Canada Geese.

It is interesting to note that records fall into discrete spring and autumn periods, strongly suggesting that they are not random occurrences of feral birds. In particular, those of 12th November 1983 were part of a wider movement documented in the *Norfolk Bird Report* for that year and considered to have involved birds from the Spitsbergen population displaced south of their normal route to wintering grounds on the Solway. Most, possibly all, of the other autumn records, most of which are in mid to late October and November, are also likely to refer to displaced Spitsbergen birds. This population usually makes its autumn landfall in Britain somewhere between Shetland and Yorkshire.

Furthermore, the flock on 14th October 1990 is likely to have been the same flock as that present at Cley from 9th to 20th October which contained six birds with Spitsbergen rings – a flock which successfully re-orientated to Caerlaverock by mid-November. Similarly, the flock of 15th October 1997 was present at Cley between 13th and 16th October and also contained two Spitsbergen-ringed birds. Most Spitsbergen Barnacle Geese arrive on the Solway between 20th September and 10th October so these displaced birds will be amongst the last arrivals on the wintering grounds.

The origin of the spring birds is less clear and may involve either feral birds or possibly birds from the newly-established Baltic population.

Dark-bellied Brent Geese. (*James McCallum*)

Dark-bellied Brent Goose
Branta (bernicla) bernicla

All three Brent Goose forms are here treated separately in recognition of non-clinal differences in morphology and to highlight their very different status. This treatment differs from that of BOURC.

Between 100 and 300 Dark-bellied Brent Geese wintered in the Harbour in the nineteenth century, arriving in October and departing in March. Rowan records them as probably commoner than Pink-footed Goose, occasionally feeding on the mudflats but usually on passage. 'Exceptional numbers' (unfortunately not quantified) occurred in the hard weather of February 1929 when 101 were shot by a gunner in the Harbour in five days.

White records a flock as having been present between October and mid-April since at least 1930, with a peak of 2-3,000 recorded, though he notes that usually fewer than this number are present. A late bird was recorded on 19th May 1964.

This rather brief summary disguises, however, the significant decline in the Dark-bellied Brent Goose population which took place in the 1930s, followed by a steady recovery and further increase to their high present-day population levels. In 1953 the largest flock was 150-200 birds. This had risen to 1,100 by 1958 and 2,500-3,000 by 1963.

Autumn arrivals from Arctic Russia now commence in September, the earliest significant movement being of 20 on the early date of 2nd September 1993. Passage gathers momentum in October and November with large westerly movements just offshore. 1,528 passed west on 27th September 2002 but the peak count is of 6,000 west on 16th October 1999.

The peak winter WeBS counts in the Harbour generally occur in November, with a mean for that month of 2,686. The overall peak winter count of 5,000 was also recorded in November in 1983. As with Eurasian Wigeon, numbers recorded by WeBS fall for the remainder of the winter – in the case of the Brent Geese to around 1,500. This may, however, be a reflection of their increasing use of inland grass as the winter progresses. Until the 1970s the geese were exclusively maritime but since then they have taken to feeding during the day on grass and cereal crops as far inland as Saxlingham and Binham. As all the geese roost in the Harbour each night, the winter population may well be more stable than WeBS counts suggest.

The species is well-known for its erratic breeding success in the Russian Arctic, with hardly any young present in some winters, whilst in other years around half of all the birds present are juveniles.

According to White most depart in March, with the last spring birds remaining until mid-April. However, in the 1990s birds have increasingly lingered into May, mirroring the pattern elsewhere in Britain, with an exceptional 1,500 still present on 2nd May 1995, a year when many Brents remained late in the county. Other high late spring counts include 412 still on 19th May 1999, 30 as late as 29th May 2000 and a further remarkable count of 1,658 on 13th May 2004.

A few birds, sometimes up to a dozen, now also spend the summer in the Harbour.

Ringing recoveries neatly illustrate the location of the breeding grounds and the migration route through northern Germany and the Baltic:-

Ringed Heligoland, Germany 26th March 1978, recovered Blakeney Point 29th January 1982.
Ringed Taimyr Peninsula, Siberia 16th July 1989, recovered Blakeney Point 27th June 1991.
A dead bird was found with a Danish ring in 1965.

Pale-bellied Brent Goose
Branta (bernicla) hrota
This form/species is not listed by Rowan.

The 1954 *Norfolk Bird Report* details 29 Pale-bellied Brent Geese in Blakeney Harbour on 5th December of that year, whilst White states that 'in 1955 many birds in a flock of 1,000 present on 8th March were considered to belong to the pale-breasted race'. This report is contained in the 1955 *Norfolk Bird Report* but is accompanied by two photographs of what are described as Pale-bellied Brents 'on the saltings of a Norfolk estuary in the 1954-1955 winter' which are in fact all Dark-bellied Brents. A query must therefore be raised over this record.

There are no known records in the 1960s and 1970s but what are termed locally 'Stranger Brents' have become more frequent since the 1980s, involving small parties from the Spitsbergen population displaced, perhaps by adverse weather, from their wintering grounds in Denmark and/or Northumberland.

All recent records are as follows:-

3 in 'early January' 1984.
30 in January/February 1985.
1st November 1985.
7 on 1st March 1986.
8 on 15th March 1987.
19th December 2000.
3 on 9th September 2001.
4 on 23rd September 2001.
1 'early in the year' in 2002.
A first-winter on 26th April 2003.
2 on 31st October 2004.
2 on 13th January 2005.
28th March 2005.

The September records in 2001 refer to 'fly-by' displaced autumn migrants during a month which saw particularly persistent northerly and northeasterly winds in the southern North Sea. The winter records largely relate to birds seen amongst the Dark-bellied Brents.

The form/species is likely to be significantly under-recorded at the Point as in many winters individuals or small parties are present with the Dark-bellied Brents feeding inland and these no doubt accompany their companions to roost in the Harbour.

Black Brant

Branta (bernicla) nigricans

One or two Black Brants have frequented the Salthouse, Cley, Blakeney, Morston and Stiffkey area with the wintering Dark-bellied Brent Goose flocks since November 1982, with the exception of a gap of six years in the early 1990s.

These are all likely to have roosted in the Harbour but the first positive sighting from within our area was of a small, poorly-marked and presumed hybrid individual (Black Brant x Dark-bellied Brent Goose) on 13th March 1999. This bird was seen frequently in the Cley, Salthouse and Blakeney area throughout the 1998/99 and 1999/2000 winters and a discussion of its appearance is in *British Birds* 95: 129-136.

Records of pure Black Brants are as follows:-

Adult on 29th April to 13th May 2001 in the outer Harbour.
First-winter on 20th April and 4th May 2002. This individual, the first Norfolk and second British record of a young bird, was originally found at nearby Cockthorpe in January, visiting Stiffkey, Wells and Cley during the winter until settling in the Harbour. A photograph of this bird appears in *Birding World* 15: 146.
Adult on 13th March 2005 at the Marrams.

Black Brants are no doubt significantly under-recorded on the Point due to their habit of feeding during the day on nearby grassland with the Dark-bellied Brents, only returning at nightfall.

Black Brants breed in Arctic Canada (west of Pale-bellied Brents) and in Arctic Russia (east of Dark-bellied Brents). Given the close association between this form/species and Dark-bellied Brent Geese, and recent records of Black Brants migrating with Dark-bellied Brents through northwest Europe, it can safely be assumed that those recorded on the Point are all central Siberian in origin. Black Brants winter on the Pacific coast of North America and, in smaller numbers, in northeast Asia.

Red-breasted Goose

Branta ruficollis

An adult wintered amongst the Dark-bellied Brent Geese in the Cley, Salthouse, Blakeney and Langham area from 7th December 1987 to 2nd March 1988. This bird presumably roosted each night in Blakeney Harbour but no specific observations to confirm this can be traced. However, the bird regularly visited Cley Eye Field during its stay and, on a number of occasions, was observed arriving from the direction of the Harbour along the shingle ridge west of Cley Coastguards, thereby securing its place on the Blakeney Point list. The bird was photographed during its stay but not on the Point.

Red-breasted Geese breed in Arctic Siberia and winter largely in southeast Europe and southwest Asia, though occasional vagrants reach Britain, historically with European White-fronted Geese but, in recent years, more typically with Dark-bellied Brents.

Egyptian Goose

Alopochen aegyptiaca

Despite being resident nearby, notably in the Glaven Valley, this introduced species is very rare on the Point. Flocks of nine on 13th October 1991 and four on 1st September 1998 are the only precisely documented records but, although the species is thought to have occurred on other occasions, no dates or details are known.

Ruddy Shelduck

Tadorna ferruginea

One flew west with a large party of Common Shelduck on 17th September 2000. The bird had been seen earlier at Sheringham and was noted subsequently at Wells, Scolt Head and Holme. Three further birds flew west on 21st July 2003.

Although their provenance is unknown, these birds are most likely to have originated from the feral population now established in the Netherlands. This seems particularly likely in the case of the first individual given its association with Common Shelduck returning from moult migration.

Common Shelducks. (*James McCallum*)

Common Shelduck (Shelduck)

Tadorna tadorna

Rowan describes the species as resident and breeding in small numbers, with up to six to eight pairs. Only two pairs had been reported in 1909.

The breeding population increased significantly after the publication of Rowan's list, with 30-40 pairs breeding between 1920 and 1940 and a further increase after the 1939-1945 war. By the early 1950s the population had reached 65 pairs, since when numbers have fluctuated according to the size of the Rabbit population. In 1954 the Rabbits were exterminated by myxomatosis and by 1956 many of the burrows in which the birds nested had become blocked through lack of use and only 20-30 pairs bred the following year.

Numbers subsequently rose again, however, with 65 pairs breeding by 1964 before a further reduction to 30 pairs by the early 1970s.

With further declines in the 1990s linked both to ongoing myxomatosis outbreaks in the Rabbits and to predation by the increasing presence of Herring and Lesser Black-backed Gulls, the Shelduck breeding population fell to an almost record low. The population was down to seven or eight pairs in 1998 and only five pairs in 2000 but numbers are, however, now rising again with 12 pairs counted in 2003 and about 18 pairs in 2004.

Rowan also records that birds were seen least in July, August and September, with largest numbers present in winter. White confirms this status, noting that most leave on moult migration to the Wadden Sea by the middle of August, returning from late November. Nowadays some eastward migration to the continent is noted in June, with most passage taking place on fine evenings in July, the birds presumably arriving at their destination by morning. Westward return movements now occur between September and November, somewhat earlier than indicated by White. Some continental Shelduck may also be involved in these movements but these would be hard to distinguish from returning British birds. Some birds also now undertake a shorter moult migration to the Wash.

White notes that 600-700 birds were in the Harbour for most of the winter in 1967/68 but numbers are now usually smaller than this, with 200-350 recorded most winters, often congregating on sandbanks in front of the Lifeboat House. There is some evidence from WeBS counts that numbers may have decreased since the mid-1990s.

A bird ringed at Seal Sands, Cleveland on 24th December 1977 was recovered at Blakeney Point on 25th January 1985, indicating that movements within Britain are also taking place.

Eurasian Wigeon, Eurasian Teal and Pintail. (*James McCallum*)

Eurasian Wigeon (Wigeon)

Anas penelope

Rowan and White describe this as the most abundant duck during the winter months and White notes peak counts of 3,000 in January 1947 and November 1955. It is still the commonest wintering duck species and noisy flocks flushed from the channels by bait-diggers are a characteristic winter sight.

Autumn arrivals from eastern Scandinavia and northwest Russia appear from the second half of August, with incoming birds passing west offshore, often mixed in with other duck species, until November, by which time large flocks have also gathered in the Harbour. Further influxes may take place during the winter in hard weather. Most departures take place in February and March.

The winter population in the Cley and Blakeney area has risen to 6,000-7,000 in the 1990s but numbers recorded in the Harbour have been lower. The peak winter WeBS count was 2,500 in January 1984 but numbers typically reach their peak in November (a mean count of 1,372) before dropping during the remainder of the winter. As with Dark-bellied Brent Geese, however, this apparent decrease may purely reflect an increasing tendency to feed on nearby grass fields as the winter progresses. In calm weather large 'rafts' of Wigeon can also form on the sea.

A drake on 23rd September 2000 showed apparent Eurasian x American Wigeon hybrid characters.

Gadwall

Anas strepera

Rowan describes the Gadwall as one of the rarest ducks but White recounts the first breeding record in the Long Hills in 1966. Six eggs were laid, five of which hatched. Birds bred again in 1967, with four young raised.

The species still breeds, with up to four pairs usually frequenting the area between the Marrams and the Hood but also occasionally near the Lifeboat House. Noisy pairs and small parties are often encountered in spring.

Birds are also present, but only in small numbers, during the winter, with little evidence of direct immigration in the autumn. Some movement to Britain from the continent has, however, been demonstrated by ringing recoveries and birds are sometimes recorded passing west at sea elsewhere along the coast.

Eurasian Teal (Teal, Common Teal)

Anas crecca

Rowan and White record the Teal as a common winter visitor and White notes 150 in very hard weather on 25th January 1963 as a notable count.

Autumn immigrants from Scandinavia and northern Russia appear very early in the season, from July, and up to a few hundred in a day can be seen passing west, often with other duck species, through until November. Further influxes may take place during the winter in hard weather and most departures take place in February and March.

High autumn WeBS counts in the Harbour include 380 in October 1988 and the highest winter count is of 900 in January 1992, though mean winter (October to February) numbers are in the range 150-225. This reflects the better feeding opportunities on nearby pools and wet grassland at Blakeney and Cley where higher numbers can usually be encountered.

Mallard

Anas platyrhynchos platyrhynchos

Rowan and White list the species as common in winter, though Rowan recounts that he once saw a small flock in July. The species is still a relatively common winter visitor (though not one of the commonest ducks) and incoming migrants from north central Europe, southern Scandinavia and the Baltic are occasionally seen in small numbers from September and particularly in October and into November.

A high count of 400 was made in December 1984 but mean winter WeBS counts in the Harbour are typically between 100 and 150. There is some evidence from these counts of a decline in the wintering population since the 1980s. Birds depart in March, leaving only a tiny breeding population.

Two nests reported east of the Watch House in 1953 probably represent the first breeding record for the Point, but White notes the first confirmed breeding for the Sandhills in 1964 when a brood of six ducklings was raised. A pair also nested in 1965 and 1966, while in 1967 five pairs nested, with two to three nests recorded in most years since.

The species still breeds, with one or two pairs usually frequenting the Marrams but also occasionally near the Lifeboat House.

Pintail (Northern Pintail)

Anas acuta acuta

Rowan describes the Pintail as one of the rarest ducks and White records it as a winter visitor in very small numbers. However, in the second edition of his list he notes it as becoming more common, with around 400 recorded in late 1976.

Numbers are now even higher. Autumn birds from Scandinavia, the Baltic States and Russia arrive and pass west, usually with Eurasian Wigeon, in September and October, notable autumn counts including 260 on 25th September 2001 and 650 on 1st October 1993. Further influxes may take place during the winter in hard weather. Mean winter WeBS counts in the harbour suggest a population between November and February of over 400 but 970 were counted in January 1997.

Most departures take place in February and March.

Garganey
Anas querquedula

Rowan does not list the species at all but White describes the Garganey as occurring in small numbers only, referring, however, to an exceptional count of 30 in the Harbour on 6th April 1948.

Garganey are now best described as rare, with all recent records occurring in autumn as follows:-

10th October 1982.
26th August 1984.
10th September 1989.
7th September 1991.
18th – 19th August 2001.
3rd September 2001.
3rd September 2002.
26th September 2004.

Although Garganey breed regularly at Cley, the preponderance of autumn records and the association of many birds with immigrant flocks of Eurasian Teal in the Harbour strongly suggest a continental origin.

Shoveler (Northern Shoveler)
Anas clypeata

Rowan and White list the Shoveler as one of the rarest ducks and this remains the case today. Birds are present, but only in small numbers, during the winter, with only sporadic evidence of westward passage in the autumn. These occasional birds are presumably continental immigrants as some movement to Britain from the continent has been demonstrated by ringing recoveries.

The occasional pair sometimes lingers into the spring in the Marrams and, although there has been no absolute confirmation of breeding in our area, this was strongly suspected in 2004 and 2005. A particularly unusual record is of eight seen on 23rd July 1997.

Red-crested Pochard
Netta rufina

Rowan and White list one 'taken in the channel near the beach' but no date is given.

The only other records are:-

Female or immature west on 7th October 1990.
A pair on 28th March 1998 in the Harbour.

The origin of these birds is unknown. The 1990 bird may have been a genuine continental immigrant but those in March 1998 are more likely to have been escapes.

Common Pochard (Pochard)

Aythya ferina

Rowan describes the species as 'unknown on the Point' and White lists only a drake on 8th October 1968.

Since a bird on 15th October 1977 there has been an increase in the number of records, typically involving small flocks of up to ten birds passing west in autumn. Some larger passage flocks have also been recorded as follows:-

20 on 30th September 1983.
20 on 16th October 1986.
15 on 6th September 1992.
28 on 9th November 2003.

All passage records fall between 6th September and 9th November with the exception of a single spring bird on 29th May 1994. Ringing elsewhere in Britain has shown that autumn immigrants are likely to be from north central Europe or west central Russia.

The occasional bird has also been recorded in winter, with up to three present in January, February and December 1995 and two in February 2001.

Tufted Duck

Aythya fuligula

Rowan states that a few occur in winter and White records the species as seen occasionally at that season, mainly in the Channel. Pinchen's diary for 1929 refers to a bird in the Harbour on 8th August 1929.

Records of Tufted Ducks are now erratic, showing no particular pattern and not confined to the winter months. Records are all of between one and five individuals, with the exception of 14 on 1st January 1985, 11 on 1st March 1985 and eight on 1st June 2001. Many records doubtless relate to local breeders but incoming migrants, perhaps from the Finnish and northwest Russian population, are also occasionally noted in autumn.

Greater Scaup (Scaup)

Aythya marila marila

Rowan lists the Scaup as one of the rarest ducks but White describes it as a passage migrant and winter visitor, usually in small numbers, but with higher counts of 60 in the Harbour in February 1954 and 50 on 1st December 1958. He quotes Ted Eales as having seen about 100 flying west on 9th October 1955, but the year given is probably incorrect as the record is listed in the *Norfolk Bird Report* for 1957.

Scaup are still scarce in autumn and winter, with records from early September, but mostly in October and November, and only occasional singles in winter. Peak recent counts include 18 on 4th September 1975, 22 on 18th January 2000 and 11 on 10th November 2003. Birds are invariably seen just flying past offshore.

Although most Scaup wintering in Britain originate from Iceland, ringing recoveries from this source have been largely in the north and west of the country. Eastern England is linked with northwest Russia through a smaller number of recoveries, implying that the birds seen on the Point are continental.

Common Eider (Eider)
Somateria mollissima mollissima

Rowan notes the species as being taken at least once and seen several times in winter. Stevenson (1890) notes the then only known instance of summering in Norfolk by this species – a bird present off the Point from July to October 1885.

By White's time the Eider had become more common in winter, but a flock of seven in the Harbour on 8th July 1950, a day of bad weather with heavy seas, was regarded as exceptional. In 1965 a duck and a drake were together off the Hood on 23rd April and subsequently birds were often seen in May and June, with seven birds summering in 1967, prompting White to suggest that the species may breed in the near future.

Peak numbers recorded in winter include 100 in December 1958 and 140-160 in February 1959, coinciding with a sudden increase in records along the whole Norfolk coast at this time. In more recent times a late autumn westerly passage has been recorded, normally of a few tens of birds, but exceptionally larger numbers are involved, for example:-

250 on 12th November 1982.
120 on 12th November 1983.
131 on 23rd November 1988.
150 on 3rd December 2003.

Smaller numbers of Eiders (sometimes up to 25) can now be seen in many winters, though over 30 wintered in 1994/95 and again in 1995/96 with a record winter count of 67 in March 1996, usually frequenting the Harbour mouth or hauled out on the sandbanks. There has, however, never been any indication of attempted breeding. British Eiders are largely sedentary and the overwhelming majority of birds recorded on the Point are no doubt continental in origin.

Long-tailed Duck
Clangula hyemalis

Rowan states somewhat enigmatically that 'many occur every winter, though not frequently recorded'. An adult male is recorded as having been secured on 8th October 1901.

White records a pair killed in the Harbour on 19th June 1907. This remains the only summer record.

The species is now a regular though rather erratic visitor in late autumn and winter from its Scandinavian and northern Russian breeding grounds, but only in small numbers, typically one to five birds, and usually only seen passing offshore. Birds are, however, occasionally seen in the Harbour, with counts here just reaching double figures in December 1972, the winter of 1976/77 and December 1982.

Larger numbers than normal were recorded in the early months of 1985, with a peak of 21 in March, and 1989, when 20 were present on 22nd April, with 16 again present in December of that year.

April records are rare, the latest being a single bird on 27th April 1985.

Common Scoter
Melanitta nigra

Rowan records the species as fairly frequently recorded in the winter months and notes that he himself once saw one in July. White notes the species as a fairly regular winter visitor, though records a pair seen on 27th June 1967.

The species is now regularly seen in small numbers at most times of year but most birds, sometimes up to several hundred in a day, pass westwards between September and December. Many early birds are males, with females and immatures predominating later in the autumn.

Occasionally much larger autumn passages are recorded, for example, 2,000 west on 20th October 1991. The vast majority of these birds are likely to be Scandinavian and northern Russian but Icelandic birds are also known to winter in British waters.

Spring movements are usually on a smaller scale though 500 flew east on 29th May 1994, 1,500 moved east on 15th May 1995 and 500 were recorded in May 2001.

Common Scoter do not normally linger to feed off the Point and large gatherings are unusual. A huge flock of up to 7,000 off the Marrams in December 2001 (with a few Velvet and one Surf Scoter) was therefore exceptional, though up to 1,550 again gathered off the Marrams in November 2004.

A few birds, usually fewer than ten, are also occasionally seen in the Harbour, though 21 were recorded here in January 1983.

Surf Scoter
Melanitta perspicillata
A drake of this Nearctic species accompanied thousands of Common Scoters off the Marrams on the morning of 23rd December 2001. It had previously been seen off Winterton and was subsequently found in Holkham Bay.

Velvet Scoter
Melanitta fusca fusca
Rowan records the Velvet Scoter as regular though scarce and White lists a record number of 40 on 8th April 1956 (although 90 had been present 'off Blakeney' in late February of that year).

The species is now regular in small numbers, typically one to five birds, in autumn between the very end of September and mid-November and very occasional in winter. Up to 18 accompanied Common Scoters off the Marrams in November 2004 but birds are normally only recorded flying by.

Spring records are very rare, the only recent sightings involving a single on 20th April 1984, three on 20th April 1985 and singles on 1st May 2001 and 15th May 2004.

Exceptional summer records concern ten in the Harbour on 10th July 1983, listed in that year's *Norfolk Bird Report*, and one on 8th August 2001.

Velvet Scoters originate from breeding grounds in Scandinavia and northern Russia, with most wintering in the Baltic.

Common Goldeneye (Goldeneye)
Bucephala clangula clangula
Rowan describes the species as uncommon, with only a few seen in winter.

By the time of White's list the species was occurring more commonly, with a count of 70 on 10th January 1968 regarded as notable, and the wintering population for 1976/77 is given as 50.

Goldeneye are now regularly seen passing west offshore in late autumn and are common in winter in the Harbour, WeBS counts recording a mean December to February figure of 50-65 birds. Higher counts are as follows:-

123 in January 1994.
177 in February 1995.
177 in January 1999.

Birds arrive late from their Scandinavian and northern Russian breeding grounds, typically from mid-October to December, and depart in February and March. Most birds are brown-headed females or immatures with, as in many species, adult males largely wintering nearer the breeding areas.

Smew
Mergellus albellus

Rowan states that an adult male was secured 'some winters back' and that 'immature birds have been observed several times'.

The species is described by White as 'rare, occasionally in the Channel'. Subsequent records of this attractive Scandinavian and northern Russian-breeding sawbill have been few and far between. All recent traced records are listed:-

A 'redhead' on 6th February 1982.
3 in January/February 1985, in the Harbour.
A 'redhead' on 1st February 1986, in the Harbour.
December 2000, precise date unknown.
A 'redhead' on 10th November 2001.

These records largely fit the typical pattern of birds displaced by hard weather from the normal wintering grounds in the Baltic and the Netherlands but the early date of the 2001 record is more unusual.

Red-breasted Merganser
Mergus serrator

Rowan and White describe the species as recorded fairly frequently during the winter months, but usually in small numbers.

The species is now regularly recorded passing west at sea in autumn, and in winter in the Harbour, arriving from September but mainly from November, peaking in December with most departing in March. In recent years counts have on occasion reached 60 although the all-time peak is of 97 on 2nd February 1994. WeBS counts reveal a lower monthly winter mean of around 20-25 birds. This species tends to penetrate further upstream in the Harbour than the other wintering diving ducks, with birds often present off the Marrams.

The occasional bird lingers into May but an exceptional record involves 14 on 14th May 2001. Three were still present in June and July of that year and further summer birds were seen on 4th July 2003 and 8th July 2004, two birds being involved in each case.

Although Red-breasted Mergansers have an extensive British and continental range, the relative proportions of those occurring on the Point are not known.

Goosander
Mergus merganser merganser

Rowan lists the species as having been taken once. White's list records it as a winter visitor, less frequent than the preceding species.

Records now usually involve small numbers, typically one to four birds, passing west offshore between late October and January, later birds often associated with hard weather. The peak counts are of ten on 29th December 1991 and 14 on 7th November 2004. Birds are not normally noted in the Harbour though singles were seen in December 2000, on 18th December 2002 and on 17th October 2004.

Spring sightings are very rare, the only records being of singles on 11th March 1990, 12th

March 2002 and 3rd May of the same year.

Goosanders have a wide breeding distribution across northern Eurasia but ringing recoveries have shown that most birds wintering in southern England are likely to originate from northern Scandinavia and western Russia. Although British-bred Goosanders could also reach our area, circumstantial evidence suggests that most, if not all, the birds recorded on the Point are continental in origin.

Red-legged Partridge
Alectoris rufa rufa
In Rowan's day this introduced, essentially sedentary species nested sporadically, with stragglers also occurring at other times outside the breeding season.

Red-legged Partridges are now resident on the Point, with two to four pairs breeding in most years, usually in marram tussocks in the Sandhills. White records five pairs breeding in 1964 and 1966 and peak numbers were attained in 1974 (12 nests) and 1975 (eight nests).

Grey Partridge
Perdix perdix perdix
Rowan accords this essentially sedentary species the same status as Red-legged Partridge. The Grey Partridge was still breeding in White's day and he notes them nesting in most years from 1961.

Regular breeding has, however, now ceased, reflecting the species' more general decline, linked to changing agricultural practices, and the only recent breeding occurred in 2002. Otherwise the species is today a rare and irregular visitor, with the only other known recent records being:-

2 on 16th April 1988.
5 on 24th October 1993.
2 on 15th May 1997.
2 on 26th March 2004.
2 on 10th April 2005.

Common Pheasant (Pheasant)
Phasianus colchicus torquatus
This species, introduced to Britain and abundant in nearby areas, is not listed by either Rowan or White.

The only known records are all very recent:-

Male in April 2003, wandering widely on the Point.
Male *torquatus*-type in spring and summer 2004. This bird wandered between the Marrams and Far Point before being found dead on the beach in July.
Male *torquatus*-type on 25th March 2005, in the Marrams.

Why Pheasants have suddenly started occurring on the Point is not known as the Harbour has traditionally represented a major barrier. It is, however, no surprise that all these records have involved males as they are known to wander more widely than females whilst prospecting.

Common Quail (Quail)

Coturnix coturnix coturnix

Rowan does not list the species but White records a pair seen several times in June 1958, though the *Norfolk Bird Report* for that year gives the dates as 29th – 30th May. Two were also seen on 20th – 21st July 1959.

Subsequent records are as follows:-

16th May 1988.
29th May 1992, seen flying in from the sea.
22nd – 23rd May 1994.
19th May 1996.
10th June 2003.
15th May 2004.

Quail are well-known as erratic summer visitors to Britain from Africa, the breeding population varying greatly between years in both its size and distribution. No link can, however, be identified between 'Quail years' in Britain and records from the Point.

Red-throated Diver

Gavia stellata

Rowan records the species as a common sight throughout the winter months in the Channel. White confirms its status as the commonest diver.

This remains the case and the Red-throated Diver is still a common winter visitor and passage migrant, reflecting the southern North Sea's importance as a wintering area for this species, the majority of which are Scandinavian breeders. The first autumn birds usually arrive in August, though the occasional bird has been seen in July, and birds are then seen regularly in increasing numbers, especially from October onwards and throughout the winter until the end of March. Occasionally significant winter 'passages' are noted, for example 318 which passed east on 3rd December 2003, but these are likely to be relatively short-distance feeding movements. Birds are usually on the open sea, with only a few seen in the Harbour. Fourteen in the Harbour on 26th November 2002 were therefore exceptional.

Late spring birds have included the following:-

23rd May 1984.
1st – 8th June 1986.
21st May 1998, in the Harbour.
4th June 2001.

A major oiling incident took place in November and December 2002, with Red-throated Divers making up most of the casualties. Thirty-two were found dead along the beach on 8th December.

A bird which flew west above the beach on 30th October 2004 was giving the loud wailing call usually associated with the breeding grounds.

Black-throated Diver

Gavia arctica arctica

Rowan lists the species as an infrequent visitor, the rarest of the divers and seldom taken. He notes one obtained by Frank Richards on 27th December 1905. White records it as occurring usually between September and April. Since then its status has remained unchanged and it is best described as scarce, though perhaps most regular in October and November. Autumn 1989 saw more records than normal, with up to seven between the Point and Sheringham between 1st and 12th November.

All records relate to birds on the open sea apart from a tame individual which frequented the Harbour in February 1963.

Out of season records include the following:-

1st June 1986.
24th August 1988.
3rd May 1994.
7th – 10th June 1994.
29th August 1995.

It is thought that Black-throated Divers in the southern North Sea originate from both British and Scandinavian populations.

Great Northern Diver. (*James McCallum*)

Great Northern Diver
Gavia immer

The species is listed in Rowan and White as an infrequent visitor, usually between September and April.

Since then it has become a scarce but regular westerly passage migrant at sea, usually in late October and November, and winter visitor, with one or two, and exceptionally up to five, lingering for long periods in the Harbour in the winter in some years. Birds in summer plumage are rare, though one such bird was noted on 25th November 1984.

British-wintering Great Northern Divers are from Iceland and Greenland, with some birds possibly from as far as the Canadian Arctic.

White-billed Diver (Yellow-billed Diver)
Gavia adamsii

A winter plumage adult was found close inshore near the Watch House with one Red-throated and three Black-throated Divers on 29th September 1985. An article on the discovery of this new bird for Norfolk appears in the 1986 *Norfolk Bird Report*.

On 28th July 1986 one, possibly the same bird, was found long-dead at the edge of the ternery. It was judged by the state of moult to have died in February, possibly following oiling. The remains of this bird are retained at the Castle Museum, Norwich.

A juvenile was seen just west of Cley Coastguards on 4th October 1986 and it or another drifted westwards along the Point on 17th October of the same year.

White-billed Divers breed widely throughout the Russian, Alaskan and Canadian Arctic and most British records are in winter and spring. This pattern of autumn records, however, hints at the possibility of a small passage to wintering grounds situated somewhere around or beyond Britain. This suggestion is further strengthened by recent spring sightings of passage birds in western and northern Scotland and the occasional bird seen moving northeast through the English Channel at this season. The mid-autumn records also illustrate neatly the early migration of this species compared with Great Northern Divers which generally occur on the Point in late October and November.

Little Grebe
Tachybaptus ruficollis ruficollis

Rowan and White describe the species as fairly regular in occurrence, mainly in the Channel from August through until spring.

It is now a scarce but regular winter visitor to the Harbour in small numbers (up to ten) but occasionally in more significant numbers. For example, 50 were counted on 9th November 1967, including groups of 22 and 14. Other large counts include 16 in February 1984, December 1988 and December 1995 and 17 in December 1998. More unusually, three were on the sea on 25th January 1992, with a further bird on 12th December 2004.

Whilst most of these birds are presumably of fairly local origin, it is not inconceivable that the occasional continental immigrant might be involved.

Great Crested Grebe
Podiceps cristatus cristatus

Rowan and White list this as the commonest of the grebes, fairly often seen in the Channel and 'mostly taken between September and January'.

The Great Crested Grebe remains a passage migrant and winter visitor, common in small numbers from August to March. Numbers passing west offshore are greatest in autumn, the largest count being of 49 on 26th October 1986. Small numbers, generally one to three but occasionally up to seven, are also encountered in the Harbour in winter and a single bird remained in the Harbour throughout July 2004.

Although most Great Crested Grebes wintering in Britain are likely to be British breeders, the westerly passages noted off the Point strongly suggest that some continental immigration is also taking place.

Red-necked Grebe
Podiceps grisegena grisegena

Rowan describes this eastern European breeding species as the rarest of the grebes and notes that one was taken on 5th January 1906. White describes the Red-necked Grebe as rare but fairly regular in winter.

Occasional birds, exceptionally up to six, are still recorded during the winter months and in hard weather this species is prone to influxes from its normal wintering grounds in the Baltic. Stevenson (1890) lists Blakeney as one of the sites from which birds were obtained in February

1865 and Pashley documents a further influx in the area in February 1922.

Since the 1970s Red-necked Grebes have become more regular. Birds move west in autumn, with the earliest recorded on 10th August 1986, and sightings are frequent from mid-September. An exceptional ten passed west on 26th October 1986 during a period of particularly heavy grebe passage. A bird in summer plumage was in the Harbour on 30th August 1975.

Late spring birds were recorded on 4th May 1998 and, latest of all, 16th May 1989.

Slavonian Grebe. (*James McCallum*)

Slavonian Grebe
Podiceps auritus auritus
Rowan and White describe the species as seen occasionally during the winter, perhaps not so regularly as the preceding species.

It is now a regular but scarce visitor in autumn and winter from eastern Scandinavia, the Baltic States and Russia, usually only in ones or twos in the Harbour in winter, but five were present on 12th November 1989 and four or five were seen on 24th December 1984.

Records are more frequent of birds passing west offshore in autumn, the earliest being on 19th September 1999 and the peak count being of 33 west during the great grebe passage of 26th October 1986.

A bird in summer plumage was present on 13th April 1991.

Black-necked Grebe
Podiceps nigricollis nigricollis
This is by far the rarest of the grebes on the Point. Rowan lists one obtained by Clifford Borrer in the Channel on 20th September 1916 and also refers to one other record.

All modern records of singles, including those detailed by White, are listed below:-

8th October 1953.
October 1963.
November 1965.

30th April 1976, in summer plumage.
2nd – 16th January 1977.
November 1977.
24th January and 10th February 1982.
24th February 1985, found dead.
12th November 1989.
25th January 1992.
2nd January 2000.

By far the most unusual run of records occurred in 1986 when seven appeared in the Harbour at the end of November, increasing to ten by 13th December. This group remained into 1987, with ten still present on 3rd January and seven still there on 10th January.

Although there have been no ringing recoveries in Britain of continental Black-necked Grebes, it seems likely from movements recorded within Europe that the birds occurring in our area are continental in origin.

Fulmar (Northern Fulmar)
Fulmarus glacialis glacialis
Rowan notes Fulmars as rarely seen, with a bird taken in September 1912. A further bird was picked up in 1916, followed by several others in subsequent years, including one found by Pinchen on 3rd November 1922.

White notes Fulmars as commoner in his day, reflecting the species' well-documented southward spread through British waters and the establishment of small local breeding colonies from 1947 onwards.

In February and March 1962 large numbers were washed up dead along the east coast, with 39 counted between the Point and Salthouse. This phenomenon was repeated in late February and March 2004 when 132 were found dead along the tideline. The 2004 'wreck' was noted all around the southern North Sea and must have involved thousands of birds. It was notable for comprising largely adult females in wing and tail moult and reflected the cumulative effect of food shortages during the 2003 breeding season and subsequent persistent poor weather.

Fulmars are now recorded throughout the year in small numbers though larger passages are sometimes noted, most frequently in September. Peak counts include:-

500 on 9th September 1989.
100 per hour on 29th September 1991.
500 in one hour on 14th September 1993, a day when a county record total of 7,600 passed Sheringham.
415 on 1st September 1994.
562 east on 28th February 2001.
300 on 9th September 2001.

An unusual summer movement was of 180 east on 26th June 1997, a day which also featured a Fea's Petrel.

Dark northern 'blue' Fulmars are occasionally recorded, mainly in late winter. Recent records include:-

6 on 14th September 1993, in the great Fulmar movement.
26th June 1997.

8th March 1998.
17 on 28th February 2001.
29th February 2004, with 24 subsequently found dead along the tideline.

The 2004 'wrecked' birds exhibited considerable variation, ranging from those with pale grey clouding on the crown and nape to much darker birds with more solid grey heads, necks and underparts, uniform grey upperparts and strongly contrasting dark grey underwing coverts. Five of these corpses are now in the British Museum of Natural History at Tring.

It is likely that Fulmars recorded off the Point have a wide variety of origins. The species has an extensive breeding range stretching from Canada to northwest Arctic Russia and young birds spend long periods foraging throughout the Arctic and north Atlantic.

Fea's (Cape Verde)/Zino's Petrel
Pterodroma feae/P. madeira
The first for Norfolk flew east close inshore at 1340 on 26th June 1997 and was later seen at Cley, Sheringham and Mundesley. Fea's Petrel breeds only on the Desertas and Cape Verde Islands, dispersing into the north Atlantic in autumn and winter, and this record reflects its recent appearances in British waters in early autumn, though it now also occurs with some regularity off the eastern seaboard of North America. Zino's Petrel is, however, extremely rare (restricted to approximately 45 pairs in two tiny colonies on Madeira) and, never having been conclusively identified away from its breeding sites, is a most unlikely visitor to British waters.

There continues to be some debate around the separation at sea of Fea's and Zino's Petrels. Nevertheless the Blakeney Point bird was seen well and the observers were confident that it showed characters fully consistent with *feae*, as have a number of other recent British records, including photographed birds. This record has been accepted by BBRC as referring to Fea's or Zino's Petrel (as have the other British records) and the species is therefore not officially counted on the British List.

As with a number of other British records, this bird appeared during a movement of Manx Shearwaters. Articles on this occurrence occur in the *Norfolk Bird Report* for 1997 and in the *Norfolk Bird Club Bulletin* 25: 8-11.

Cory's Shearwater
Calonectris diomedea borealis
The only records are as follows:-

2 on 26th August 1984.
27th August 1993.
26th July 1999.
7th July 2004.

Currently only the Atlantic islands form *borealis* is on the British List, and this is clearly the predominant form in British waters, but the occurrence of the nominate Mediterranean form (Scopoli's Shearwater) in British waters has now also been proven. As with most British records, none of the birds listed above was identified to form though they are assumed to have been *borealis*.

Great Shearwater
Puffinus gravis
A single bird flew west then east past Cley Coastguards at 1030 on 9th September 1997. Although observed from outside our area (see the recording policy in the introduction to the Systematic

List) it was clearly seen to enter Blakeney Point waters and therefore just warrants an inclusion on the list.

Great Shearwaters breed on Tristan da Cunha and Gough Island in the South Atlantic, departing in spring for the eastern seaboards of South and North America before returning to the breeding areas in autumn via the northeast Atlantic.

Sooty Shearwater
Puffinus griseus

The species is not listed by Rowan but White records it as a rare autumn visitor.

Sooty Shearwaters are now regular in small numbers in onshore winds in autumn between late August and October, mostly in September. Peak counts are:-

150 on 3rd September 1986, an unprecedented number and a county record.
35 on 4th August 2001.
55 on 9th September 2001.
45 on 22nd September 2002.

There are two records of singles in the first week of November, with an exceptionally late bird on 30th December 1989 which was also seen off Hunstanton on the same day.

Along with the Arctic Tern and Great Shearwater, this species vies for the distinction of being the furthest-travelled of all the birds recorded on the Point, originating from breeding colonies in Australia, New Zealand, Chile and the Falkland Islands. Many of the Sooty Shearwaters seen in the North Sea are thought to be non-breeders as these southern hemisphere colonies are re-occupied from mid-September.

Manx Shearwaters. (*James McCallum*)

Manx Shearwater
Puffinus puffinus

Rowan describes this species as a rare vagrant, taken once on 11th September 1895, but White notes it as a passage migrant, usually in small numbers and mostly in the autumn.

Spring records are rare, with two on 30th April to 1st May 1991 the only ones traced. Records become more frequent from the last week of May, with moderate numbers occasionally seen at this time, for example 32 on 5th June 1986 and 29 on 2nd June 2001. The species is thereafter regular through the early autumn in moderate numbers, typically up to 80 in a day, mainly in onshore winds. Larger numbers are occasionally seen as follows:-

500+ on 27th August 1989.
123 on 22nd September 2002.
1,076 on 29th August 2003.

Records are rare after the end of September, by which time the birds should be well on their way to the wintering grounds off Brazil. With breeding colonies scattered throughout the eastern Atlantic, the origins of those recorded on the Point are not clear.

Although some Manx Shearwaters are seen close inshore, many seen from the Point are little more than 'blips' on the horizon.

Balearic Shearwater
Puffinus mauretanicus

Rowan does not list this species but White notes the first record of two 'Levantine Shearwaters' shot by George Long, a local wildfowler, on the Bar on 22nd September 1891, one passing into the Connop collection (*British Birds* 2: 313). These were the first for Norfolk. The next record for the county was a bird seen off the Point on 7th August 1955 and another was seen on 29th August 1956.

Since White's list the species has been recorded in a further eight years, with records falling between 15th August and 2nd October. All records involve singles with the exception of two on 27th September 1970.

Several birds have lingered offshore, actively feeding, most notably a bird between the Point and Weybourne on 1st – 8th September 1990.

This scarce and threatened species is confined as a breeding bird to the Balearic Islands and its regular occurrence in the southern North Sea is therefore perhaps surprising. However, the entire population is known to leave the Mediterranean to spend the late summer and early autumn in the Bay of Biscay and around southern England.

Little Shearwater
Puffinus assimilis baroli

A female of the Azores, Madeira and Canaries form *baroli*, picked up by Pinchen along the high water mark on the Point on 11th May 1929, is now in the Castle Museum, Norwich. His book *Sea Swallows* recounts the event:-

> 'One day I was escorting two ladies round the neighbourhood and pointing out items of interest when, on a very small tide, I discerned some feathers of a bird sticking up out of the water. I always examined such things so picked up the bird and took it home. I thoroughly cleaned it and discovered that it was a very rare specimen, the Little Dusky Shearwater, in a state of good preservation.'

This specimen, the second record for Norfolk, was examined during the preparation of this book and is indeed in remarkably good condition. It is mounted alongside a number of other seabirds in the glass cabinets in the Castle Museum's 'British Bird Gallery' public display area. An account of this record is published in *British Birds* 23: 41.

Amazingly, another, also of the form *baroli*, was found freshly dead along the beach on 1st May 1960 and forwarded to the British Museum where it is now preserved at Tring. An account of this record, including a description and measurements, is also contained in *British Birds*.

The dates of these records are particularly surprising given the scarcity of all 'tubenoses' off Norfolk in spring.

The taxonomy of the small black and white shearwaters is complex but recent studies have proposed that *baroli* is perhaps best treated as a form of a more widely-defined Audubon's Shearwater *Puffinus lherminieri*.

European Storm-petrel (Storm Petrel)

Hydrobates pelagicus

According to Rowan and White this species 'has been seen and taken on the Bar, chiefly in autumn, rarely in spring'. It is now best described as rare, much rarer than Leach's Storm-petrel and tending to appear in mid to late autumn in onshore gale conditions. All recent records are as follows:-

25th January 1987, an unusual date for Norfolk.
29th October 1989, notable for occurring in a southwesterly gale.
13th October 1997.
9th September 2001.
3 on 10th September 2001.
9th October 2001.
8th November 2001.
10th November 2001.
2 on 24th September 2004.

The high percentage of late autumn, and even winter, sightings is surprising given that the number of Storm Petrels at large in the North Sea declines rapidly after September. Storm Petrels breed in northern and western Britain and Ireland, the Faeroes and Norway and most winter off western and southern Africa, with some entering the Indian Ocean.

Leach's Storm-petrel (Leach's Petrel)

Oceanodroma leucorhoa leucorhoa

Rowan notes this species as irregular in autumn, taken twice on the Bar. White notes a further record on 15th September 1957, though other published records from the time include a bird on 15th October 1956 and one shot in the Harbour on 27th October 1939.

Since the 1970s Leach's Petrels have become more regular though they are still rare and less than annual. Records are always associated with strong onshore winds and fall between 4th August and 10th November, though almost all have occurred in September. Records are normally of single birds, though two have been recorded on a small number of occasions. Larger counts have included:-

7 on 9th September 1989, the day of an unprecedented movement, with 75 recorded passing Sheringham.
10 on 29th September 1991.

4 on 9th September 1997.
3 on 10th November 1999.

There are two spring records of single birds - one on 12th June 1978 and an undated record in the spring of 1994.

Birds are typically seen close inshore, slinking in the wave troughs, though birds have also been observed in the Harbour on at least one occasion.

Although most birds doubtless originate from the colonies in the northeast Atlantic, it is also possible that the occasional Nearctic bird is involved as these birds are also known to move southeast into British waters on passage to wintering grounds in the tropical mid-Atlantic.

Northern Gannet (Gannet)
Morus bassanus

Rowan notes this species as regular, sometimes quite plentiful, especially in September, a few also appearing now and then throughout the winter.

White records the Gannet as a regular passage migrant, chiefly in September, sometimes very numerous, and also seen occasionally at other times of year.

Gannets have increased steadily in Norfolk throughout the twentieth century and they can now be encountered in ones or twos at any season but are most common in mid-autumn, with counts in the hundreds frequent in periods of onshore winds. Even higher numbers have been recorded occasionally, for example 2,000 on 27th August 1989 and 1,500 on 9th September 1989, whilst 350 per hour were passing on 29th September 1991.

White notes Gannets in the Harbour on 26th July 1950 at a time of bad weather but birds are otherwise invariably passing at sea on migration from colonies in Scotland, the Faeroes, Iceland and Norway to wintering grounds off southwest Europe and west Africa. Evidence for this is provided by a Gannet ringed in the gannetry on Bass Rock, Lothian on 11th July 1971 which was recovered on the Point on 20th May 1978.

White notes five birds on 16th June 1970 as noteworthy but much higher numbers have now been recorded in the spring and summer, for example 72 on 4th May 2002 and 300 on 17th June 2001.

Great Cormorant (Cormorant)
Phalacrocorax carbo sinensis (Continental Cormorant)
Phalacrocorax carbo carbo (North Atlantic Cormorant)

Rowan notes this species, somewhat enigmatically, as:-

> 'irregular but common on the Point. They usually appear singly and practically in every month of the year'.

This status is confirmed by White.

Cormorants have increased significantly during the twentieth century and they are now present in moderate numbers throughout the year, but particularly in autumn and winter, fishing, passing offshore and day-roosting in the Harbour. Up to around 40 birds may be encountered in these roosts though WeBS mean counts in winter are in the range 20-25.

The majority of birds today are of the continental, and now increasingly British, form *sinensis* following its rapid increase and expansion in northwest Europe since the 1970s. Although birds of the North Atlantic form *carbo* doubtless occur, there are no confirmed recent records of this form from the Point. Records from the nineteenth and early twentieth centuries are, of course, more likely to have involved a higher percentage of *carbo*.

Most of the Point's Cormorants will no doubt be from English breeding colonies but there continues to be some recruitment to the British population from the near-continent.

Shag (European Shag)
Phalacrocorax aristotelis aristotelis
Rowan gives this species the same status as Cormorant but with the comment that the former species is more common. White refers to Shags as not commonly seen.

This is still true today as the Shag remains a scarce visitor, usually in late autumn and early winter. Records normally involve singles though three were present in December 2001 and up to nine were recorded in November and December 1984. Unseasonal birds were present on 1st – 2nd June 2001 and 9th May 2003.

Shags undertake a southward dispersal from the breeding colonies but this falls short of a real migratory movement. As a result, most Shags recorded on the Point are probably wanderers from the nearest colonies in northeast England and eastern Scotland, as evidenced by a bird ringed on the Farne Islands, Northumberland on 29th June 1961 which was recovered on the Point on 8th April 1962.

Eurasian Bittern (Great Bittern, Bittern)
Botaurus stellaris stellaris
According to Rowan the Bittern has been taken once on the Point. Despite their breeding at Cley and, at least in some years, regularly visiting Blakeney Fresh Marsh (outside our area), there are no other known records.

Little Egret. (*James McCallum*)

Little Egret
Egretta garzetta garzetta
The dramatic increase of this delightful species across southern Britain in the 1990s, doubtless linked to climate change, is neatly reflected in sightings on the Point.

The first record appears to be of one on 21st September 1989, the year of the first large influx from northwest France into southern England. There were three records in autumn 1993 (again a major influx year), since when records have become annual, initially of singles, but up to six were present in July 2001 and seven in August 2004, increasing to a record nine by October. It is now the commonest species of heron, present daily throughout the year, though the peak time appears to be autumn when locally-bred juveniles swell the numbers. Winter records are clearly linked to the wintering population established since 1993/94 on the Stiffkey and Warham saltings, from where the birds flight to roost at Holkham. By the winter of 2004/5 evening roost flights from the south side of the Harbour were exceeding 50 birds.

Favourite feeding locations on the Point include the Glaven channel at the Marrams, the salt-marsh between the Watch House and the Hood, Blakeney Pit and Pinchen's Creek, and at high tide birds sometimes roost communally perched high in the *Suaeda*.

With a new breeding colony now established nearby, this delightful species seems destined to become a permanent feature, adding a touch of the exotic and still appearing somewhat incongruous alongside the Dark-bellied Brent Geese.

Grey Heron
Ardea cinerea cinerea
Rowan notes that the species may cross over from the 'mainland' but is never common. He personally notes single birds in April and July and remarks that it had been taken in September.

White notes that Grey Herons can be found at any time of year and that passage migrants may occur. He records a peak count of 12 arriving from the sea on 24th September 1955.

Their status remains unchanged with, in most years, small flocks, doubtless from the near-continent, seen arriving from the sea, particularly from the second week of September to the first week of October. The peak counts are of 15 on 6th October 2001 and 17 on 25th September 2003.

Single birds are also regularly seen on the saltings, often mobbed by gulls.

Purple Heron
Ardea purpurea purpurea
The only record of this southern European heron concerns a bird which flew down the Glaven, crossed the Point between Cley Coastguards and the Marrams and flew north out to sea on 16th June 1991.

White Stork
Ciconia ciconia ciconia
Two flew west on 2nd April 2000, having first been seen at Incleborough Hill, Cromer and later that day were tracked along the coast to Holme. Presumably the same two birds subsequently roosted in Holkham Park.

A possibly high proportion of the White Storks occurring in Norfolk are escapes or free-flying individuals from collections at home or abroad or from reintroduction programmes in the Netherlands, Belgium and Germany, so the origin of these two birds cannot be known with certainty.

Wild White Storks breed in central and southern Europe and winter in Africa.

Eurasian Spoonbill (Spoonbill)
Platalea leucorodia leucorodia
Rowan gives records of Spoonbills in May and August 1903 and White cites an earlier record of three birds on 6th June 1879. He also lists six further records up to 1974, involving eight birds

between May and September. There are, however, at least two more published records, including a group of five birds on 4th June 1948.

Since the 1980s Spoonbills have become more regular, doubtless originating from the increasing Dutch population, and during the 1990s have become almost annual in spring. Most records are in May but the earliest record is of a bird on 22nd April 2004 and a late bird was seen on 7th June 2003. Further flocks include four on 30th May 1998 (resting in the Harbour) and five on 18th May 1993 but a record group of six occurred on 28th April 2002, flying in from the sea at Cley and heading low west past the Point.

A few Spoonbills have been seen in autumn between the end of August and the end of September and an exceptionally late bird was seen on 19th November 1989.

Most Spoonbills are seen flying past but the occasional bird has lingered in the Harbour.

Honey-buzzard (Honey Buzzard, European Honey-buzzard)
Pernis apivorus
Rowan lists one taken by Frank Richards near Pinchen's Creek on 5th September 1913. This bird was downed with an 8-bore from the deck of Pinchen's houseboat, the *'Britannia'* – a particularly productive spot! (see Red-breasted Flycatcher). All subsequent records are listed:-

24th May 1976.
17th September 1976, circling over the Plantation.
Dark juvenile on 13th October 1990, arriving from the sea at the Sandhills.
Juvenile on 20th September 2000, passing inland through the Harbour during that day's astonishing influx, when at least 40 were reported in the county.
Adult on 7th July 2002, high west over the Harbour, mobbed by Oystercatchers.

The influx of September 2000 was a result of strong easterly winds which displaced birds west from their normal southerly route out of Scandinavia.

Red Kite
Milvus milvus milvus
The only record concerns a wing-tagged bird fitted with a radio transmitter seen on 25th July 1990. This bird had been released in the Chilterns earlier in the month as part of the Red Kite reintroduction programme and was also seen at a number of other sites between the Point and Paston on this date.

Although Red Kites, both from the reintroduction programme and genuine continental immigrants, are increasingly recorded in Norfolk they have so far shown a marked reluctance to venture out to the Point.

White-tailed Eagle (Sea Eagle)
Haliaeetus albicilla
The first record of this huge eagle was in 1949 when an immature bird was seen hunting the Bar on 10th December. It remained for some time and was seen almost daily along the coast between Weybourne and Burnham Overy until 20th January 1950, being seen on several occasions on the Point, passing at sea, hunting in the Sandhills and resting on the tideline.

In 1961 one was seen by Ted Eales on 6th December and again on 15th. This bird later wintered in the Holme/Scolt Head area.

In 1962 a further bird was seen and filmed by Ted Eales, also on 6th December.

White and Gantlett (1995) list another bird in late December 1963, though with no precise date given, seen feeding on a dead seal and last seen on 4th January 1964. However, this record does not appear in the *Norfolk Bird Report* for those years.

White-tailed Eagles breed widely across northern Eurasia and have recently been reintroduced into western Scotland but these birds were doubtless all wanderers from the wintering population around the Baltic.

Marsh Harrier (Eurasian Marsh Harrier, Western Marsh Harrier)
Circus aeruginosus aeruginosus

Rowan does not list this species but it does appear in White's list where he notes it as a scarce species which can be encountered at any time of year.

It is worth recalling that as recently as 1971 there was only one British nest of Marsh Harrier (in Suffolk). The species is now widespread in Norfolk and breeds as close to our area as Blakeney Fresh Marsh.

In line with the rising fortunes of a number of birds of prey, Marsh Harriers are seen increasingly regularly on the Point, the records largely involving spring migrants from the near-continent and, as the year progresses, birds wandering and dispersing from their nearby breeding strongholds.

The first Marsh Harriers are usually seen in April and records of apparent migrants, including birds arriving from the sea, are then not unusual in April and May, though the presence of local breeding birds probably masks the true occurrence level of migrants. Local birds are seen regularly through the summer and early autumn and occasional birds are seen in late autumn and winter but they are scarce at this season.

Hen Harrier
Circus cyaneus cyaneus

Rowan states:-

> 'As far as I can determine no Harriers have been obtained on the Point itself. Mr. E.C. Arnold tells me that on September 15th 1903 he saw a bird which was almost certainly a female or immature Hen Harrier. An immature bird of this species was shot on the Morston Marshes on September 10th 1907. It was seen to rise from the sandhills on the Point and cross the channel.'

By the time of White's list, the species was an occasional visitor and regular passage migrant between October and March. Five were present for several weeks in the severe winter of 1978/79, preying on weakened waders.

Hen Harriers are still regular on the Point, being almost a daily sight in winter, usually single birds hunting the *Suaeda* and the Sandhills. Most are brown 'ringtails' but the occasional grey male is also seen. Some individuals may visit the Point daily for several weeks at a time, roosting at nearby Warham.

Most Hen Harriers wintering in eastern England are thought to be continental in origin and there is some evidence of spring and autumn passage. The occasional autumn bird has been seen arriving from the sea, strongly suggesting immigration from the continent. In autumn, birds are seen from the third week of September whilst in spring a few birds are recorded passing west through April and often into early May, usually occurring singly, though two flew west on 12th April 2003. More unusually, a 'ringtail' was predating Oystercatcher chicks on 18th June 2000.

Pallid Harrier

Circus macrourus

A first-summer bird was disturbed in the Long Hills and flew west through the Sandhills on 16th May 2003, occurring the same day as a Tawny Pipit and a Thrush Nightingale. What was presumably the same bird was also seen briefly the following morning near the Hood.

This record reflects the recent upsurge in British records of this western Russian and Central Asian steppe breeder, possibly attributable to the collapse of collective farming regimes in these ex-soviet areas. This was the second record for Norfolk and follows hot on the heels of the first – a first-winter individual which roosted off Warham from 24th December 2002 to 30th March 2003. This bird wandered widely and was seen as close to our recording area as Cley, Blakeney Fresh Marsh and Morston.

Montagu's Harrier

Circus pygargus

No records are listed by Rowan but White describes the species as an occasional visitor and regular passage migrant between April and September. A juvenile was present on 28th August 1964 and Cant's notes refer to a further individual on 4th May 1966.

Since the 1970s, however, further records have been very few:-

'Ringtail' on 14th May 1990.
'Ringtail' on 14th May 1992.
6th June 1993.
Female on 11th July 1994.
'Ringtail' on 10th May 1999.
Female on 21st April 2003.
Female on 23rd April 2004.

Montagu's Harrier is a central European and western Asian breeder, wintering in Africa, but occasional breeding also takes place in eastern England.

Eurasian Sparrowhawk. (*James McCallum*)

Eurasian Sparrowhawk (Sparrowhawk)

Accipiter nisus nisus

Rowan describes Sparrowhawks as occasional, mostly occurring between September and April. He himself only saw the species once, in January 1913.

In White's time the Sparrowhawk was still rare, 'although it was seen in 1965'.

Sparrowhawks are now regular at all times of year, particularly in April and mid to late autumn, and are regularly seen predating small migrants, particularly thrushes, in October and November. Records normally involve singles, with only occasional sightings of two birds. Some records may refer to local birds but many are likely to be continental migrants, as a number of Scandinavian-ringed Sparrowhawks have been recovered in Norfolk. A female found dead on the beach in the second week of September 2004 may also provide some circumstantial evidence of immigration.

Common Buzzard (Buzzard)

Buteo buteo buteo

Rowan makes no mention of the species but Pinchen's diaries include a 'Buzzard' on 24th October 1926 and also a reference to a 'large black Buzzard' (*sic*) on 2nd March 1927. White lists one seen on 20th August 1966 as the first documented record. There were no further records until an undated bird in 1983. Since then records have increased in line with the species' changing status in the county, with numbers of both local breeding birds and presumed continental migrants now rising steadily.

All known subsequent records are as follows:-

25th August 1985.
1986, but date not known.
7 west in a flock on 10th September 1995, later seen on the ground at East Hills, Wells.
5th June 1996.
20th May 2001.
17th August 2001.
12th April 2003.

The flock of September 1995 may be linked to a local Institute of Terrestrial Ecology release scheme operating from 1994. Eight birds were released in 1995 but that autumn also saw a noticeably larger than normal Buzzard passage.

Rough-legged Buzzard

Buteo lagopus lagopus

Rowan makes no reference to the species and White lists two records only – one on 28th March 1963 and a bird which hunted between Cley and the Point from 31st October to 15th November 1966 during a large autumn influx of the species.

This Scandinavian breeder is noted for its periodic winter influxes into eastern England but it remains rare on the Point, with all subsequent records as follows:-

'Some' in autumn and early winter 1973 (though no precise details known), during that year's invasion which began on 20th October.
1st and 4th May 1974, the final records from the 1973 influx.
26th October 1974, during a further influx.
21st March 1986, resulting from an influx in autumn 1985.
29th October 1988.

20th October 1994, during a further influx.
10th May 1999.
25th April 2004.
13th October 2004.

Osprey
Pandion haliaetus haliaetus

The species is not listed by Rowan. White notes the first record as a bird hunting Far Point on 6th – 7th September 1948, with a further seven records to the end of 1965. However, Pashley records birds as having been seen in May 1903 and 1904 and on 12th – 13th May 1913. He also refers to a pair in another year which fished in the Harbour from 16th – 29th May, roosting in the woods at Stiffkey.

Around seven were recorded in the 1970s and again in the 1980s but since 1990 the species has become annual.

Most records are in spring and fall between the middle of April and the end of May, though an early bird occurred on 2nd April 2000. Birds are typically seen passing west through the Harbour, causing panic amongst the gulls and waders, but they have also been noted fishing, particularly off the far spits. 2001 was the most prolific season, with a record seven birds seen, including three on 16th May.

There were only four autumn records before the 1990s but they have since become more frequent, with over ten records between August and the very beginning of October. The earliest of these was on 2nd August 1992, with the latest on 1st October 1979 and 1st October 2000.

Both British and Scandinavian breeders are likely to be involved in these movements. Birds passing west early in the spring seem most likely to be bound for Scotland whereas later birds may be displaced from the continent. A number of autumn birds have been seen arriving from the sea in weather conditions highly suggestive of a Scandinavian origin. Ospreys from all European populations winter in Africa.

Common Kestrel (Kestrel)
Falco tinnunculus tinnunculus

Rowan describes the Kestrel as fairly regular, though not abundant, in winter and also observed more than once in September. White describes it as an occasional visitor.

The species is now more common and may be encountered at any season, with individual birds often lingering for long periods. There is some evidence of slight spring and autumn passage and birds have been noted arriving from the sea so some interchange with the continent seems likely.

A pair bred in the roof of the Lifeboat House in 1974. Five young were raised, one of which was later found drowned in a water tank. Each parent bird went off with two young, the female and two juveniles frequenting Yankee Ridge from 21st July to 3rd August. The pair is reported to have fed their chicks mainly on young Little Terns.

Kestrels can have a huge impact on nesting terns, particularly Little Terns, sometimes taking all the young from a colony. In 1995 a male Kestrel took all the young from a colony of 15 Arctic Terns in under three days.

A bird ringed at Lode, Cambridgeshire on 14th March 1985 was recovered on the Point on 25th August the same year.

Red-footed Falcon (Western Red-footed Falcon)
Falco vespertinus

There are five records of this engaging falcon, all in mid to late May:-

Male on 15th May 1959.

Female east on 14th May 1992, at the Hood.

First-summer male west on 14th May 1992, at the Long Hills.

Female on 29th May 1992.

Female on 21st May 2002, at the Marrams, hawking insects and landing on the shingle beach.

The two birds on 14th May 1992 occurred within an hour of each other and formed the vanguard of a record invasion of 150 Red-footed Falcons into Britain in long-range, hot southeasterly winds - an influx which produced over 40 in the county. Record numbers of Red-throated Pipits were also recorded at this time and this species was also noted on the Point on the same day. The bird in 2002 occurred in similar conditions and a Red-throated Pipit was also seen at the Marrams immediately afterwards, the same day also producing a Subalpine Warbler!

After leaving their southern African savannah wintering grounds many Red-footed Falcons enter Europe through Tunisia and Sicily and are then liable to westward displacement from their preferred northeasterly heading towards breeding grounds in eastern Europe and western Russia. These displacements are now occurring more frequently, bringing ever greater numbers to Britain.

Merlin. (*James McCallum*)

Merlin

Falco columbarius aesalon

In Rowan's time Merlins were irregular but fairly frequent winter visitors, a status reiterated by White.

Since the 1980s Merlins have become more frequent and are resident on the Point during the autumn, winter and spring, with up to two or three birds frequently present, hunting the shingle ridge and the far spits for wintering and migrant passerines. They also frequently hunt over the sea, awaiting incoming small birds, and follow Hen or Marsh Harriers, ready to pursue birds disturbed by their larger relative.

The first Merlins appear early in the autumn, often in August, though birds were present on 19th July 1992 and 26th July 2001. Birds also linger late in the spring, often until the third week of May, and one was still present on 6th June 1998.

The vast majority of birds seen on the Point are likely to be British breeders, as evidenced by their early autumn arrival. Icelandic Merlins winter largely in Ireland and the west of Britain, and ringing elsewhere has shown little evidence of immigration into eastern England from the continent.

Hobby (Eurasian Hobby)
Falco subbuteo subbuteo
Rowan does not list the species and White notes only three records – the first involving two birds on 5th August 1953 at a time when fewer than ten were recorded each year in the county. Further singles occurred on 8th July 1965 and 6th July 1967.

Another bird was seen on 27th May 1975 but there are no further known records until 1994, when four passed east on 20th June, and 1996, when one occurred on 21st September.

Since 1996, however, Hobbies have become annual and can be expected at any time between May and September, extreme dates being 4th May and 29th September. Birds are sometimes observed resting on the shingle ridge, and in September 2002 two birds inhabited Far Point and appeared to be feeding on migrants.

This welcome increase reflects the species' success as a breeding bird across Norfolk, though some occurrences, perhaps particularly those in autumn, are also likely to be of continental birds, displaced from passage to wintering grounds in southern Africa.

Gyr Falcon
Falco rusticolus
White notes one seen on 20th December 1953, 'considered to belong to the Icelandic form *F. r. islandus*', though the species is now best regarded as monotypic but with variable morphs. This bird, seen by M.F.M. Meiklejohn, is described as being accompanied by a 'similar but much darker bird', with an implication that this too may have been a Gyr Falcon. Meiklejohn's notes from the time record that:-

> 'At 1100 hours on 20 December 1953 at Blakeney Point, Norfolk, I saw a large bird of prey (approximately buzzard size) fly down behind the sand-dunes.
>
> The bird was a large falcon… above grey with brown admixture on wing coverts; underparts appeared white, but possibly had few dark streaks; head pale; thin streak downwards from gape… larger and stouter than Peregrine; tail rather long; head protruding more forward of shoulders than in Peregrine; slower wing flaps than Peregrine, but giving impression of great power and speed; wings set at right angle to body and in flight not sloping backwards so much as in Peregrine; wings also broader. The bird's crop was distended and protruded, as if it had just been feeding.
>
> When the bird was flying away, I caught sight of a second similar bird flying over the sea at some distance, and following it. This second bird was not seen well, but was generally much darker in plumage. It too had the crop distended. It was flying with faster flaps, as if to catch up to its companion…'

Further reports from our area followed. Notes in the county archive from an unknown observer (thought possibly to be Archie Daukes) record the following:-

'Dec. 26th – a large lazy-flying dark slate-grey falcon, strikingly light below – observed at considerable distance flying over the W. end of Blakeney harbour. A better view of this bird was obtained on Jan 2nd when it flew past on Morston Marshes at about 100 yards.'

and:-

'Dec 29th – a much paler and somewhat larger bird which gave the impression of being about 1/3 larger than a Peregrine female was seen in flight near Stiffkey Channel… A very good view was obtained as the bird flew past in a heavy squall of wind at about 30 yards. Very light underparts and a partial moustachial stripe were plainly discernible.'

The differences between these descriptions perhaps lend weight to Meiklejohn's observation of two birds. Further reports of Gyr Falcons outside the immediate Point area came from Cley on at least 1st and 7th January 1954 and from Wiveton Marshes on the former date.

White also notes a further record on 1st October 1954. This bird is noted simply in the 1954 *Norfolk Bird Report* and in Taylor *et al.* (1999) as 'a very large, pale grey falcon with no 'moustaches' and pale greyish underparts'.

It is unfortunate that these records are not documented in more detail. All accepted modern British records of Gyr Falcons have been in the north and west and have involved the white *'candicans'* morph, presumably originating from Greenland. Claims in Britain of grey birds are now hopelessly clouded by the presence of escaped Sakers *Falco cherrug* and large hybrid falcons, firm identification of which is often effectively impossible.

Peregrine Falcon (Peregrine)

Falco peregrinus peregrinus

Rowan notes Peregrines as taken on 19th October 1909 and on one or two other occasions. The species had also been observed several times. Pinchen's diaries note occurrences on 2nd June 1922, two on 17th October 1922, 24th July 1926, 24th October 1926 and 2nd December 1929. White records the species as occasional, usually in September and October. He notes one on 28th September 1947 taking a Common Redstart and lists a further record on 22nd October 1950, at a time when the Peregrine population was at a low point after control by the Air Ministry during the 1939-1945 war.

Peregrines remained at a low ebb during the 1960s and 1970s and no further records are known from the Point until 22nd February 1982, followed by several other occurrences in the 1980s, largely in the winter. Several birds were also recorded in 1990, since when the species has become annual, with several now seen each year.

Peregrines can now be encountered at most times of year, with records regular until May and again from August. British winterers are thought to be largely Scandinavian in origin though some birds from the increasing British population are perhaps also involved.

A wide variety of prey species has been recorded at the Point, including Dark-bellied Brent Goose and Bar-tailed Godwit, and on one occasion a bird was seen to chase a Leach's Storm-petrel.

Water Rail

Rallus aquaticus aquaticus

Rowan notes that a specimen was taken in autumn 1902 and White records further occurrences on 23rd October 1955, 27th January 1957 and 13th April 1958.

Water Rails are now scarce autumn migrants from the continent, though their extremely skulking habits in waterlogged *Suaeda* and creeks must lead to many going undetected. Most records are of singles, more often heard than seen, between early October and mid-November, though two were recorded on 8th November 2003 and 30th October 2004.

Winter birds were seen on 27th January 1962 and 13th January 1990, with two on 1st December 1998 and further singles on 16th January and 3rd March 2004. It is possible, however, that the species is present, largely unrecorded, throughout the winter as Cant notes Water Rails being present in the 'big freeze' of January 1963, so emaciated that they could be picked up.

A further, more recent, spring individual occurred on 15th May 2001.

Corn Crake (Corncrake)

Crex crex

Pashley's diary records one of his rare visits to the Point on 8th May 1891:-

> 'The only birds in the bushes were a few pairs of Reed Buntings, a Pied Flycatcher on the wires of the coastguard flag staff and a Corn-Crake'.

Rowan does not list this record but does note that a specimen was obtained in autumn 1902. Pinchen's diary records a 'Landrail' on 7th October 1922 and White notes further singles on 8th September 1955, 25th – 27th April 1957 and 11th October 1966.

There are only two subsequent records:-

26th August 1968 (though Cant's notes give the date as 25th).
18th – 19th September 2002.

All records are presumably of continental birds, where large populations still exist in parts of eastern Europe, displaced west whilst on passage to wintering grounds in Africa.

Moorhen (Common Moorhen)

Gallinula chloropus chloropus

Rowan notes that a Moorhen was taken once amongst the *Suaeda* bushes. He also believed the species to have been seen in the Channel.

White lists further records behind the Lifeboat House in the hard weather of January 1963 and in the Plantation in October 1968.

The only other traced records are of birds in the *Suaeda* on 3rd November 1984, 25th May 1991 and 25th March 2005. More bizarrely, a bird was seen in the tern colony from a seal trip boat on 9th June 2004 before it flew to the mainland.

This species is surprisingly scarce given that it is a common breeder on Blakeney Fresh Marsh and at Cley. As with the following species, however, ringing recoveries to and from the near-continent have shown that Moorhens can be surprisingly mobile and it is therefore likely that some of the Point records relate to migrants.

Common Coot (Coot)

Fulica atra atra

Rowan lists a Coot taken on 31st December 1906. White states that in very bad weather such as 1947, when inland waters are frozen over, several hundred may occur in the Harbour and the 1947 issue of *Wild Bird Protection in Norfolk* refers to 'a big company of Coots' on 18th February of that year.

The only recent records of which we are aware concern up to 16 in January and February 1985, 31 in February 1991 and a single bird on 29th December 2000, all linked to hard weather. In this context, a particularly unusual record was of one close inshore on the sea off the Sandhills on 24th August 2003. As with the preceding species, ringing recoveries to and from the near-continent have demonstrated that Coots can be surprisingly migratory so it is possible that this individual may have been an immigrant.

Common Crane (Crane)

Grus grus grus

Pashley's diaries record nine Cranes east over the Bar on 29th August 1899. The next record is of two passing west on 25th April 1956.

Rowan, however, fails to mention the first of these records and White refers only to a record in May 1968 (actually on 3rd May). A further bird occurred on 2nd November 1986, arriving from the sea.

Since the establishment of the resident Broadland breeding population in the 1980s records have become more frequent. Groups of one to four birds are now virtually annual, typically heading high to the west in the late morning on bright spring days from mid-April but with most in the first three weeks of May. It is assumed that these are all birds from Broadland indulging in short distance wanderings as this pattern is noticeably different from that in the rest of Britain where a marked mid-March peak occurs, coinciding with Crane passage through northwest Europe into Scandinavia. There are no recent records which fall outside this pattern, with the exception of the 1986 individual which could well have been Scandinavian in origin, displaced from its route to winter quarters in Iberia.

Oystercatchers. (*James McCallum*)

Oystercatcher (Eurasian Oystercatcher)

Haematopus ostralegus ostralegus

Pashley notes that, due to human persecution, Oystercatchers were absent as a breeder from the Point between 1892 and 1905. The first nest for the Point was not found until 1906. Rowan records the species as a scarce breeder, with no more than three clutches per season. At no time of year was it described as plentiful.

White notes the six nests found in 1922 as:-

'eminently satisfactory because only a few years ago one nest in this area was quite an event.'

No more than eight nests were to be found in the 1920s but the number had risen to 22 pairs in 1931. Numbers remained at around this level until the 1939-1945 war when, in 1940, 47 nests were located.

After the war numbers again increased, rising to a maximum of 92 pairs in the 1950s, 120 pairs in the 1960s and 200 pairs in the 1970s. Numbers fluctuated between 140 and 200 pairs through the 1980s and 200 pairs were still present in 1998, declining to 140 pairs by 2002, 154 pairs in 2003 and 148 pairs in 2004. Breeding success is currently pitiful due to predation by Common Gulls. In 2003 only two young fledged and in 2004 only three young were seen. Breeding Oystercatchers on the Point are hard to ignore due to their vigorous mobbing of intruders but this seems to do little for their breeding success.

Oystercatchers are also common autumn migrants and winter visitors from the continent and in winter this is the commonest wader in the Harbour. The first birds appear in July and ringing elsewhere has demonstrated that many of these originate in western Norway. White lists peak counts of 350 in the winter of 1953/54 and a maximum count of 600 on 17th October 1956. Modern-day counts have regularly reached and exceeded these levels, with 1,000 present in October 1993 and again in August 2003, though WeBS mean counts for October to March are in the range 500-600.

An Oystercatcher ringed on the Point on 27th July 1953 was recovered at Southampton, Hampshire on 30th January 1957, illustrating the southward dispersal of British-breeding Oystercatchers in winter. Some British birds reach France or even Iberia.

Avocet (Pied Avocet)

Recurvirostra avosetta

Rowan records that the Avocet was probably a common sight until the early part of the nineteenth century but at the time of his writing it was an irregular spring migrant. He notes that one was taken on 19th May 1905 and that four were seen near the Watch House on 2nd September 1907.

White lists the next record as three birds on 10th June 1947, the year in which Avocets re-established themselves as a British breeder in Suffolk, and another on 1st May 1967, though this latter record is not mentioned in the *Norfolk Bird Report* for that year. Further records around this time include a single on 14th April 1948, five on 26th July 1952 and a further single on 22nd September 1963.

Since the 1980s, by which time the Cley population had become established, Avocets have become scarce though regular in the Harbour, most frequent in spring and summer. A particularly high total of 33 was recorded on 17th April 1999. Avocets breeding nearby will sometimes move their flightless young into the Harbour to feed. The species is rare in winter though increasing numbers are now wintering as close as Cley.

Stone-curlew (Stone Curlew)

Burhinus oedicnemus oedicnemus

White notes the first record of a bird flushed in the Sandhills by Ted Eales on 10th May 1951.

Subsequent records are as follows, all either spring migrants or early autumn birds presumably dispersing from Breckland breeding grounds:-

9th June 1988.
23rd April 1990.
Juvenile on 13th August 2000.
15th August 2001.
5th June 2002.
26th July and 1st August 2004.
28th May 2005.

Birds have frequented both the shingle ridge and the Harbour muds and the individual in 2000 accompanied a flock of Oystercatchers.

Collared Pratincole

Glareola pratincola pratincola

This southern European and southwest Asian rarity, which winters in Africa, flew west over Far Point on 6th July 1995 together with Swifts and a few Sand Martins. This was the adult bird, the fourth for Norfolk, which toured the north of the county in the summers of 1994 – 1998, normally frequenting Cley or Titchwell but also visiting Snettisham, Burnham Norton, Holkham, Berney and even Lancashire, Northamptonshire, Kent and the Netherlands. The bird was well-photographed during its stay in Norfolk and pictures have been widely published but it was not photographed on the Point.

Oriental Pratincole

Glareola maldivarum

The sole record concerns a first-summer bird which lingered at the Watch House from 0800-1015 on 4th June 1993 before heading west. This bird had been present at Gimingham since 14th May and was subsequently seen at Burnham Norton, Titchwell and Thornham.

The bird was well-photographed during its stay in Norfolk and pictures have been widely published, though no photographic record is known of its occurrence on the Point. This is a far-eastern species breeding in eastern Asia and wintering largely in Australia. Not surprisingly, there-fore, this was only the third British record and the first for Norfolk. A full account of its occur-rence can be found in the *Norfolk Bird Report* for 1993.

Little Ringed Plover (Little Plover)

Charadrius dubius curonicus

White records the first as seen near Pinchen's Creek on 6th September 1949, at a time when the species was still very rare in the county. A pair was seen between the Hood and the Watch House on 16th May 1952 and in 1954 two were seen on 10th and 14th May and two on 4th October. These latter birds are particularly late records for Norfolk.

Subsequent records have been few but appear to be becoming more frequent, normally involving single birds flying over:-

4th May 1986.

30th May 1997.

20th May 2000.

20th August 2000.

4 juveniles on 18th August 2001.

3 on 24th June 2003, with one intermittently to 4th July, often song-flighting.

4th September 2003.

12th August 2004.

2 on 21st April 2005, with one to 22nd.

Although the species has an extensive Palearctic distribution it is likely that many of these records are linked to the presence of breeding birds at Cley. European Little Ringed Plovers winter in Africa.

Ringed Plover (Great Ringed Plover)

Charadrius hiaticula hiaticula

Charadrius hiaticula tundrae (Tundra Ringed Plover)

Rowan records the species as a resident, breeding in fair though variable numbers but never with more than 20 pairs in a season.

White notes the Ringed Plover as a common breeding bird, with significantly larger numbers breeding than in Rowan's day. Between 40 and 85 pairs bred during the 1950s and 100 pairs were recorded for the first time in 1961, rising to 114 pairs in 1962. Many Ringed Plovers were, however, victims of the severe 1962/63 winter and the population dropped sharply in 1963 to 54 pairs, only to rise rapidly to a new peak of 140 pairs by 1967. Numbers then remained high until the mid-1970s with an all-time peak of 180 pairs reached in 1972.

Only up to around 100 pairs, however, bred in the 1980s and in the 1990s the population fell further, down to 50 pairs by 1997, with only 15–18 pairs by the turn of the century, mirroring once more their status in Rowan's day. The population remained at 15 pairs in 2004, with only two young fledged.

The Ringed Plover is notoriously susceptible to human disturbance in its preferred sand and shingle habitats. It also suffers from predation, for example adult birds have on a number of occasions been taken from the nest by Sparrowhawks.

These breeding birds show the pale upperparts typical of the nominate form which breeds in Britain, France, southern Scandinavia, Iceland, Spitsbergen, Greenland and Canada. British breeders tend to winter a little to the south in western Europe, with those from further afield wintering progressively further south along the Atlantic coast and those from the Nearctic reaching west Africa. These continental and Nearctic birds no doubt also occur on passage as autumn counts of largely migrant Ringed Plovers in August and September regularly reach 200, with 341 counted in September 1994 and 345 in August 2003.

There is in addition a noticeable passage in May and again in August and September of small, dark birds of the form *tundrae* from northern Scandinavia and northern Russia moving to and from wintering grounds in west Africa. A notable count of 75 of these dark birds was made in May 1994. These can be strikingly different from the larger, paler local breeders and earlier spring migrants of the nominate form.

The winter population in the Harbour is generally in the region of 60-100 though 161 were counted in November 1994.

Kentish Plover

Charadrius alexandrinus alexandrinus

Rowan records this widespread but largely southern species as having been taken once, many years earlier, by J.H. Gurney on the Hood. The bird is described as 'immature' though no date is given. Pashley's diaries contain a record of three on the Point on 3rd August 1899.

Further records, including those given by White, are as follows:-

30th December 1927.

September 1938, but precise date unknown.

2 on 18th April 1952.

3rd October 1956.

Female and young-looking juvenile on 31st August and 7th – 8th September 1975.

9th May 1976.

A pair for two weeks from 7th June 1976.

28th August 1976.

8th August 1977, with two on 12th and 14th, the year in which the species attempted breeding at Salthouse.

First week of June 1978, but precise date unknown.

26th – 30th May 1979.

A pair in 1983, making two unsuccessful breeding attempts, the female remaining until 30th August.

A further record at 'Blakeney' on 11th June 1970 may have been in our area.

Greater Sand Plover

Charadrius leschenaultii subsp.

The second for Norfolk, a female, commuted between Cley and Blakeney Harbour from 30th July to 22nd August 1985 and was seen again on 2nd September. When in the Harbour it often frequented a creek in the northeast corner and was also noted roosting on the Point itself near the Lifeboat House. A photograph of this bird roosting on the Point with Ringed Plovers is in the *Norfolk Bird Report*s for 1985 (in black-and-white) and 1992 (in colour). A full account of its occurrence appears in the *Norfolk Bird Report* for 1985.

A further individual in similar plumage again commuted between Cley and the Harbour between 5th and 8th August 1992 before being relocated in Essex and Kent. This bird was also photographed but not on the Point.

It is difficult to assign Greater Sand Plovers to form, but both individuals are perhaps most likely to have been of one of the western forms *columbinus* or *crassirostris*, from southwest and Central Asia respectively.

Dotterels and Northern Wheatears. (*James McCallum*)

Dotterel (Eurasian Dotterel)

Charadrius morinellus

Rowan records the Dotterel as a rare September visitor, taken in 1901, 1902 and, in 1903, in breeding plumage. Pashley's diaries refer to a bird brought in 'from the bushes' on 21st September 1892.

White also records the species as rare, quoting the next record as 24th August 1963 and three other records involving four birds up to 1976.

Since the 1980s Dotterel have been almost annual in occurrence although a decline has been noted over the last ten years. Most records fall in late August and September, the earliest being on 9th August 1981 and the latest on 12th October 2003, the only record for that month. Birds are normally seen singly but two or three birds have been seen on four occasions.

The first spring record was of one on 10th May 1975. The next bird at this season occurred on 11th May 1986, since when there have been a further seven records involving at least eleven individuals. Spring records fall between 8th and 31st May and, as in autumn, normally involve singles, though three were recorded on 24th – 31st May 1989 and on 8th May 1995.

Some birds have just been noted flying through but most are seen on the ground. Such birds invariably frequent the shingle areas, with the flat stretch at the east end of the Sandhills ('Dotterel Flats') being a particularly favoured spot.

The Dotterel recorded on the Point are doubtless of Scandinavian stock and they generally, but not exclusively, occur in easterly conditions. The small British population is thought to leave the breeding grounds and head directly south for Morocco.

European Golden Plover (Golden Plover)

Pluvialis apricaria

Rowan describes the species as regular and by no means uncommon between September and December while White describes it as a regular passage migrant, with a few wintering.

Golden Plovers are now regularly seen passing west in autumn and are also present in the Harbour in considerable numbers at this season, throughout the winter and into the following spring. They form typically tight, dense flocks in the inner Harbour and commute to feed inland at Cley and Blakeney and also beyond Morston and Stiffkey.

Returning autumn migrants occur from late July and peak in early August when around 500-1,000 are present. Numbers typically build up to around 2,000 in winter, though 3,000 were present in January 1999 and 2003 and 3,200 in January 2004. Somewhat inexplicably, WeBS counts rarely exceed 100 but this may be because counts have occurred when the birds are feeding elsewhere. Birds are seen until the final departures in April and May. More unusually, a bird was present on 8th – 10th June 1993.

Amongst those seen in apparently full summer plumage, birds showing characters of both northern and southern 'types' can be seen though the relative proportions of each are not clear.

Only a small fraction of Britain's wintering Golden Plovers use coastal mudflats so Blakeney Harbour is an important such site for this species. The overwhelming majority are doubtless Scandinavian in origin as Icelandic birds have been shown to winter mainly in Ireland.

Grey Plover

Pluvialis squatarola

Rowan notes the species as occurring between mid-September and March in fair numbers, with 'exceptionally large numbers' recorded in 1908. White describes it as a passage migrant and winter visitor, though with records at all times of year.

A steady westerly passage of this Arctic Russian breeder is noted offshore in August and several hundred can be found in the Harbour at this time, with a peak of 800 in August 1987. During the winter WeBS mean counts for November to February are in the range 100-120 though 190 were present in January 2001.

A return passage is noted in spring of birds which have wintered to the south in west Africa, the largest count at this season being of 1,000 on 4th May 1981. A few non-breeding individuals can also be found in the Harbour in summer.

Northern Lapwing (Lapwing)

Vanellus vanellus

Pinchen's diairies make frequent reference to passages of 'Green Plovers', including 'more than I ever remember seeing before' in autumn 1929, and Rowan records large numbers crossing the Point in autumn, mostly in September but also in October. White also reports large parties of autumn immigrants and records that a pair nested for the first (and only) time in 1961, laying four eggs from which two chicks flew.

White also notes that in the severe weather of January 1963 most Lapwings left the Point just before the worst weather arrived and returned two days after the thaw started, with large numbers seen coming in off the sea on 2nd and 3rd March of that year.

Along with the Sky Lark, the Lapwing is known to have suffered significant declines across northwest Europe due to changing agricultural practices and this has been reflected in their increasing scarcity as an autumn immigrant since the 1970s. Large westerly movements used to be noted in October but any counts of over 200 in a day would now be regarded as noteworthy. The Lapwing is noted as the earliest 'autumn' migrant, with the first returning failed or non-breeders often noted in late May.

Winter numbers are, however, still high, with WeBS counts recording a few hundred, but 2,000 were counted in December 2000 and 3,000 in February 2001 and again in January 2004, reflecting the fact that eastern England now represents the most important British wintering area for Lapwings.

Red Knot (Knot)
Calidris canutus islandica (Greenland Knot)
Rowan and White note Knot as annual in large numbers from the end of August to May, becoming scarce towards mid-winter, especially in years of severe weather.

Small parties of Knot are regularly seen coasting westwards in autumn from mid-July but the Harbour is not an important wintering site for this species by comparison with the huge numbers which winter in the Wash. Currently around 300–600 winter in the Harbour, with the largest numbers present between November and February, though occasional much larger counts have been made as follows:-

4-5,000 on 17th February 1901.
4,000 on 2nd March 1955.
An estimated 10,000 on 22nd December 1962.
4,000 on 5th February 1968.
4,400 on 25th January 1985.

The Knot occurring on the Point, as those throughout Britain, are almost entirely of the Greenland and Arctic Canadian form *islandica*. Both this form and nominate *canutus* from Siberia stage on the Wadden Sea but Siberian birds are thought to continue directly onwards to Mauritania, largely bypassing Britain.

Sanderling
Calidris alba
Rowan and White both note the species as annual in considerable numbers between September and April, much scarcer in the winter months.

Numbers now peak in spring in May, when over 200 have occurred, and birds return from July, peaking in August and September, when up to 100 have been recorded. Sanderlings occur both on the outer beach and on the stretches of firm sand in the Harbour, typically running along the water's edge like clockwork toys. WeBS counts in the Harbour show a mean winter population of only 20-30 birds. A few non-breeding birds are also present in summer.

British-wintering Sanderling are known to originate both from Greenland and Arctic Russia, but the relative proportions of those occurring on the Point are not known. The passage peaks reflect their migration to and from the main wintering grounds in west Africa.

Little Stint
Calidris minuta
Rowan notes the occurrence of a few Little Stints in most years in September, though they are never abundant and usually associate with flocks of larger congeners. They are recorded as much more plentiful in some years than others. White notes the species as an uncommon passage migrant in small numbers.

Little Stints remain annual though scarce, larger numbers naturally coinciding with the periodic autumn influxes for which they are well known, linked either to easterly conditions during their passage from Arctic Russia to Africa or to high population levels (or both).

Autumn records, involving normally only one or two individuals in a day, occur between July and September, though nine were present in September 1993 as part of a wider influx.

Spring Little Stints are rare. Cant's notes refer to a bird on 16th June 1967 and more recent records occurred on 2nd June 1991, one or two in May and to 13th June 2000 and in May 2001.

Temminck's Stint
Calidris temminckii

Rowan notes Temminck's Stints as rare and irregular autumn passage migrants, taken several times. Birds are noted as having been taken 'in recent times' by Frank Richards on 24th September 1902 and by M.A. Catling on 14th September 1907.

White was not aware of any other records. Pashley's diaries, however, refer to a record of a bird seen by himself on one of his infrequent visits to the Point on 30th August 1914 and Pinchen's diaries record that he heard a bird on 1st September 1927.

There are only four recent records of Temminck's Stints, involving seven individuals:-

2 on 23rd May 1987.
4th May 1997.
3 on 21st May 2002.
25th August 2003, flying east and subsequently seen at Cley.

This paucity of records compared with the pools at nearby Cley reflects the species' preference for freshwater habitats. Temminck's Stints are Scandinavian breeders and these records relate to migrants travelling to and from their African wintering grounds.

Curlew Sandpiper
Calidris ferruginea

Rowan and White both record the species as annual in small numbers in September and the first half of October and, more rarely, in April. In some years they were regarded as very plentiful in autumn.

This remains broadly the case today, with a few observed each autumn and, as with Little Stint, larger numbers recorded in invasion years, linked either to easterly conditions during their passage from Arctic Russia to Africa or to high population levels (or both). Birds occur between July and September and, as with all waders, moulting adults precede the pristine juveniles. The highest numbers recorded recently have been 45 adults on 31st August 1992, an influx year, and 75, mainly juveniles, on 9th September 1985, also part of a wider influx.

Spring records are rare, normally involving one or two birds only and normally in May.

Purple Sandpiper
Calidris maritima

Rowan notes Purple Sandpipers as occasional between September and December. White records them between late August and April.

Purple Sandpipers remain annual autumn migrants in very small numbers, often seen just flying past along the shoreline but sometimes very tame juvenile birds can be encountered on the shingle ridge. Early autumn records include three on 2nd – 12th August 1946 and one on 28th July 1954 but records fall mainly between mid-August and late September, although there are records throughout October and into November. Peak counts are of eight on 13th September 1971 and eight on 28th November 2000.

Plate 1   The heligoland trap on the Hood, looking west towards the Lifeboat House, 1954. (*Richard Richardson archive*)

Plate 2   The Plantation in the 1950s. (*Richard Richardson archive*)

Plate 3 Blakeney Point – aerial view from the east at high tide. (*Mike Page*)

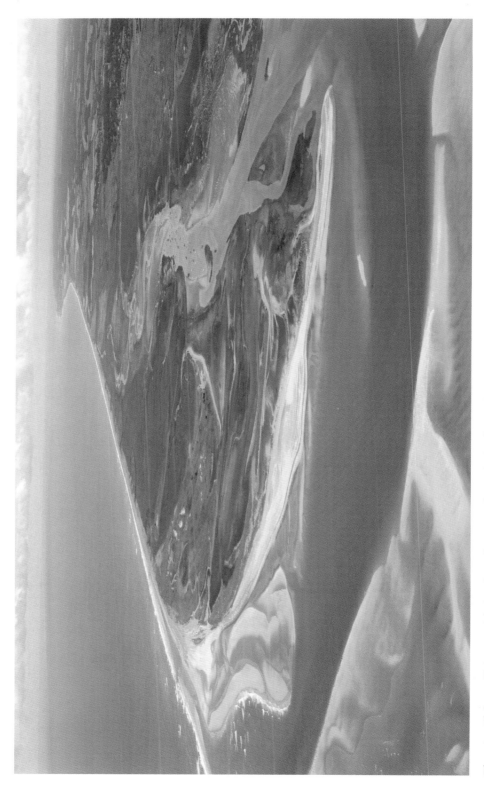

Plate 4 Blakeney Point – aerial view from the west at low tide. (*Mike Page*)

Plate 5 The Watch House. (*Richard Porter*)

Plate 6 The blue-and-white boat WH 272, marooned in the Marrams, looking west towards the Lifeboat House. (*Richard Porter*)

Plate 7   Blakeney Harbour, looking southeast towards Blakeney Church. (*Richard Porter*)
Plate 8   The *Suaeda* between the Hood and the Long Hills, looking west towards the Sandhills. (*Richard Porter*)

Plate 9   The wreck of the '*Yankee*', looking north towards the Sandhills. (*Richard Porter*)
Plate 10 The Lifeboat House, now housing the National Trust information centre and Wardens' accommodation. (*Richard Porter*)

Plate 11 Looking northeast towards the Plantation and the Laboratory. (*Richard Porter*)
Plate 12 The Plantation today. (*Richard Porter*)

Plate 13 The Laboratory and the Tamarisk. (*Richard Porter*)
Plate 14 The *Suaeda*, looking west towards the Watch House. (*Richard Porter*)

Plate 15 Red-breasted Flycatcher, June 2003. (*Richard Porter*)
Plate 16 Male Dotterel, May 2004. (*Richard Porter*)

Plate 17 Ortolan Bunting – a formerly regular autumn migrant, now increasingly scarce. (*Julian Bhalerao*)

Plate 18 Male Red-spotted Bluethroat, May 1987. (*Tim Loseby*)

Plate 19 Pallas's Grasshopper Warbler, September 2001 – the third record for England. (*Dave Nye*)
Plate 20 Radde's Warbler, October 1961 – the second record for Britain. (*Richard Richardson archive*)

Plate 21 Pied Flycatcher on the Plantation fence – a 'classic' early autumn sight. (*Richard Porter*)
Plate 22 Siberian Chiffchaff, October 2004. (*Richard Porter*)

Plate 23 Female Desert Wheatear, November 2003. (*Richard Porter*)
Plate 24 Female Northern Bullfinch, October 2004. (*Richard Porter*)

Plate 25 Arctic Warbler, September 1993. (*Julian Bhalerao*)
Plate 26 Greenish Warbler, August 2000 – the traditional early autumn rarity on the Point. (*Julian Bhalerao*)

Plate 27 Pallas's Warbler, October 1989. (*Barry Jarvis*)
Plate 28 Male Asian Desert Warbler, May/June 1993 – the first spring record for Britain. (*Julian Bhalerao*)

Plate 29 Siberian Stonechat, September 1991. (*Robin Chittenden* www.harlequinpictures.com)
Plate 30 Red-throated Pipit, September 1991. (*Robin Chittenden* www.harlequinpictures.com)

Spring records are rare, the only traced birds being singles on 16th May 1950, 14th May 1988 and 8th May 2004, whilst an exceptional summer record involves one in the Harbour on 18th June 1977.

The origin of these Purple Sandpipers is not entirely clear. Some are likely to be from Norway but Canadian breeders are now also thought to make up a proportion of the British wintering population.

Ringed Plover, Grey Plover, Little Stint, Curlew Sandpipers, Dunlins and Bar-tailed Godwits. (*James McCallum*)

Dunlin

Calidris alpina alpina (Northern Dunlin)
Calidris alpina schinzii (Southern Dunlin)
Calidris alpina arctica (Greenland Dunlin)

Rowan notes that, although Dunlin are seen throughout the year, they are most numerous in spring and autumn. He records them as probably the commonest of the Point's waders while White refers to them as undoubtedly the commonest.

Dunlin of all the above three forms occur but their relative status is unclear, with subspecific identification in the field only possible with summer plumage adult birds. The southern Greenland, Iceland and British form *schinzii* occurs mainly in July and August on passage to its wintering grounds in Mauritania and predominates in the large flocks present at this season, either passing west offshore or in the Harbour. Amongst these flocks can also be found the occasional bird showing characters of the northern Greenland form *arctica*, which shares a similar migratory strategy, but the occurrence of this form has not been definitively proven from trapped or measured birds. As with all waders, the early arrivals consist exclusively of adults, but juveniles become progressively more common through August.

Within these early autumn flocks can be found a few much brighter adult birds showing characters of the Scandinavian and Russian form *alpina*. It is this form which progressively replaces passage *schinzii* during the autumn, with larger numbers arriving and passing west off-shore in October and November after moulting on the Wadden Sea. Peak autumn counts are made at this time, typically of around 700 birds, but 960 were present in October 1994. The British wintering population is thought to consist entirely of *alpina*. Numbers in winter typically reach 500-600 but over 1,000 were present in December 2001, 2,000 in January 2003 and an exceptional 3,600 were counted on 25th January 1985. The Dunlin is now the second commonest wintering wader in the Harbour after Oystercatcher.

In spring many birds depart in March and April, when returning birds once again use the Wadden Sea, but some are seen well into May, often in the company of *tundrae* Ringed Plovers. The species is rarely recorded in June. The proportion of *schinzii* involved in spring movements is not known but is likely to be much lower as this population traditionally stages through the Irish Sea estuaries at this season.

Broad-billed Sandpiper
Limicola falcinellus falcinellus
There are five records of this stripy rare wader, involving six individuals:-

13th August 1895, shot by Pinchen. This record is listed in Gantlett (1995) as referring to two birds.
2 on 5th September 1950, near the Watch House. This record is described in detail in the 1951 issue of *Wild Bird Protection in Norfolk*, leaving no doubt that two birds were involved, but White's list refers to only one bird.
Adult on 5th – 6th August 1990, near the Watch House, previously present at Cley since 28th July.
Juvenile on 12th September 1993, near the Watch House, previously present at Cley since 8th. This bird was photographed on the Point.
Adult on 25th July 1996, previously present at Cley since 24th.

Broad-billed Sandpipers are elusive breeders in Scandinavian and northern Russian bogs, with a southeasterly migration route to wintering grounds around the northern Indian Ocean. It is therefore, not surprisingly, a rarity in Britain. Although a high percentage of Broad-billed Sandpipers in Britain (and in Norfolk) occur in spring, it is interesting that none have yet been recorded on the Point at this season.

Buff-breasted Sandpiper
Tryngites subruficollis
Rowan and White list one obtained by Arnold on 8th September 1899 and this date is confirmed in Richard Richardson's hand-written extracts from Arnold's notes. However, Gantlett (1995) and Taylor *et al.* (1999) incorrectly give the date as 7th.

This is one of the very few exclusively Nearctic species to have occurred on the Point. It breeds in northern Alaska and northwest Canada, wintering in Argentina and Paraguay.

Ruff
Philomachus pugnax
Rowan notes the species as uncommon, with a few recorded most years in September, and more rarely in spring. White notes a flock of 20 seen by Ted Eales outside the Lifeboat House in September 1965.

Ruff are still scarce migrants to the Point from Scandinavia and northern Russia, most being on passage to wintering grounds in Africa. They are regular in ones or twos in the Harbour in autumn, particularly with the Golden Plovers, but also in winter, when occurrences may be linked to hard weather. Higher numbers include seven in October 1997, 12 in December 2003 and a record 24 in January 1998.

Jack Snipe

Lymnocryptes minimus

Rowan notes the species as merely occasional and White records it as only occurring very occasionally, usually during hard weather. He lists autumn records on 29th September 1960 and 22nd September 1966.

Jack Snipe are now regular in ones or twos as an early spring and late autumn migrant en route to and from breeding grounds in Scandinavian bogs. Spring birds are generally recorded in the second half of March, with returning birds in autumn appearing from mid-September but with most seen in October. Birds are generally flushed from the saltmarsh on the outer edges of the *Suaeda* and are no doubt under-recorded.

Common Snipe (Snipe)

Gallinago gallinago gallinago

Rowan notes Snipe as merely occasional. White, by contrast, notes the species as frequent, mainly as a passage migrant but also a winter visitor. It is likely, however, that the species is now scarcer as a migrant due to its well-documented decline as a breeding bird in northwest Europe. However, data from the Point are not sufficient to provide robust evidence of this.

Snipe are still regular passage migrants, particularly in autumn from August onwards, when small 'wisps' can be encountered passing over or flushed from the saltmarsh. The species is doubtless under-recorded due to the extent and inaccessibility of the saltmarsh areas.

Good numbers are also present during the winter, with a particularly high count of 181 in the Harbour in 1997.

The Snipe recorded on the Point are presumably exclusively of the widespread nominate form as the Iceland, Faeroes, Orkney and Shetland form *faeroeensis* winters largely in Ireland.

Great Snipe

Gallinago media

Rowan refers to the species as 'taken once on the Sand Hills' by Ramm, though no date is given. White gives no further records.

This species was historically much commoner in Norfolk and must at that time have been more regular on the Point. Taylor *et al.* (1999) refer to Thomas Gunn securing 'a Great Snipe and a Bluethroat with right and left shots in the sandhills' though again no date is given for this record.

Recent accepted records are as follows:-

28th August 1976, near the Watch House.
Juvenile on 25th – 27th August 1987, ranging widely along the shingle ridge. This bird occurred during a large 'fall' which also produced two Greenish Warblers. It was photographed and an account of its occurrence is contained in *Twitching* 1: 218-219.
Juvenile on 12th September 2002, in the Sandhills and ranging to Yankee Ridge.

In addition, a further bird was seen on 22nd September 1996 in the Sandhills but was not submitted to BBRC.

This species breeds in Scandinavia and western Russia and winters in Africa. It is now, however, rare and a bird of some conservation concern. It therefore seems unlikely ever to increase its occurrence rate on the Point much above the current one per decade.

Woodcock (Eurasian Woodcock)

Scolopax rusticola

Rowan merely lists the species but White describes it as annual, usually in October.

Woodcock now occur as very scarce early spring and more common late autumn migrants, also appearing in winter in hard weather.

Spring birds are occasionally recorded in March, coinciding with the departure of continental winterers, though late birds were seen on 20th April 2003 and 3rd May 2001. Pinchen's diaries refer to a bird on the somewhat unusual date of 2nd August 1929.

Autumn immigrants normally occur from the second week of October, though two were seen on 4th October 1998 and Pinchen notes a bird on 28th September 1922, at a time when arrivals of this species occurred slightly earlier in the season than they do today. Passage continues into November, with birds normally seen in easterly conditions, often associated with 'falls' of Blackbirds or Goldcrests. Numbers are generally small, normally fewer than ten in a day, but 18 were counted on 25th October 1988 and 13 on 21st October 2001. They are, however, probably under-recorded due to their habit of sitting tight until almost trodden on. One or two are still recorded in the winter months in hard weather and Cant notes birds in the 'big freeze' of January 1963 being so emaciated that they could be picked up.

British Woodcock are known from ringing recoveries to be largely sedentary and all the birds recorded on the Point can therefore be assumed to be continental in origin. Birds wintering in southeast England originate largely from Russia, Finland and the Baltic States.

Black-tailed Godwit

Limosa limosa limosa
Limosa limosa islandica (Icelandic Black-tailed Godwit)

Rowan notes that the Black-tailed Godwit was reported to have been seen on the Point more than once but had never been taken. This accords with Pashley's remark that he did not see the species pass through his hands until 1917, although they occurred more frequently thereafter. For example, Pinchen notes birds on 30th April 1922, 11th May 1922 and 'about a dozen' on 31st October 1922.

White records the species as rare and quotes records in August 1954, December 1958 and 'a nice flock' in 1961.

Although the form involved in these early records is not clear, many are likely to have been of the larger, longer-billed and longer-legged nominate European (and British) form as it was these birds which bred sporadically at Cley between 1964 and 1970. Birds of this form winter largely in west Africa, with a few also in southwest Europe. The occasional migrant *limosa*, thought to be from the current tiny British breeding population on the Nene Washes, Cambridgeshire, is still recorded at Cley but this form has not recently been noted on the Point.

Since the 1980s there has, however, been a huge increase in the number of Black-tailed Godwits of the Icelandic form *islandica* staging through the area and these birds are now regularly seen in the Harbour in both spring and autumn, commuting between here and Cley. They are, however, scarcer in winter when most winter further south in Britain and western Europe. Numbers peak in March and April and again between July and September and can reach 500 on occasion.

Bar-tailed Godwit

Limosa lapponica lapponica

Rowan lists Bar-tailed Godwits as regular visitors in some numbers between autumn and spring, most plentiful during September and early October, but with many also staying through the winter.

White quotes a particularly high count of 450–500 on 17th – 18th October 1977.

Bar-tailed Godwits, breeding from northern Scandinavia into Arctic Russia and wintering largely in west Africa (but with some wintering in western Europe), remain common passage migrants and scarcer winter visitors in the Harbour. Small numbers can be seen passing westwards offshore in early to mid-autumn, initially adults in July and August, followed by juveniles in September. A high autumn count was of 400 in August 1986.

In winter around 100 are frequently seen in the Harbour but higher counts have been recorded recently including 450 in January 2001, 360 in December 2001and 330 in March 2004. Red summer plumage individuals have been noted several times in mid-winter.

Wintering birds generally depart in February and March to pre-migratory feeding grounds on the Wadden Sea. However, an exceptional spring movement, undoubtedly involving west African winterers, occurred in 1984, with 400 recorded on 29th April. A few non-breeding birds can also be encountered during the summer.

Whimbrel
Numenius phaeopus phaeopus

Rowan records the Whimbrel as regular in early autumn and irregular in spring, noting that he had also seen it himself in summer. White suggests that it had become commoner, with the first spring migrants appearing in mid-April and the majority in May, with stragglers to the end of June. Autumn migrants are noted as appearing from early July and continuing until the end of September, with peak numbers in August. White refers to flocks of 100 as being common in autumn and notes flocks of 200 in August 1959 and 1963.

This status summary remains accurate today, with counts of up to 45 recorded in May and up to 250 in August. They are very much birds of the saltmarsh. An early bird was recorded on 13th March 2003 and a late spring migrant was present on 15th June of the same year. In autumn, Whimbrel are rare by October and particularly late records involve a single on 6th November 1984 and two on 1st November 2000. Even more unusually, a winter bird was seen in the Harbour on 5th December 1966.

A few early autumn Whimbrel may be from the small Scottish population but the majority will no doubt be from elsewhere within their much larger range which extends from Iceland and the Faeroes to Scandinavia and Russia. Winter quarters lie in west Africa.

Eurasian Curlews. (*James McCallum*)

Eurasian Curlew (Curlew)

Numenius arquata arquata

Rowan notes Curlews as most numerous in autumn and spring, scarcest in summer. He describes the species' 'weird and not at all unpleasing call' as 'one of the characteristics of the Point'.

White records that some Curlews are present throughout the year and notes high counts of 400 in the Harbour on 18th – 23rd September 1954 and 900 in mid-September 1957.

Curlews are now a common sight in autumn, with females and failed breeders being amongst the first waders to return from the continent. Birds pass westwards singly or in small parties as early as June but are particularly prominent in July. As many as 110 have been recorded in the Harbour in June but as the autumn progresses numbers in the Harbour increase further as juveniles appear in force. Peak counts are generally in the 250–500 range, though 650 were present in August 2001 and 800 in August 2003. The true numbers of Curlews are often hard to establish as they gather on the more inaccessible outer fringe of the saltmarsh, but disturbance by planes or raptors tends to flush the flocks, revealing their true numbers.

Over 100, and occasionally over 200, may still be found in the winter before departures to Scandinavian breeding grounds take place between March and May, noisy flocks often being seen departing to the north and northeast at this season. A few non-breeding birds are also present in the summer.

A Curlew found freshly dead on the Point on 25th January 1958 had been ringed as a young bird in 1926 about 50 miles west of Stockholm, Sweden, illustrating the origin as well as the longevity of these birds.

Spotted Redshank

Tringa erythropus

Rowan notes this Scandinavian and northern Russian breeder, which winters in Africa, as a rare passage migrant in September, rarer in spring, with one winter record on 20th February 1904. Pinchen's diaries also record a few sightings.

White records it as rare, but quotes a record of 25 on 16th April 1958 – an astonishing number on a remarkable date.

Spotted Redshanks remain scarce at both migration seasons, especially so in spring. The period from July to October sees most records, normally only of one or two birds, but four were seen on 1st September 1996 and an autumn record of nine was counted on 28th July 1991.

Notably late birds were seen on 14th November 1964 and 16th November 2001, two were shot in the Harbour in February 1904 and a bird wintered in the early months of 1968.

Spotted Redshanks are typically seen wading actively in the Channel but can also be flushed from the saltmarsh creeks.

Common Redshank (Redshank)

Tringa totanus totanus
Tringa totanus robusta (Icelandic Redshank)

Rowan notes the Redshank as a resident and annually breeding species, usually only one pair, occasionally two. It is recorded as most plentiful in autumn and spring, scarcer in winter.

White documents the increase in the breeding population and by 1950 there were 45 pairs. The population fell in 1952 before rising again until in 1962 60 nests were recorded. Following the severe winter of 1962/63, during which many Redshank were found dead, the breeding population crashed to only four pairs in 1963. This had, however, recovered to 30 pairs by 1970.

Following the severe winter of 1978/79 the population fell once more to nine pairs and has remained at a low level ever since. Only two pairs were recorded in 2001, though this had risen to five pairs in 2003 and six in 2004.

Peak numbers in the Harbour occur in September and October, counts normally falling in the 200-300 range, but higher totals include 350 in September 1992 and 450 in October 1997. An easterly passage of Redshank, thought to involve migrant British breeders, has been recorded at Sheringham but there has been little evidence of this on the Point. The mean winter population is around 150 birds though 286 were counted in December 1994.

At all seasons Redshank are typically noisy and neurotic companions on the walk out along the Point, fully living up to their reputation as 'sentinel of the marshes'.

In addition to British-breeding birds of the nominate form, ringing elsewhere has shown that continental nominate birds and Icelandic *robusta* also occur on British estuaries, though the proportions of each on the Point are not known. British and Icelandic birds are thought to winter mainly in northwest Europe, therefore accounting for the winter birds in the Harbour, with birds from Scandinavia and the Baltic passing through in spring and autumn on passage to and from wintering grounds further south in western Europe and in west Africa.

Greenshank (Common Greenshank)

Tringa nebularia

Rowan notes Greenshank as a regular though uncommon passage migrant in autumn. White notes that it can also be encountered in spring and occasionally in other months.

Its status today remains unchanged, with birds frequently noted in the Harbour in spring and autumn, peak months being May, August and September. A high total of 40 was recorded in autumn 1985 and 26 were counted in May 2001.

An early bird was seen on 10th April 1994, November birds were recorded in 1993, 1998, 1999 and 2001 and birds were present in January 2000 and 2004.

Greenshanks on the Point are typically flushed from creeks, loudly announcing their presence across the Harbour. They are also regularly seen actively feeding in the Channel.

Greenshanks breed predominantly in Scandinavia and Russia and winter in southern Africa.

The small population in northern Scotland is thought to winter mainly in Ireland, suggesting that the overwhelming majority of birds recorded on the Point are continental.

Green Sandpiper

Tringa ochropus

Rowan states that this species has been 'taken more than once on the Marrams' and lists a record of one on 8th September 1910. Pinchen records two on 23rd May 1922. It is also described by White, perhaps surprisingly, as 'frequently seen passing over'.

Green Sandpipers are now barely annual migrants to the Point and there are only around 16 records since 1990, mostly between late June and early September, with the exception of spring birds on 6th May 1990, 22nd April 2003 and 15th April 2004.

Green Sandpipers are scarce on the Point due to its lack of freshwater habitat. The few birds seen are usually passing over high, announcing their presence with their distinctive and far-carrying fluting calls.

The species breeds in Scandinavia and Russia and winters in southern Europe, around the Mediterranean and in central Africa.

Wood Sandpiper

Tringa glareola

Rowan states that the species was 'observed on one occasion near the Watch House' by Gurney, while White, as with the previous species, records it, again somewhat surprisingly, as 'frequently seen passing over'. A record count of four was obtained on 26th August 1966.

Wood Sandpipers are now barely annual migrants to the Point and there are only around a dozen records since 1990, all falling between the second week of August and the end of September, with the exception of singles on 2nd and 5th May 1995 and 21st May 2002. The latest recorded was on 6th October 1969.

A bird on 24th August 2003 was briefly singing and display-flighting over the Watch House.

Wood Sandpipers are scarce on the Point due to its lack of freshwater habitat. The few birds seen are usually passing over high, announcing their presence with their distinctive and far-carrying calls.

The species breeds in Scandinavia and Russia, wintering in Africa south of the Sahara.

Common Sandpiper. (*James McCallum*)

Common Sandpiper

Actitis hypoleucos

Rowan and White record this species as a regular autumn passage migrant, never plentiful, and occasionally seen in the summer months.

It is now almost exclusively a spring and autumn migrant, passing between Scandinavia and its African wintering grounds. Up to half a dozen birds can typically be flushed noisily from the creeks in the second half of April and May and again in July, when the first adults return, and August and September, when juveniles predominate. Larger numbers occasionally occur, for example 28 on 30th July 2003.

A favourite location for this species is along the Glaven Channel, immediately west of Cley Coastguards.

Turnstone (Ruddy Turnstone)

Arenaria interpres interpres

Rowan and White note that one or two Turnstones may be seen at any time of year, though they are more plentiful in September and less so in March and April.

Turnstones remain common passage migrants and winter visitors, frequenting both the outer beaches and the Harbour muds. Adults appear from late July, with juveniles predominating from August. Numbers typically reach 100 (occasionally up to 160) in September and October, though an exceptional 350 were counted on 20th August 1986. The winter population is around 60 birds, though 225 were counted in December 2001. The main spring exodus takes place in April.

Ringing has shown that most British-wintering Turnstones are from Greenland and Canada, with only a minority from Scandinavia. These latter birds winter largely in west Africa.

Red-necked Phalarope

Phalaropus lobatus

Rowan lists birds taken in September 1901 and on 8th October 1903, 1st September 1905 and 14th September 1906. White lists a further record on 23rd August 1966 but no subsequent occurrences are known. Although some of the earlier records may have involved Scottish breeders at a time when that population was larger, any modern-day Red-necked Phalarope would now be most likely to originate from Scandinavia, displaced from an overland route to wintering grounds in the Arabian Sea.

Grey Phalarope (Red Phalarope)

Phalaropus fulicarius

Rowan notes only one taken, on 2nd October 1911, though he states that others had been observed.

White lists this record as 2nd August 1911 but this date would be most unlikely and this is presumably a transcription error. Further records listed are four together on 21st October 1947, a truly remarkable record of a summer plumage female in the Harbour on 13th July 1963 and a single on 14th September 1975.

All subsequent traced records are as follows:-

13th September 1976.
9th – 10th September 1996.
10th November 1999.
10th September 2001.
22nd September 2001.

22nd September 2002.
5th October 2003.
8th October 2004.

Grey Phalarope is a true Arctic species, breeding in Greenland, Arctic Canada, Iceland and Spitsbergen, with an autumn heading towards western Europe on the way to wintering grounds at sea off west Africa. Most records on the Point are of birds passing offshore, although the occasional bird has wandered over the shingle bank or lingered to feed in the surf.

Pomarine Skua
Stercorarius pomarinus

Rowan notes that the species had been observed on several occasions in autumn beyond the Bar but had never to his knowledge been taken. Gurney is quoted as believing that one was shot in the area in 1879. This coincides with a large influx of gale-driven Pomarine Skuas in north Norfolk in mid-October of that year, described by Stevenson (1890) as the great ornithological feature of that autumn. They were reported as 'swarming in our harbours, bays and estuaries' and many must have been in our area at this time. White notes the species as a regular autumn passage migrant in small numbers.

Records have been annual since at least 1980. The first autumn birds, largely adults, are usually seen in late August though birds are sometimes seen earlier in the month or even at the end of July. Records then increase through September and peak in October and November, largely of juveniles, and normally involving only small numbers in periods of strong onshore winds. Records are distributed on average three to four weeks later in the autumn than both Arctic and Long-tailed Skuas, and Pomarines may be expected to predominate in late autumn skua movements.

Occasionally, much larger passages take place as part of major influxes into the southern North Sea. Such an event was clearly occurring in the autumn of 1916 when 70 were noted passing inland on 14th September. More recent large movements have occurred as follows:-

34 on 28th and 29th October 1983.
110 on 2nd and 200 on 10th November 1985, part of an exceptional passage which saw around 780 recorded in the county, many being adults with full tail 'spoons'.
30 on 29th September 1991, part of an unusual seabird movement in near-calm conditions.

A further large movement occurred off the north Norfolk coast in late October 1997 but there are no known counts specifically from the Point.

Late autumn influxes of juveniles are clearly caused in part by weather conditions in the North Sea but probably also reflect years of high breeding success on the Russian tundra.

This species is more likely to be seen in winter than Arctic Skua and recent records at this season include birds on 3rd – 18th January 1986, 28th February 1998, 1st January 2001 and 8th March 2005.

An exceptional spring passage record involves a pale phase bird on 22nd May 2004. The species' rarity at this season can readily be understood as their northeasterly passage through British waters from wintering grounds off west Africa leads them well away from north Norfolk.

200 on 17th October 1986.
150 on 5th November 1989.
223 on 17th November 2000.
430+ on 16th October 2002.

Records outside this season are scarce though there are a few records for the period July to September and during the winter. A further recent spring record involved a full summer plumage adult resting on the sea close inshore on 2nd May 2004.

Sabine's Gull
Larus sabini
Rowan notes that immature birds are said to have been seen during the autumn. None had been obtained in the area though there were at least three sight records.

White notes Sabine's Gulls as very rare, citing occurrences on 11th October 1911, 27th December 1953 and 12th October 1974. The December 1953 record would now be regarded as exceptional and is 'square-bracketed' in the 1953 *Norfolk Bird Report*.

Sabine's Gulls are now recorded regularly, though not annually, in autumn between the last week of August and mid-November, with most seen in September, typically in strong onshore winds. Records, involving both juveniles and adults, are normally of single birds but three were seen on 27th August 1977. Birds are normally seen under 'sea-watching' conditions but late August adults have been seen resting on the beach on at least one occasion (24th August 1983) and a partially summer plumage adult lingered on 5th – 12th September 1984.

Sabine's Gull is one of the few truly Nearctic breeding species occurring in our area, with those seen from the Point doubtless from the nearest breeding grounds in Greenland and eastern Canada. After passing through British waters they proceed to wintering grounds off southwest Africa.

Black-headed Gulls. (*James McCallum*)

Black-headed Gull
Larus ridibundus ridibundus
Pashley records that:-

'There are almost every summer a few Black-heads about the Harbour and marshes but I have never heard of their breeding here.'

At this time the Black-headed Gull was subject to severe persecution and there were even fears that it might be driven to extinction as a British breeding bird.

Rowan notes the species as plentiful throughout the year but it is not listed as breeding. In White's list it is finally recorded as a breeding species, having nested for the first time in 1925 when two nests were found. By the end of the 1939-1945 war the colony had increased to such an extent that their numbers were controlled to protect the nesting terns.

Numbers thereafter remained low during the 1950s and 1960s but by 1973 200 pairs were breeding, with 400 pairs in 1978. Numbers then fell back slightly before continuing to increase, with 1,000 pairs recorded in 1985, rising to 1,500 pairs in 1988 and 3,000 pairs in 1991. Numbers remained steady at 2,500 - 3,000 pairs throughout the 1990s but declined dramatically to 200 pairs in 2000 and 50 pairs in 2001, rising slightly to 310 pairs in 2002, 750 pairs in 2003 and about 800 pairs in 2004.

British-breeding birds winter largely within Britain, though some have been recovered as far afield as France and Spain, but Black-headed Gulls are also abundant passage migrants and winter visitors. Very large numbers arrive from northern Europe and Russia from July onwards and form massive autumn and winter roosts in the Harbour. Although these have not been counted systematically they involve many thousands of birds and this is by far the commonest gull species. For example, a single count in January 1983 produced a figure of 32,800 birds. The Harbour roost is thought to draw birds from a large inland area of the county.

Ringing recoveries have been recorded as follows:-

Ringed Colne Pt., Essex 27th June 1976, recovered Blakeney Point 11th May 1982.
Ringed Deeping St. James, Lincolnshire 3rd November 1965, recovered Blakeney Point 10th June 1982.

A bird with an Estonian ring was found dead on the Point on 31st January 1994, illustrating the eastern origin of many winterers.

Slender-billed Gull

Larus genei

An adult pair in summer plumage commuted between Cley and Blakeney Harbour on 12th – 15th May 1987. The larger male was very protective towards the female, chasing away other gulls, and copulation was observed on a number of occasions. These were the first for Norfolk.

These Mediterranean, northwest African and western Asian rarities were well-photographed during this period (though not on the Point) and an account of their occurrence occurs in the *Norfolk Bird Report* for 1987.

Common Gull (Mew Gull)

Larus canus canus

Rowan notes the Common Gull as the least common of the British breeding gulls on the Point, fairly abundant in some autumns and winters, with a few present throughout most summers.

White repeats this status but documents the species' first attempted breeding on the Point and in Norfolk in 1964. This attempt was unsuccessful but a pair bred again in 1965, raising three chicks which were subsequently taken by a Short-eared Owl. In 1966, however, two young were successfully raised – the first breeding success in the county.

One or two pairs of Common Gulls bred regularly until the early 1990s but four pairs bred in

1992, since when the breeding population has fluctuated between three and seven pairs. Breeding success has, however, been consistently low.

Common Gulls are present throughout the year in moderate numbers with, in addition to the local breeding birds, strong spring and autumn passages in March and April and August to November as well as sizeable autumn and winter roost gatherings in the Harbour. As with Black-headed Gull, these roosts attract birds from large parts of the county. Common Gulls are regularly observed calling and heading high to the northeast in spring, doubtless bound for breeding grounds in Scandinavia and western Russia, and returning birds appear in August and September. Britain is an important wintering area for this species, although some British breeders move south and west as far as France or Spain.

The very occasional much darker adult has been seen, showing apparent characters of the eastern form *heinei*, but the forms are clinal and the occurrence of eastern birds would be hard to prove without a ringing recovery.

Lesser Black-backed Gull

Larus fuscus graellsii (Western Lesser Black-backed Gull)
Larus fuscus intermedius (Continental Lesser Black-backed Gull)

Rowan notes the species as present throughout the year but never, with the exception of some summers, as abundant as Herring Gull. He describes it as most numerous in autumn.

White documents the first breeding record of the species in 1978 when a pair of the pale British form *graellsii* nested in the ternery and raised one chick. This was the first breeding record for the Point and for Norfolk. Two pairs bred in 1979 and between one and eight pairs bred until 1999 when a massive increase to 120 pairs took place. Numbers rose to 180 pairs in 2000 and the following year 340 pairs of Herring/Lesser Black-backed Gulls were nesting, coinciding with a major reduction in the number of breeding Black-headed Gulls and Sandwich and Common Terns. Following a degree of 'discouragement', however, only five pairs bred in 2002 and none in 2003.

Birds showing characters of the whole cline from pale British *graellsii* to dark continental *intermedius* (including apparently intermediate birds most likely to originate from the Netherlands and Germany) are now common in the spring, summer and autumn. *Intermedius* tends perhaps to be more common in spring and again in the autumn.

The first migrant adult Lesser Black-backed Gulls appear as early as mid to late February and during the summer and autumn the species is a major component of the large gull gatherings in the Harbour. Somewhat contrary to Rowan and White, however, the species is particularly scarce in winter, the occasional records at this season usually being of juveniles/first-winters. Although an increasing winterer well inland in eastern England, the Lesser Black-backed Gull is scarce on the Point, and at nearby inland feeding sites, at this season. Despite increasing numbers wintering in Britain, however, the bulk of the population continues to winter in Iberia and Morocco.

Herring Gull. (*James McCallum*)

Herring Gull (European Herring Gull)

Larus argentatus argenteus
Larus argentatus argentatus (Scandinavian Herring Gull)

Rowan notes the Herring Gull as present throughout the year, plentiful in winter but in varying numbers in summer.

White records the species' first breeding on the Point (and indeed in Norfolk) in 1972, when three young were reared. Two pairs bred in 1973, with one pair in 1974 and 1975. No further breeding was attempted between 1976 and 1978 but two pairs again bred in 1979. Since then numbers have fluctuated but rose to 40 pairs by 1989, 60 pairs in 1995, 100 pairs in 1996 and a peak of 180 pairs in 1999. Numbers were, however, down to ten pairs in 2002 following some 'discouragement' and none are known to have bred in 2003.

The breeding birds are all of the pale-mantled west European form *argenteus* but between October and March large numbers of the darker-mantled Scandinavian form *argentatus* (largely from coastal Arctic Norway) can also be seen. These latter birds are often recorded passing west in late autumn and also, especially in hard weather, during the winter but they also make up a high proportion of the large number of wintering Herring Gulls. These are typically found roosting on favoured sandbanks in the Harbour or feeding in the intertidal zone off the end of the Point. Herring Gulls are, however, always outnumbered by Great Black-backed Gulls in the Harbour roosts. Many of the wintering Herring Gulls fly inland in the morning to feed on the local refuse tip and pig fields, returning to their roost in mid-afternoon. Sizeable westward spring movements, involving hundreds of birds in a day, are also noted in March and April.

A bird ringed on Texel, Netherlands on 11th July 1984 was recovered on the Point on 9th September 1985.

A first-winter Herring x Glaucous Gull hybrid lingered between Cromer and the Point from 1st July 1989 to 20th April 1990.

It is perhaps worth noting in passing that White cites records of 'Siberian Herring Gulls (*L. a. heuglini*)' (*sic*) on 4th January 1960 and 14th – 20th December 1965. These records, however, reflect an incomplete knowledge in the 1960s of large gull taxonomy and identification and should clearly be discounted.

Yellow-legged Gull

Larus michahellis michahellis

This form is currently (as at 2005) treated by BOURC as a form of Herring Gull, but is widely treated elsewhere as a full species in its own right. The *British Birds* list accords the form separate treatment but refers to it as *Larus cachinnans michahellis* (i.e. 'lumped' with the following species).

Records on the Point reflect the Yellow-legged Gull's recent marked increase in Norfolk and in the rest of Britain, with the species increasingly developing a northward post-breeding migration to Britain from its Mediterranean colonies presumably fuelled, at least in part, by climate change. Since the first known record of an adult on 4th August 1990 they have become regular with, for example, up to five on Far Point in late July and early August 1995.

Yellow-legged Gulls were seen almost annually through the 1990s but larger numbers occurred in 2001, with up to four birds present with the other roosting large gulls in the Harbour throughout July and August though the turnover of birds was high and more individuals were involved. The species is now to be expected almost daily in July and August and there are now also records for March, April, May, June, September, October and November. There are, however, as yet no winter records.

A ringed first-summer bird was seen in autumn 2002 with a white colour ring with black lettering on the right leg and a metal ring on the left leg – a combination indicating an origin in the French Mediterranean, where large scale ringing has taken place at a number of colonies.

Caspian Gull (Pontic Gull)

Larus cachinnans

This form is currently (as at 2005) treated by BOURC as a form of Herring Gull, but is widely treated elsewhere as a full species in its own right. The *British Birds* list 'lumps' this form with Yellow-legged Gull under the name *Larus cachinnans cachinnans*.

Caspian Gulls breed in western Russia and the Ukraine but have in recent years expanded to the northwest and now breed as near as Poland, wintering in moderate numbers in northern and central Germany and parts of the Netherlands. Although only recently added to the Norfolk list they have become regular in the county and could now be encountered at any time of year.

In 2001 second-summer birds were recorded in the Harbour on 21st and 24th July as part of a record influx of Yellow-legged Gulls.

Iceland Gull

Larus glaucoides glaucoides

Rowan describes the species as a rare winter visitor and notes a bird taken on 30th September 1905. White lists a further individual accompanying 15 Glaucous Gulls at the Watch House on 19th November 1952.

Subsequent records are as follows:-

First or second-winter on 22nd November 1987.
First-winter on 16th April 1989.
Second-winter on 25th November 1989.
First-winter between 3rd January and 22nd May 1993, roosting on the Point and feeding off Sheringham.
Adult on 1st – 5th March 1993, roosting on the Point.
First-winter on 10th November 2001.
20th March 2002.

Iceland Gull is one of the few truly Nearctic breeding species to occur in our area, nesting in Greenland and wintering in the northeast Atlantic.

Glaucous Gull
Larus hyperboreus hyperboreus

In Rowan's day the Glaucous Gull was a fairly regular winter visitor in small numbers between December and March. White records that 15 were seen with Great Black-backed Gulls and an Iceland Gull near the Watch House on 19th November 1952 – a truly exceptional count for south-east England. In 1958 two birds were seen on many dates from 14th January, one staying until 26th June and the other remaining until 1st August when it was found dying.

Since the 1960s Glaucous Gulls have remained regular, though this is largely due to the presence of two long-staying returning individuals. A particularly faithful individual, known as 'George', took up winter residence between 1963/64 and 1980/81 (though Taylor *et al.* 1999 only describe it as present to spring 1979), only to be replaced by a further bird, inevitably known as 'Boy George', from 1982/83 until 1989/90. These individuals sometimes lingered into May and occasionally returned as early as late August. Further scattered singles occurred throughout this period and have continued to do so since 1990 but averaging barely annually, records of these additional birds falling between November and May, with March proving to be a particularly productive month.

A first-winter Glaucous x Herring Gull hybrid lingered between Cromer and the Point from 1st July 1989 to 20th April 1990.

Glaucous Gull is a High Arctic species, breeding throughout the Arctic region and wintering further south. Hybridisation with Herring Gull has been recorded frequently in Iceland, the most likely source area for the hybrid individual.

Great Black-backed Gull
Larus marinus

Rowan notes the species as present throughout the year, plentiful even in summer. Of their occurrence he says:-

> 'In autumn the sandbanks in the Channel and on the bar are often black with them,
> the vast majority then being adults'.

White expands on this theme, describing the birds present in the summer months as 'in various immature plumages'.

Great Black-backed Gulls are still common, mostly so in autumn from July and in the winter, and are the dominant species in the roosts of large gulls in the Harbour, always outnumbering Herring Gulls. Systematic counts have been few but a couple of hundred are often present and some birds also remain during the summer.

The Great Black-backed Gulls seen on the Point originate from British colonies and also from coastal Norway and northwest Arctic Russia. The North Sea is an important wintering area, holding 45% of the world population at this season.

Ross's Gull
Rhodostethia rosea

A pink summer plumage adult, the first for Norfolk, flew east along the outer beach at the end of the Point on 10th May 1984. It had been present at Cley on 9th and returned there on 11th – 12th, before moving to Titchwell on 13th – 14th.

An account of this exciting Arctic Siberian rarity, accompanied by photographs taken at Titchwell, is contained in the 1984 *Norfolk Bird Report*.

Kittiwake (Black-legged Kittiwake)

Rissa tridactyla tridactyla

Rowan notes the Kittiwake as the scarcest of the British breeding gulls, more plentiful in some winters than others, occasional in summer.

White describes the Kittiwake as much commoner than in Rowan's day with some large flocks noted in summer between the mid-1940s and mid-1960s. In 1964 350 were present on 28th – 29th July while in 1965 there was a concentration of about 3,000 birds in July. Large flocks were again present in July 1966 and June 1967 and in 1976 4,000 were present on 9th August.

Such large summer concentrations are now rare and, although the species can be seen at any time of year, the Kittiwake is noted mostly as an autumn migrant, occasionally in large numbers in strong onshore winds. The peak recent counts have been 2,500 east on 4th November 1984 and 1,000+ on 29th September 1991. Numbers are generally small in winter though 500 were noted in January 1998.

For the first (and only) time, two pairs bred amongst the Sandwich Terns in 1958. The nests were found on 13th June and the next day one egg was present in one nest with two in the other. One nest was destroyed by a Great Black-backed Gull but the eggs from the other hatched on 8th and 9th July. Unfortunately both young were found dead on 14th July. These were the first Kittiwakes to be hatched in Norfolk. Photographs of one of the nest sites with an attendant adult and also of the two chicks can be found in the 1958 *Norfolk Bird Report*.

A summer concentration occurred again in 1995, with 350 present on Far Point on 23rd June, building up to 600 by 25th. Most were first-year birds but much noisy display was noted, particularly between adults, and seaweed was even arranged into nests.

The Kittiwake is the world's most abundant gull, with colonies from eastern Canada through Greenland, Iceland, Britain and western Europe to Norway and Arctic Russia. Birds winter widely at sea in the north Atlantic, reaching as far south as Iberia. The precise origins of those occurring on the Point are therefore not known, although an apparent decline in numbers may be linked to the well-publicised recent poor breeding success in Shetland.

Gull-billed Tern

Sterna nilotica nilotica

White lists four records of this species, all of which are also included in the relevant issues of the *Norfolk Bird Report*:-

25th – 26th October 1967.
'Immature' on 29th August 1971.
27th August to 3rd September 1972.
25th August 1974.

There are no subsequent records. Gull-billed Tern has a wide but discontinuous world distribution, with the closest breeding birds traditionally being in Denmark and the western Mediterranean. With the recent extinction of the Baltic population, however, this species is perhaps unlikely to reappear on the Point.

Caspian Tern
Sterna caspia

An adult which had wandered between Breydon and Hickling Broad in July 1993 flew west past the Point on 29th July and was later seen at Brancaster, Holme and Spurn Point, East Yorkshire.

A further bird was reported flying west on 23rd July 2001, although this record appears never to have been submitted and does not appear in either the 2001 *Norfolk Bird Report* or BBRC Report. However, a Caspian Tern had been present in the Yare Valley and at Great Yarmouth on 16th – 17th July and this was possibly the same individual.

Caspian Tern has a wide but discontinuous world distribution and the origin of these birds cannot therefore be known with any certainty.

Lesser Crested Tern
Sterna bengalensis emigrata

An adult, the first for Norfolk and the second for Britain, was found on 9th August 1983. Initially thought to be a Royal Tern *Sterna maxima*, it was later identified as Lesser Crested. It was present with the Sandwich Terns almost daily until 17th September, during which period it was also seen at Scolt Head and Holme. The bird was photographed during its stay and an account of its occurrence is in the 1986 *Norfolk Bird Report*.

This bird is assumed to be the long-staying female, which became known as 'Elsie', which summered (and bred) on the Farne Islands, Northumberland between 1984 and 1997, raising four Lesser Crested x Sandwich Tern hybrid young during this period.

The pale form *emigrata*, breeding in coastal Libya and wintering off west Africa, is presumed to account for this and the other British records.

Sandwich Terns. (*James McCallum*)

Sandwich Tern

Sterna sandvicensis sandvicensis

The first record appears to be of a juvenile on 1st August 1891, the species not being known to the Cley gunners before this date. Thereafter records increased and the species was seen in most years but only in small numbers.

By the time of Rowan's list the Sandwich Tern was an annual passage migrant in small numbers, normally in September and October, less commonly in the spring. The species was present and thought possibly to have bred in 1893, 1895 and 1897 and three or four birds were present throughout the breeding season in 1914 but no eggs or young were found and it is presumed that they did not actually breed. Rowan notes that the species appeared to be on the increase.

The first confirmed breeding occurred in 1920 and breeding took place again in 1921, when two nests were found. This rose to nine nests in 1922, 100 in 1923 and by 1924 300 pairs were breeding, with other similar-sized colonies at Cley and Salthouse and a smaller colony at Scolt Head.

However, in 1925 the whole colony relocated to Scolt Head. This has become a familiar pattern, with the birds alternating between the two sites and, for a time, Stiffkey/Warham. By 1926 the birds had returned and the colony increased in size, reaching 1,000 pairs in 1928 and 1,500 in 1929.

Breeding was spasmodic between 1930 and 1944 with no more than 50 pairs in any year, but 1,000 pairs returned in 1945, dropping to only two pairs in 1946, and only small numbers bred until 1950 when 194 pairs were recorded. The storm surge of January 1953 washed away much of the breeding areas and no birds bred in either 1954 or 1955 but by 1956 103 pairs had returned. 600 pairs bred in 1957, with 750-800 pairs in 1958, after which time the colony relocated to Stiffkey/Warham.

A single pair bred again in 1962, with no further breeding until 105 pairs in 1966, after which the Point was again deserted until 1970 when 35 pairs nested, albeit unsuccessfully. 45-50 pairs returned to the Point in 1976 but in 1977 the colony increased dramatically to 1,700-1,800 pairs, with 3,000 pairs in 1978 and a record 3,800-3,900 pairs by 1981.

The colony remained stable at over 3,000 pairs until 1984 when it fell to 2,500 pairs, to 1,000 pairs in 1985 and 1986 and to 450-500 pairs in 1987, before rising once more to 1,000 in 1988, 1,500 in 1989 and 3,000 in 1990 and 1991.

A near-record 3,700 pairs bred in 1992 and, with the exception of 1994 and 1995 when 1,000-1,500 pairs bred, over 3,000 pairs were present throughout the 1990s.

In 2000 only 75 pairs bred, with 250 in 2001 and 750 in 2002 but numbers rose once more to 2,900 pairs in 2003 before falling back to 1,260 pairs in 2004. Sandwich Terns have always nested at the very end of the Point though their preferred location changes from year to year as the habitat itself changes.

The erratic breeding history of Sandwich Terns on the Point can most readily be understood by considering all the north Norfolk breeders to belong to one highly mobile population. In years when the Sandwich Terns are scarce or absent at the Point, their numbers at Scolt Head tend to be correspondingly higher (and vice versa). In recent times, the protected sites on the spits at the end of Blakeney Point and on Scolt Head have been their only breeding locations, with other sites formerly used, notably Salthouse and Stiffkey/Warham, no longer suitable.

The high numbers present on the Point in the 1990s formed the largest colony in the country, holding around 22% of the British population, with the bulk of the remainder in northeast Scotland and Northumberland. With Britain holding 10% of the world population, it is clear that north Norfolk is an important composite site for this species.

Sandwich Terns are notoriously disturbance-prone until breeding is well underway and this may partly explain their erratic breeding history on the Point, the other key factor being the availability of suitable breeding habitat. The configuration of the Point's far spits changes constantly, with breeding areas washed away only to reform elsewhere. When the colony is successful in forming the breeding adults fly considerable distances to feed and during the summer a constant stream of birds can be seen returning to the colony with food, largely sand-eels.

In addition to human disturbance (including egg collectors), uncertain food supplies, weather and tides the breeding terns also have to contend with a significant variety of predators. Although the persistent pattern of nesting with Black-headed Gulls affords a degree of protection, the list of these predators is long and includes Foxes, Stoats, Weasels, Rats, Hen Harriers, Short-eared Owls, Kestrels, Oystercatchers, Rooks and Herring, Lesser Black-backed, Great Black-backed and Common Gulls. It is only thanks to active management of all these threats, including the fencing off and wardening of the breeding areas, trapping of Rats and Stoats and night-shooting of Foxes, that the terns have been able to thrive.

In the 1940s arrivals were expected from mid-April, though now the very first birds are seen from the third week of March, with most returning in April. At this time the high vocal displays of newly-arrived pairs are a particularly evocative feature. Passage of more northerly-breeding birds continues into May.

In August locally-bred birds mix with those from further north and from the near-continent and most depart during September, but occasional birds linger into October. Even later singles have been recorded on 8th November 1987 and 5th November 1989 and two were present on 3rd December 2000, with one remaining to 6th.

A first-summer bird was present on 6th – 23rd June 1994, an unusual record as birds of this age normally spend their first summer on the wintering grounds. These extend the length of the west African coast from Morocco to South Africa but with the majority in central west Africa between Senegal and Ghana where, along with other wintering terns, they are vulnerable to trapping and killing by children with noose traps baited with dead fish.

Many Sandwich Terns have been ringed on the Point, with recoveries as follows:-

Two ringed Blakeney Point summer 1928, recovered Angola 1929.
Ringed Blakeney Point 15th June 1958, recovered Esmoriz, Portugal September 1958.
Ringed Blakeney Point 18th June 1958, recovered Aberlady, Lothian 24th August 1958.
Ringed Blakeney Point 23rd June 1958, recovered Dakar, Senegal 30th October 1958.
Ringed Blakeney Point 29th June 1984, recovered Eboue, Ivory Coast 28th February 1985.
Ringed Blakeney Point 29th June 1984, recovered Teesmouth, Cleveland 27th July 1984.
Ringed Blakeney Point 29th June 1984, recovered Pegwell Bay, Kent 26th July 1984.
Ringed Blakeney Point 29th June 1984, recovered Luanda, Angola 4th November 1984.

The birds from Angola represent the most distant recoveries, a distance of around 7,000 km. The northerly autumn movements to Cleveland and Lothian are particularly interesting and the Kent bird demonstrates a notably early departure from the colony.

Sandwich Terns from elsewhere in Britain have also been recovered as follows:-

Ringed Farne Islands, Northumberland 28th June 1969, recovered Blakeney Point 18th July 1982.
Ringed Leverton, Lincolnshire 28th August 1980, recovered Blakeney Point 14th July 1983.

Richard Richardson's notes provide a beautifully-crafted description of this special Blakeney Point bird:-

'Suddenly, as if alarmed, the entire assembly rises as one, silently at first but quickly bursting into a great surge of jubilant cries as the birds mount into the blue sky to cascade down like snow-flakes in the wind. Odd pairs will break away from the main concourse and, with strident calls of 'kirrik', climb steeply to a thousand feet or more, glittering like twin stars in orbit before setting their narrow, angular wings for the exhilarating descent, swerving in unison, criss-crossing at high speed and alternating the 'kirriks' with a harsher 'karr karr karr karr'. Arrived back among their companions on the sands they patter round and round each other in mutual display with black top-knots erected and drooped wings arched outwards from the shoulders so the tips are scissored beneath their elevated tails.'

Roseate Tern
Sterna dougallii dougallii

The earliest traced record for the area was a pair, both apparently females, shot on the Bar on 24th June 1896. The man who shot these birds was prosecuted by the Society for the Prevention of Cruelty to Animals and was convicted, but Pashley paid his fine and costs amounting to 23 shillings and sixpence.

A bird lingered in the colony between May and July 1902 and paired with a Common Tern. Two eggs hatched and the hybrid fledglings were said to resemble very much the young of the Sandwich Tern only, naturally, much smaller (Pinchen, 1935). Thereafter occasional birds were noted regularly in the colony.

Rowan records the Roseate Tern as a vagrant, identified on several occasions and said to have been taken twice in August. White notes the species as a rare and irregular summer visitor and occasional breeder in the main ternery.

The first breeding record listed by White was in 1921 but some confusion surrounds this. Pinchen's diaries certainly describe breeding in 1922, with the nest first found on 26th May, but a photograph of this nest is said to have been that of a Common Tern (Bloomfield, 2003). Taylor *et al.* (1999) list the first confirmed breeding as having occurred in 1923. White states that between one and three pairs of Roseate Terns bred in each year of the 1920s except for 1924 and 1926, but Pinchen notes breeding in 1926, the nest being shown to Harry Witherby who visited the site with Jim Vincent of Hickling.

In the following decade they bred only in 1939, when one pair laid one egg which hatched, but the chick died. Photographs of the nest and chick by Reginald Gaze appear in the 1939 edition of *Wild Bird Protection in Norfolk* and also in his 1947 book *Bird Sanctuary*. A pair again bred, although unsuccessfully, in 1948 on Far Point. In this year the first egg was laid on 23rd June, with the second on 26th. On 2nd July the eggs were blown out of the nest by a northerly gale, one egg being replaced and further incubated until the site was badly flooded on 8th July, after which the birds deserted.

Breeding attempts then petered out but one or two and occasionally up to five birds have still been noted in the ternery in many summers from the 1950s to the present day. More sightings occurred from the 1990s with two non-breeding pairs present in 1993 and a summering pair in the following two years. Following an unsuccessful breeding attempt near Wells in 1996, Roseate Terns attempted to breed on the Point in 1997 and 1998 but predation and flooding led to failure.

Colour-ringed birds from the Farne Islands, Northumberland have previously been noted in autumn and in 1999 the male of a Roseate Tern pair was observed with double metal rings, apparently originating from Coquet Island, Northumberland. The female of this pair had a short left tail streamer, a feature also noted on a bird in 1994 and 1995, suggesting that a returning pair might be responsible for many of the recent records. Up to five adults were noted in 1999. Given the recent decline in the British Roseate Tern population this species seems unlikely ever to consolidate its tenuous foothold.

The first birds are occasionally noted returning from wintering grounds in the Gulf of Guinea in May, but Roseate Terns are also sometimes noted as autumn migrants in August and September, as evidenced by juveniles seen in 1988, 1990 and 2001. The latest records appear to be of birds on 20th September 1978, 8th October 1964 and a particularly late bird on 14th and 21st October 1984.

Of the Roseate Tern Pinchen noted the following:-

'The Roseates are very difficult to recognise and their note is the only safe guide; the more expert ornithologist can only with difficulty identify them by sight... The expert uses a very powerful pair of field glasses to assist him in his study but these fail at times whereas the notes never deceive.'

Common Tern
Sterna hirundo hirundo

The Common Tern has probably nested on the end of Blakeney Point since time immemorial and has certainly been documented since at least 1830. Rowan, writing in 1915, could find out little about the history of the colony but believed it to be very old. In his checklist he describes the species as a summer resident, with numbers increasing irregularly, noting that in July 1914 there were about 600 clutches of eggs, the largest number then on record. Prior to protection, however, predation and disturbance had been serious problems, with human activity being a significant factor in the nineteenth century. The birds were freely shot and in 1898 Rooks and Rats so harassed the terns that they fled to Stiffkey.

Numbers increased rapidly after Pinchen's appointment as Watcher in 1901. In that year 140 pairs were thought to have nested but by 1923 numbers had exceeded Rowan's recorded levels and reached 2,000 pairs, a level largely maintained between 1935 and 1950. Much research work on the breeding Common Terns was undertaken by University College London in the 1920s, for example that of Watson (1921).

Numbers have fluctuated throughout the latter half of the twentieth century. Peak numbers of around 2,000 pairs were still recorded in 1950-1952, with between 1,000 and 2,000 pairs breeding until 1959 when numbers fell to 970 pairs. Numbers fluctuated between 800 and 1,200 pairs until a temporary increase to 1,400-1,900 pairs took place between 1971 and 1977.

In 1978, however, numbers declined to 950 pairs and the colony was down to 175 pairs in 1981, since when numbers have never regained their former levels, the population being around 200-300 pairs until 1997, when it declined further to 170 pairs. Numbers fell to an all-time low of 30 pairs in 2000 but have since recovered to between 120 and 200 pairs. Common Terns have always nested at the very end of the Point though their preferred location changes from year to year as the habitat itself changes.

The first Common Terns usually appear from wintering grounds in west Africa in mid-April but particularly early birds were seen on 1st April 1985 and 1st April 2001. Most arrivals take place in late April and early May but there is little evidence of passage as birds are thought to travel over-land directly to their colonies. Birds showing apparent first-summer plumage are frequently seen but many of these are likely actually to be second-summer birds.

Numbers in autumn are augmented by passage migrants from the continent and considerable movements have been recorded in August. Numbers drop sharply in September and very few are present by October. Notably late birds occurred on 1st November 1994, 7th November 1969, 11th November 1986 and, latest of all, 14th November 1985.

Ringing recoveries have been recorded as follows:-

Ringed Blakeney Point summer 1951, recovered Dakar, Senegal November 1951.
Ringed Blakeney Point summer 1951, recovered Dakar, Senegal April 1952.
Ringed Blakeney Point 15th July 1957, recovered Holland 8th September 1957.

Arctic Tern
Sterna paradisaea

Rowan records the Arctic Tern as an irregular autumn passage migrant, 'probably more frequent than supposed', and makes no mention of it as a breeding species. White notes that in most years a pair, sometimes two, nest among the Common Terns. Arctic Terns are thought to have bred for the first time in 1922 and ten pairs were present in 1923, with four nests found. A peak of six nests was found in 1947, after which one to three pairs were present annually until 1984 when six pairs again bred. This had risen to 15 pairs by 1991 and a record 22 pairs in 1992. Numbers remained at around 20 pairs until 1998, after which the colony declined to four pairs in 2000 before rising to 18 pairs in 2003, falling again, however, to six pairs in 2004. Arctic Terns on Blakeney Point are at the extreme southern limit of their range and it is unlikely that their numbers will ever be anything other than modest.

The first birds arrive in mid-April and passage takes place in late April and early May. There is occasional evidence of direct northward passage of small parties appearing from inland and continuing rapidly due north out to sea. A bird was seen on 25th June 2003 showing apparent first-summer plumage.

Arctic Terns are regularly seen in very small numbers, rarely more than ten in a day, as autumn passage migrants, though 17 were counted on 30th September 1992. Sightings are regular into October, for example eight were still present on 16th October 1988, and two particularly late birds were seen on 16th November 1996.

An Arctic Tern ringed as a chick at Isefjord, Denmark on 4th July 1981 was recovered on the Point on 23rd November 1981, though this latter date is given as 12th August in Taylor *et al.* (1999), and it is therefore unclear which is correct.

This species is the greatest wanderer of all those recorded on the Point (with the possible exception of the Great and Sooty Shearwaters), with breeding grounds around the fringes of the Arctic and winter quarters around the Antarctic pack ice. The species shows little breeding site fidelity between seasons, with Blakeney Point-bred birds mixing subsequently with migrants from Scotland and Scandinavia and even as far afield as Arctic Canada, perhaps returning to colonies elsewhere the following spring.

Sooty Tern
Sterna fuscata fuscata

The first Norfolk record of this tropical, pelagic rarity was of an adult seen by J.S. Wing from a boat in the Harbour on 11th September 1935.

The second record was of a single adult which wandered between the Blakeney Point and Scolt Head terneries from 14th – 19th June 1966. Cant's notes refer to it also being present on 25th June. This bird had been seen at Minsmere, Suffolk on 11th June and was seen again at Scolt Head on 11th July. In between, a Sooty Tern, presumably this bird, appeared on the Farne Islands, Northumberland on 21st June.

Little Terns. A male presenting a female with a Sandeel. (*James McCallum*)

Little Tern
Sterna albifrons albifrons

Rowan notes the Little Tern as an erratic breeder, 'its numbers varying enormously and quite unaccountably'. There were rarely fewer than ten pairs or more than 40. Rowan notes their arrival in the first week of May, normally a few days before the Common Tern, departing at the end of August and the beginning of September.

White records that there were 100 pairs in 1912 but this was the only year prior to 1937 in which the number of nests exceeded 50. After the 1939-1945 war numbers rose and, until the 1990s, numbers only fell below 70 pairs in 1954 and 1955. The upward trend continued into the 1960s and the peak was reached in 1970 when up to 220 pairs bred. Numbers remained high throughout the 1970s and into the 1990s at between 110 and 200 pairs.

215 pairs bred in 1996 but numbers subsequently fell to only 60 pairs in 1998 and 85 pairs in 2002, rising briefly to 116 pairs in 2003 before falling back to 75 pairs in 2004.

Little Terns breed in two discrete colonies – one with the Common Terns on Far Point and one east of the Watch House. Both colonies are fenced off to reduce casual disturbance and wardening efforts are focused on frustrating the efforts of the egg collectors who still visit the Point each summer.

The terns' predators are many and varied and have included Kestrels, Oystercatchers and Short-eared Owls. Kestrels are particularly problematic, for example a pair took all the young from the Watch House colony in 1993.

The first birds are now typically seen in mid-April, though the occasional bird may appear as early as the second week of the month, the earliest being on 9th April 1957.

Late summer gatherings can be large and, due to the numbers recorded, must involve a considerable number of birds from elsewhere, presumably from the near-continent and other colonies in eastern England.

Most Little Terns depart during September but singles are occasionally recorded into early

October. Sightings thereafter are rare as by this time the birds should be well on their way to wintering grounds in west Africa but a notably late bird was still present on 13th November 1988.

Black Tern
Chlidonias niger niger

Rowan and White both note that a few are recorded annually in spring and autumn. Pashley, however, notes 'thousands' passing on 15th May 1893. Pinchen records a bird on 4th July 1929 and 'many' in the Harbour in the August of that year.

Occurrences of Black Terns are rather erratic. In some years only a few are seen whilst both spring and autumn can, in other years, produce large influxes.

Spring influxes are typically associated with warm southeasterly winds in early May. High counts include:-

40 on 11th May 1946.
30 on 9th May 1954.
21 on 22nd May 1989.
200 on 2nd May 1990, a day when over 1,000 passed through Cley.

Early birds have been seen in the last week of April and very occasionally birds are recorded into early June. Birds at this season are usually seen heading eastwards through the Harbour and are presumably leaving the country following an earlier displacement into central England.

In autumn, birds are seen annually offshore in small numbers in August and September, but in some years greater numbers are displaced from the large early autumn gatherings in the Netherlands. Significant counts have included up to 80 in late August 1990 and again up to 80 in early August 1994. At such times birds have often lingered for some days, roosting with other terns on the outer sandbanks and beaches, before finally leaving for wintering grounds along the western coasts of Africa.

White-winged Black Tern (White-winged Tern)
Chlidonias leucopterus

The history of this species on the Point is, to say the least, somewhat confused and it is impossible even to guess at the total number of records.

Rowan notes a bird seen near the Sandhills in August 1902. Pashley makes no reference to this bird but refers in his diary pages to two birds seen on a buoy in the Harbour on 16th May 1893. He also notes a bird seen 'quite close' on 1st August 1900 but although the location of this bird may have been the Sandhills the text is slightly ambiguous on this point. Neither of these records is, however, included in his Systematic List where the species is given square brackets, together with the comment that he has never seen the species in the flesh 'although it has been reported several times, but from unreliable sources'. He then proceeds to cite a record of three birds seen by E.M. Connop on a buoy just over the Bar in May 1903 (which do not appear in his diary pages) and a further record from June 1910 which 'turned out to have been a Black Tern.'

To complicate matters further, White lists a further four more recent records involving five birds as follows:-

September 1938. This was actually in the first week of the month according to the 1938 edition of *Wild Bird Protection in Norfolk*.
2 on 21st June 1950. However, the 1950 edition of *Wild Bird Protection in Norfolk* refers to two birds in Morston Creek on 24th May 1950, with three in the Harbour next day and a

further single bird seen on Far Point on 21st June.

September 1968. However, the 1968 *Norfolk Bird Report* notes this bird as being present between Morston and the Point from 27th August to 11th September.

September 1969. However, this record is not listed in the *Norfolk Bird Report* for that year.

The only recent record, and the only one around which there is no confusion, concerns a juvenile which spent most of 24th August 2001 feeding over the sea off the Sandhills, having previously been at Sizewell, Suffolk.

White-winged Black Terns breed in eastern Europe and western Russia, wintering widely in Africa.

Common Guillemot (Guillemot)

Uria aalge aalge (Northern Guillemot)

Uria aalge albionis (Southern Guillemot)

Rowan notes that Guillemots usually put in their first appearance in October and are often seen until the beginning of March in small numbers, usually singly. He records that they are often picked up dead. Pinchen refers to many in the Harbour on 21st August 1926 and White describes them as a regular passage migrant from September to March.

Guillemots remain regular, particularly in autumn and winter, often up to a few hundred, either lingering and feeding close inshore or passing at sea in significant movements. Recording difficulties arise, however, due to identification difficulties with distant auks and many such passges can only be recorded as involving either this species or Razorbill.

Large numbers include 500 passing east in half an hour on 20th February 1994, a day on which an estimated 10,000 passed Sheringham, and 5,000 were present in the second half of December 2000. These figures are, however, dwarfed by a movement of 20,000 on 4th January 2001. On this day up to 500 per minute were passing west between 0815 and 0900 with, at one point, 1,200 in the air at once and a further 600 on the sea. Unusual numbers were then seen in the summer of 2001, with 344 east on 2nd June and 500 east on 17th June at a time when birds should be at or near the breeding colonies.

89 were found dead in the auk 'wreck' of February 1983, caused by severe gales and high seas in the North Sea, and smaller numbers are unfortunately regularly found dead from oiling. Amongst these tideline corpses have been brown-toned birds of the southern form *albionis*, breeding in England, Ireland, France and western Iberia, and blacker individuals of the more northerly-breeding Scottish, Icelandic, Faeroes and Norwegian form *aalge*. The nearest breeding colony to Blakeney Point is at Flamborough Head, East Yorkshire.

Razorbill

Alca torda islandica

Alca torda torda (Northern Razorbill)

Rowan notes Razorbills as fairly regular in small and varying numbers between August and November, occasionally at other times of year. He also notes a bird picked up dead in July 1912. White reiterates these comments and their status remains unchanged today, though it should be noted that identification difficulties apply as described for the preceding species. The Razorbill is, however, generally less numerous than the Guillemot.

A notable easterly movement of at least 2,000 occurred on 5th October 1984 and an unseasonal record was of three birds lingering between April and July 2001, whilst an adult was feeding a half-grown chick close inshore on 16th July 2003.

161 were found dead in the auk 'wreck' of February 1983, more than the total of Guillemots.

It is of course difficult to determine the form of the Razorbills occurring off the Point. Many will doubtless be of the British and Irish, French, Faeroes and Icelandic form *islandica* though the slightly larger more northerly Scandinavian nominate form presumably occurs as well. Razorbills winter further out at sea and further south than Guillemots, in the Bay of Biscay, in the western Mediterranean and off northwest Africa. The nearest breeding colony to Blakeney Point is at Flamborough Head, East Yorkshire.

Black Guillemot
Cepphus grylle arcticus
Rowan notes one record only, picked up exhausted on the beach, but does not give the date. White lists a bird in the Harbour on 11th – 14th March 1971.

Other known records include:-

10th February 1956, found dead.
2nd September 1963.
26th October 1968.
1st – 16th January 1983.
3rd October 1985.
24th October to 21st November 1992, between the Point and Weybourne.
Juvenile on 24th September 2003.

Black Guillemots are largely sedentary, with juveniles being only slightly more dispersive. It is likely therefore that all the Point records refer to birds from the nearest populations (of the form *arcticus*) in Scotland and Scandinavia.

Little Auks. (*James McCallum*)

Little Auk
Alle alle alle
Rowan records that Little Auks are irregular, but by no means uncommon, numerous in some winters. White reiterates this status and lists two records in the 1950s.

The status of Little Auk on Blakeney Point is understated in the literature as many of the recent influxes involving several hundred birds have only been counted from nearby sites such as Cley and Sheringham. Although all these birds will have passed the Point minutes afterwards they are not included here in line with the recording policy outlined in the introduction to the Systematic List.

Periodic influxes of Little Auks have been occurring since local recording began. Pashley notes that birds were 'everywhere' after the gale of 20th – 22nd November 1893, with several killed against the rigging of the steamboat *'Leven'*, ashore at the Watch House. A further large influx was noted in 1895.

Such influxes continue to occur mainly in late October and November, but are not recorded every year, and in some years only one or two birds are seen. Birds invariably pass west close inshore, singly or in small parties, sometimes in company with waders. Peak numbers noted as specifically recorded from the Point include 150 on 29th October 1983, the day of a large movement off Norfolk with many birds tagged onto groups of Knot and Dunlin, and 171 on 20th October 1991. Other significant passages occurred along the north Norfolk coast in late October 1974, December 1990 and October/November 1995. Particularly early birds were recorded on 29th September 1984 and, earliest of all, on 23rd September 2003.

Winter records are scarce but two were close inshore on 13th January 1991 and one was found dead on 17th March of the same year. 17 were found dead in the auk 'wreck' of February 1983.

It is of course difficult to determine the form of the Little Auks occurring off the Point. Most will doubtless be of the widespread Arctic-breeding nominate form though the occurrence of the slightly larger Franz Josef Land form *polaris* (Franz Josef Land Little Auk) cannot be discounted. This form has been found dead in Shetland and is therefore likely to be occurring in the northern North Sea, the source area for those recorded on the Point.

Puffin (Atlantic Puffin)

Fratercula arctica grabae

Rowan notes that Puffins can be picked up exhausted on the beach but are more frequently found dead. White adds that occasional birds are seen in the Harbour, usually in August or September, possibly on the strength of a record of a juvenile there on 25th August 1955. Such records in the Harbour are not now the norm.

Puffins are now scarce visitors, most common in autumn, but significantly rarer than Little Auk. Records normally involve very small numbers of birds offshore, with peak recent numbers being eight on 4th October 2003, ten on 8th October 1989 and 23 on the early date of 17th June 2001. Unseasonal birds were seen on 22nd April 1984 and 22nd May 2004.

Occasional birds are found dead on the beach but 35 were found under such circumstances in the auk 'wreck' of February 1983.

It is of course difficult to determine the form of the Puffins occurring off the Point. Most will doubtless be of the British and Irish, French, Faeroes and southern Norwegian form *grabae* though the occurrence of the widespread, slightly larger, more northerly nominate form (Northern Puffin) cannot be discounted.

Pallas's Sandgrouse

Syrrhaptes paradoxus

White quotes Stevenson (1890) in noting that on 26th June 1863 four females were killed from a flock of about 30 birds near the Pit and that in the last week of July another flock of 30 birds was seen. The precise location of these birds is, however, not known.

Rowan records that 'two (?)' specimens were obtained by Pinchen on the Point in the great invasion of summer 1888, with others observed by Gurney during the same season. He notes it as quite probable that they had also occurred during other invasions but fails to mention any occurrences in 1863.

Pashley's diaries refer to 33 Pallas's Sandgrouse being brought to him in 1888 from the immediate neighbourhood, at least 10-12 of which are referred to as having been shot 'on the beach', 'in the Marrams' or 'in the Sandhills', and therefore presumably from within our area.

The 1888 records are attributable to the flock of up to 180 birds which settled that year on a bare, stony knoll in a turnip field at Morston belonging to a Mr. Woods. The birds arrived in the late spring and remained until the third week of October. In all, between 1,100 and 1,200 were estimated to have occurred in the county as a whole.

Pinchen's diaries provide a unique perspective on the events of that year, indicating that the whole flock was visiting the Point at the time:-

'These birds came from Central Asia. I well remember the excitement there was in Cley with the gunners when these birds arrived. It was in the close season for shooting but the Sandgrouse were not on the list so they had a warm reception. Lots of people were out after them but I can assure you they took some stopping as they were the fastest flying birds I have ever shot at. Golden Plover can move pretty fast but the Sandgrouse was faster. You could shoot straight up and they would pass without taking the slightest notice. A great many used some of the fields at Morston, feeding on the seeds in turnip crops. I have been in the sandhills, if the wind was in the south you could hear them as soon as they started to fly 'chiz-a-witt, chiz-a-witt' and very soon you would see them coming across the mudflats making for the sandhills, their favourite place. I noticed they picked the seed from various plants that grew along the beach...

I must tell you that they passed a law, no Sandgrouse to be shot for four years. Well by the time they got that into force all birds had gone and I have not seen one since. They were in great demand amongst the collectors who would give a good price, the usual price was 10 shillings which we thought was a lot at that time. The later end of the time I was offered two pounds, two shillings for one but I did not get one.'

A handful of further records occurred in the county in 1889, 1890, 1906 and 1908 but none were seen on the Point in these years. With no further invasions into northwest Europe it is no surprise that the species has never again been recorded.

The 1888 irruption of this species from its Central Asian semi-desert range must be one of the most exciting bird events ever witnessed on the Point and one that many would wish to see repeated!

Rock Dove (Rock Pigeon, Feral Pigeon)
Columba livia livia

This species is not listed by Rowan or White but Pinchen's diaries frequently refer to westward movements of pigeons.

Feral Pigeons are still regularly seen and on some days significant numbers of racing pigeons can pass, invariably to the west.

This probably qualifies as the most ignored species on the Blakeney Point list!

Stock Dove (Stock Pigeon)
Columba oenas oenas

Rowan notes that the species used to breed in the Sandhills. White repeats this comment but adds no further status update and omits it from his list of breeding species.

A pair of Stock Doves now regularly breeds in the Lifeboat House and during the 1990s they also occupied Rabbit burrows in the Sandhills, with small numbers frequently seen around the

Near Point Black-headed Gull colony.

The species is absent outside the breeding season and, although some coastal passage of Stock Doves has been noted elsewhere in north Norfolk, there has been little evidence of this from the Point. The only such record known concerns a lone bird which arrived from the north on 29th October 2004 and landed in the saltmarsh.

Woodpigeon (Common Wood Pigeon)
Columba palumbus palumbus
Rowan notes that a few usually stray over during the autumn and that the species is occasional in spring. This status is repeated by White.

In 1949, however, Ted Eales noted a 'big immigration' on 26th March, with birds seen coming in over the sea from the north. The 1959 *Norfolk Bird Report* also notes an 'immense influx' around the coast of Norfolk, including at Cley, on 19th – 24th November of that year but to what extent this movement was witnessed on the Point is not known.

There are no known recent large influxes but since the 1980s the species has become regular in very small numbers and is frequently encountered, particularly in spring, feeding in the salt-marsh at the Marrams. The only recent 'large' counts are of 30 on 4th May 1992 and 24 on 3rd April 2003. These are, however, all local birds on short excursions from Blakeney Fresh Marsh. Records at other seasons are rare and there has been no recent evidence of any passage at either season – indeed the whole question of the movements of this essentially sedentary species, at least in Britain, remains controversial.

After prospecting in a couple of recent years around the Laboratory, a pair bred successfully in the adjacent Tamarisk in 2003, rearing two young. They subsequently re-nested in the Plantation but were not successful. In 2004 a pair arrived on 12th July and nested successfully, rearing two young in the Plantation.

Collared Dove (Eurasian Collared Dove)
Streptopelia decaocto decaocto
Collared Doves spread spectacularly from China through Central Asia to Europe and Britain between the 1930s and the 1950s and are therefore, of course, not listed by Rowan. White, however, notes two very tired birds in the Plantation on 4th May 1960 (only four years after the first Norfolk birds at Overstrand in 1956) and, writing in 1981, he records 'several during the last few years'.

The Collared Dove is still rare but almost annual in spring. Records fall between 3rd March and 27th May but most are in May and all involve singles apart from three on 14th May 2000.

The species is even rarer in autumn and only two records are known at this season – singles on 4th October 1989 and 20th October 1990.

Turtle Dove (European Turtle Dove)
Streptopelia turtur turtur
The species is not listed by Rowan, a surprising omission given the species' former more common status, and its absence from his list seems likely to be an oversight. The species' historical status on the Point is therefore unfortunately not known.

This omission is then perpetuated by White. As a result, all known records have occurred since 1989, at a time when the species has experienced a massive decline in numbers in Norfolk and nationwide. Almost all records are from May, as follows:-

19th May 1989.

146

8th May 1990.
27th May 1991.
21st and 23rd May 1992.
25th May 1993.
6th May 1995.
25th May 1996.
16th May 2000.

There is only one autumn record - on 8th September 1990.

With ongoing declines linked to agricultural intensification, a deterioration of its African wintering habitat and excessive shooting and trapping in the Mediterranean, future observers may do well to see this species on the Point again.

Rose-ringed Parakeet (Ring-necked Parakeet)
Psittacula krameri subsp.
An individual of this introduced species was seen in 1989 but the date of the record is not known.

Great Spotted Cuckoo
Clamator glandarius glandarius
A juvenile, the fifth record for Norfolk, was present in and around the Plantation on the afternoon and evening of 7th July 1992, having previously been seen briefly at Cley. It was still present early on 8th but flew off towards Stiffkey. Somewhat surprisingly, it was again seen on the Point on 11th July. A photograph of it in the Plantation is in *Birding World* 5: 248.

Great Spotted Cuckoos are amongst the earliest of all migrants to arrive in their north African and Iberian breeding grounds, the first returning 'spring' birds often appearing in December and January. The occurrence of a vagrant juvenile in early July is therefore not that extraordinary, as early summer marks the beginning of their 'autumn' migration. It is interesting to note that the few July records of this species in Britain have all been on the east coast.

Common Cuckoo (Cuckoo)
Cuculus canorus canorus
Rowan records Cuckoos as rare, occasional in September and October. White notes that they are also occasional in spring and have bred. A juvenile was seen on 4th August 1954 and one was reared in a Sky Lark's nest in 1963. A chick was again seen in a Sky Lark's nest in 1966.

Cuckoos are still recorded on the Point as summer migrants from southern Africa, though not annually, typically singly in May and early June and again (largely juveniles) in August. They can, however, sometimes be heard singing from the south side of the Harbour on calm days in spring. There is some evidence of a recent decline in numbers.

Barn Owl
Tyto alba alba
Neither Rowan nor White list the Barn Owl, but one or more birds were often seen during night-time Fox-shooting carried out by the National Trust between 1998 and 2000. There are no known daylight occurrences though the species is probably under-recorded if it crosses to the Point at dusk or after dark. A bird hunted west of Cley Coastguards at the very edge of our recording area on the evening of 17th April 2002 and this may be a regular habit as Barn Owls are resident nearby and frequently hunt Blakeney Fresh Marsh.

Eurasian Scops Owl

Otus scops scops

One of these tiny southern European and western Asian owls was seen on 6th October 1922 by Pinchen who, not surprisingly, described it in his diaries as 'the first I have seen'. The wind was strong from the northeast at the time.

Scops Owl remains a major rarity in Britain, with the vast majority occurring in spring. The date and weather conditions associated with this record are therefore most surprising. Although this was the seventh record for Norfolk there has been only one since.

Snowy Owl

Bubo scandiacus

A second-winter male of this High Arctic species, the 14th for Norfolk and the first since 1938, was found perched on the roof of the westernmost chalet on the morning of 23rd March 1991. It subsequently moved to the fence overlooking the Lupins before flying off strongly high to the southwest after spending around three hours on the Point. It was relocated at Stiffkey that afternoon. Next day it was at Burnham Overy and on 25th at Scolt Head. It reappeared at Easington, East Yorkshire on 30th March and was probably the bird seen around Orkney in April.

This was the bird which had wintered at Wainfleet, Lincolnshire from 24th December 1990, last seen there on 18th March 1991. Good photographs of this bird were taken in Lincolnshire and poor, though identifiable, 'record shots' were taken of it on the Point.

A full account of this occurrence appears in the *Norfolk Bird Report* for 1991 and the ageing of the bird is discussed in *Birding World* 5: 96-97.

Although Scandinavia or northern Russia is, of course, the most likely source area for this bird, a Nearctic origin cannot wholly be excluded as Canadian birds have in the past reached northwest Europe on ships.

Little Owl

Athene noctua vidalii

Pinchen's *Sea Swallows* contains the following:-

> 'One of the most destructive of the raptorial birds is the Little Owl. As an illustration of its destructive nature I may recount how, on one occasion, a tern was sitting on eggs when it was attacked by one of these owls. Its body was still in position on the nest but the head was severed completely and lay at some little distance. These creatures gave us an anxious time when Roseate and other terns were on the nesting ground and we had to keep a sharp look-out to guard against their depredations.'

Rowan does not list this introduced species and White cites only three records – on 8th September 1957, 8th October 1957 and 6th October 1960. The only other records traced are as follows:-

3rd October 1989.
28th August 1991.
13th September 1992.

A clear pattern of autumn occurrences is therefore emerging, reflecting the species' pattern of limited autumn dispersal from local breeding sites. Although Little Owls are largely sedentary, their more extreme wanderings are clearly able to bring them to the Point, albeit only occasionally.

Tawny Owl
Strix aluco sylvatica

A bizarre tale surrounds the only occurrence on the Point of this highly sedentary species. A Tawny Owl was picked up by a regular Blakeney Point birdwatcher on the road between Attleborough and Dereham and placed, presumed dead, in the car's boot. On arrival at Morston Quay the boot was opened, only for the owl to fly out. The next day a Tawny Owl, doubtless the same disorientated individual, was flushed from the *Suaeda* on Yankee Ridge. Although this record occurred in the early 1980s, the precise date has now unfortunately been lost.

Long-eared Owl
Asio otus otus

Rowan notes that the species had only been taken by Ted Ramm. White notes Long-eared Owls as very rare and lists seven records between 1960 and 1975.

Long-eared Owls, originating from Scandinavia, are now almost annual in autumn. Extreme dates are 10th September and 16th November but most occur in October in conditions favouring arrivals from the continent. Between one and three birds in a season is typical but four birds occurred on 13th October 1990 and a record eight on 27th October 1991, perhaps indicative of one of their periodic irruptions. Birds are sometimes seen arriving from the sea but are normally flushed from the *Suaeda* or the dunes, although roosting birds have been noted in the Plantation.

Spring birds are very rare, with singles recorded as follows:-

14th May 1988.
7th June 1995.
24th April 2002.
13th March 2003.

Short-eared Owl. (*James McCallum*)

Short-eared Owl

Asio flammeus flammeus

Rowan records this, the most migratory and nomadic of the owls, as irregular, recorded several times between October and April. White notes that in some years birds nesting on the 'mainland' have taken many tern chicks and the occasional sitting adult. This is a habit still prevalent today, with either passage or local owls sometimes making predatory visits in spring and even summer.

Short-eared Owls are, however, most familiar as late autumn immigrants from northwest Europe, with several birds noted each year between late September and November, sometimes seen arriving from the sea but normally flushed from the *Suaeda* or the shingle ridge. Birds are usually recorded singly but larger numbers have included five on 13th October 1990 and six on 4th October 1992. A further influx occurred over 29th – 31st October 2004 when at least five were recorded.

European Nightjar (Nightjar)

Caprimulgus europaeus europaeus

Pashley notes one 'from the bushes' on 8th September 1899 and one taken from a fishing smack on 11th October 1902.

Rowan records Nightjars taken two or three times in September and White lists records on 21st May and 3rd September 1956 and 21st August 1977.

The only recent records are as follows:-

5th October 1998, flushed from the beach on Far Point. It flew off across the Harbour, flushing all the gulls which presumably took it to be a raptor.

25th June 2003, a bird heard 'churring' in the Sandhills at 2330 (this record is incorrectly listed as 25th July in the 2003 *Norfolk Bird Report*).

It is likely that most, if not all, autumn records refer to continental birds as the Nightjar has a large population in eastern Europe and European Russia. The 1977 record coincided with a large 'fall' of continental migrants while the 1998 record occurred as part of that year's memorable influx of continental Robins.

Common Swift (Swift)

Apus apus apus

Rowan notes the Swift as rare but observed several times. Pinchen, however, notes 'hundreds' passing on 16th and 17th June 1927 and 'many' on 8th May 1929. White notes that they may frequently be seen hawking over the Point during the summer months. On 30th August 1935 many entered the Lifeboat House in the evening and roosted there overnight.

An early bird occurred on 10th April 1966 but the first returning Swifts from Africa are not usually seen until the end of the month or early May. Thereafter it is scarce but regular in small numbers, with most appearing to be wandering local breeders whenever feeding conditions or southerly winds lead them out over the Harbour. Occasionally, though, heavy passages can take place in late spring and early summer. For example, hundreds passed on 30th May 1993 and 2,000 moved west on 19th June 2001. Whereas the first of these movements may have involved migrants, the June count is more likely to have been a feeding movement.

Swifts are decidedly scarce in autumn after August but Pinchen's diaries note a bird on 28th September 1922. An unidentified swift seen over the Harbour on 13th November 1995 was presumably either this species or Pallid Swift. Three further unidentified swifts, also either this species or Pallid Swift, occurred on 29th October 2004 (see below).

Pallid Swift
Apus pallidus subsp.

Three Pallid Swifts were over the beach at the Marrams in the late afternoon of 20th October 2004 – at the same time as a Dusky Warbler at the Laboratory.

A further Pallid Swift flew slowly west along the Point shortly after 1300 on 29th October 2004 and lingered to feed for a couple of minutes between the Long Hills and the Sandhills. It had been seen earlier, along with two other swifts, either Common or Pallid, at Sheringham, Weybourne, Salthouse and Cley and all three birds were subsequently noted at Wells. As it departed to the west from the Sandhills the Pallid Swift was briefly accompanied by one of these other swifts but the views were poor and this second bird could not be identified.

At 1500 two further swifts flew west which were also either Common or Pallid Swifts. These latter birds had been seen previously at Sheringham and identified as Pallid Swifts but the views obtained on the Point were inconclusive.

At the time of writing (May 2005) these records are under consideration by BBRC.

These records coincided with a widespread influx of Common and Pallid Swifts into northwest Europe in late October 2004. These southern European and north African swifts, which winter south of the Sahara, are expanding northwards in southern Europe and are increasingly seen in Britain – a trend likely to be encouraged by climate change. They occur typically in October and November in strong southerly or southwesterly winds associated with the warm sectors of low pressure areas. Although the form involved in these records is not clear, they are likely to refer to the most widespread form *brehmorum*.

Alpine Swift
Apus melba melba

The only accepted record of this southern European and southwest Asian species, with a winter range in Africa, is of a bird seen at the Hood on 14th June 1962.

It is perhaps worth noting that White records six seen between Cley and the Point between May and September 1966. However, no trace can be found elsewhere of any of these records and they are presumably best discounted.

Common Kingfisher (Kingfisher)
Alcedo atthis ispida

Rowan notes a bird taken by Clifford Borrer on 20th September 1916 as the only record though he refers to it being seen commonly at Cley. White cites a further record on 20th September 1957 and one ringed in 1967.

Kingfishers are regularly seen singly, or occasionally in pairs, in autumn along the Glaven Channel west of Cley Coastguards and wandering along the outer edges of the Marrams but the only known record from further along the Point involves a bird in Pinchen's Creek on 10th September 2003. Most birds are presumably local in origin but Taylor *et al.* (1999) list Blakeney Point as one of a number of sites where birds have been seen arriving from the sea.

European Bee-eater (Bee-eater)
Merops apiaster

The only record of this colourful Mediterranean and southwest Asian species is of a juvenile seen on 3rd September 1988.

Bee-eaters are increasingly recorded in Norfolk, with several birds having been tracked along the entire length of the coast. However, no others have yet ventured out to the Point.

Hoopoe (Eurasian Hoopoe)

Upupa epops epops

There are nine records of this delightful southern European and Asian species which winters in Africa. Eight or nine individuals have occurred:-

11th September 1963.
21st August 1966.
8th and 22nd August 1968.
18th – 20th April 1972.
7th – 15th May 1985.
18th April 1987.
2nd – 6th June 1992.
18th – 19th September 2001.

The equal distribution of records between spring and autumn is at variance with the national picture, where 78% of Hoopoes occur in spring and only 22% in autumn. This is no doubt a reflection of the fact that, due to its north-facing aspect, the Point receives little in the way of direct arrivals from France and Iberia, the source of many British occurrences in spring. It is also note-worthy that the few such records fall decidedly late in the season, whereas a high proportion of spring Hoopoes in Britain occurs in March. This may suggest either onward passage following an earlier landfall on the south coast or may also hint at a more easterly origin.

Given the predominantly eastern origins of the Point's migrants in autumn it is also possible that some Hoopoes at this season originate from more easterly populations, conceivably even of the greyer eastern form *saturata*. For example, the bird in September 2001 occurred in easterly weather conditions which brought birds not only from central Europe but also from Siberia.

Wryneck and Willow Warbler. (*James McCallum*)

Wryneck (Eurasian Wryneck)

Jynx torquilla torquilla

Blakeney Point has long been famous for Wrynecks and they are an eagerly-anticipated compo-nent of early autumn 'falls'. In easterly conditions they are displaced from their route between Scandinavian, north European (and perhaps even northern Russian) breeding grounds and winter quarters in Africa. The all-time total is impossible to calculate but in excess of 250 birds have occurred since the 1939-1945 war.

Pashley notes that he received many specimens 'from the bushes' in autumn. Rowan records them as fairly frequent, though irregular, in September. White notes them as occurring in late August and September, usually singly, but refers to unprecedented numbers between 2nd and 28th September 1965 when 25-30 occurred between the Point and Salthouse.

Most Wrynecks still occur in late August and September, with extreme dates being 8th August (in 1969) and 24th October (in 1976). The species is very nearly annual but often only one or two birds are seen in a season. More productive years have been:-

1954 with around 15 (including 11 on 22nd August).
1958 with 12 (including 8 on 4th September).
1965 with 25 - 30 (on 4th – 6th September).
1968 with around 16.
1976 with 10–15.
1977 with 15 (including 14 on 19th August).
1987 with around 20 (including 15 on 26th August).

Wrynecks sometimes linger for several days to feed on ants, making precise numbers difficult to determine. This is in notable contrast to the situation in Orkney and Shetland where birds move on rapidly in response to poor feeding conditions.

Nine or ten Wrynecks have occurred in spring, all since 1985:-

Up to 3 on 12th – 15th May 1985, coinciding with a major Bluethroat arrival.
23rd May 1987, also coinciding with a Bluethroat arrival.
24th April 1994.
21st May 1994, again coinciding with a Bluethroat arrival.
12th and 14th May 2000.
29th April 2003.
30th April to 1st May 2004.

It is doubtful whether this represents a real increase at this season as the spring has only been watched regularly for passerines since the mid-1980s. The three April records reflect the fact that this is an early migrant to northern Europe.

At both seasons Wrynecks are usually seen feeding on the ground in the dunes and grassy areas but birds can also frequent the Lupins and the Plantation, as described in Richard Richardson's unpublished notes:-

'A favourite haunt on Blakeney Point is the little clump of white poplars and decay-ing, flood-killed pine trees where, in late August and early September, one or two of these Scandinavian migrants can usually be watched flaking the bark from the rotten branches for the earwigs and woodlice hiding there and displaying the intricate tap-estry-pattern of their 'Nightjar' plumage.'

Green Woodpecker (European Green Woodpecker)

Picus viridis viridis

Rowan notes that this species has been taken three or four times in autumn. White notes it as occasional, most common in the autumn. In 1953 one was seen on 8th February and, remarkably, five were apparently present on 20th November. Further birds were seen on 16th November 1967 and 30th January 1968.

The only subsequent traced records of this highly sedentary species are of singles on 25th January 1986 and 6th November 1988.

Great Spotted Woodpecker

Dendrocopos major major (Northern Great Spotted Woodpecker)

Rowan notes a single record but provides no details. White records that the occasional bird may be seen, usually in September, and lists four records between 1959 and 1972. There are, however, a further four records from this era and all known records are listed below:-

10th September 1953.
6th September 1956.
21st October 1957.
11th October 1959.
24th September 1961.
19th September 1962, an influx year.
15th September 1968, also an influx year.
16th September to 17th December 1972.

There is then an apparent long gap in records until a run of more recent sightings:-

20th October 1997, in the Long Hills.
18th September 2001, on Near Point.
19th September 2001, in the Marrams.
2 on 25th September 2001, both found dead on the beach.

As British Great Spotted Woodpeckers are essentially sedentary, all records are doubtless of continental immigrants and therefore of the nominate form, although this can only truly be confirmed in the hand. The 2001 arrivals coincided with a large irruption of Great Spotted Woodpeckers into northwest Europe which extended to Britain in strong northeasterly winds.

Short-toed Lark (Greater Short-toed Lark)

Calandrella brachydactyla subsp.

Though only recorded for the first time in 1988, this Mediterranean and southwest Asian species has become regular, with increased coverage producing a total of eight records in spring and two in autumn. All records are as follows:-

1st October 1988, on the shingle ridge at the Watch House.
7th – 10th May 1990, on Yankee Ridge (listed in Gantlett (1995) as 8th – 10th).
4th May 1992, in the Marrams.
30th May 1997, possibly to 31st, between the Long Hills and the Sandhills (listed in the 1997 *Norfolk Bird Report* as 31st).
13th May 1998, in the Marrams.

bird was seen on 7th November 1998. Significant passages have occurred in both spring and autumn, almost always of birds heading west. Spring sees by far the largest numbers, with most passing in May. At this time a few hundred in a day may be seen, but occasionally even larger movements occur, for example 2,000 on 26th May 2003 and an exceptional 2,500 per hour on 8th May 1994.

Records from the Point presumably involve a majority of British breeders but continental birds doubtless also occur.

An apparent Swallow x House Martin hybrid was seen on 10th September 1991.

House Martin (Common House Martin)
Delichon urbicum urbicum

Rowan notes that House Martins bred in 1915 and 1916 (two nests) in the Lifeboat House but that otherwise the species was merely an occasional straggler in the spring and occurred more rarely in the autumn. White notes the species as a passage migrant.

House Martins are now regular westerly passage migrants at both seasons, returning from Africa in April and May and departing in August and September, usually in small numbers. Occasional larger passages occur, for example 100 on 25th September 1988, 505 on 28th May 2001 and 300 on 28th April 2003.

These numbers are significantly smaller than counts made elsewhere in north Norfolk and demonstrate clearly that the Point is not well sited for observing diurnal 'visible migration'.

A few birds are seen into October but an exceptionally late bird occurred on 29th November 1986. Pinchen notes 'a martin' on 3rd November 1922, presumably referring to this species.

Records from the Point are assumed to involve a majority of British breeders but continental birds doubtless also occur.

An apparent Swallow x House Martin hybrid was seen on 10th September 1991.

Richard's Pipit
Anthus richardi richardi

The large 'Richard's Pipit' complex is perhaps best separated into the Siberian and northeast Asian Richard's Pipit, wintering largely in southeast Asia, and other large pipit groups in Africa, Indochina, Indonesia and Australasia. The scientific name quoted above is therefore at variance with that given in the BOURC and *British Birds* lists.

Some confusion surrounds the early history of Richard's Pipits on the Point. Pashley refers to a bird taken in grass at the Point (and later passing into the Connop collection) on 27th October 1909. Rowan refers to the first for the Point being shot near the Lifeboat House by W. Bishop but does not give the year – it may well, however, be a reference to this same bird. Rowan also states that 'another is said to have been shot and mistaken for a thrush'. To complicate matters further, White lists the first for the Point as one shot by W. Bishop in October 1907 but gives no exact date – it is possible that this is a transcription error in referring to the 1909 bird.

White lists subsequent records on 5th – 6th September 1964, at the time the earliest ever recorded in the county, and another on 25th. This latter record may, however, be a transcription error as it is listed in the 1964 *Norfolk Bird Report* as having occurred on 25th October. Further birds occurred on 14th September and 6th October 1968 but these are not listed by White who does, however, refer to further records on 20th September and 22nd November 1970 and 13th October 1977.

Since the 1970s there have been a further 19 autumn records, all falling in the 'classic' Richard's Pipit 'slot' between 25th September and 20th October. This apparent increase may, however, have much to do with increased observations as Richard's Pipits were regularly recorded by Gätke on

Heligoland, Germany in the late nineteenth century and must also have been reaching Britain in some numbers at this time.

Two have also occurred in spring - one in the Sandhills on 30th April 1989 and one at the Watch House on 26th April 2001. The near-coincidence of dates is interesting and reflects a recent pattern of late April and early May occurrences in Britain, presumably involving birds returning from winter quarters situated somewhere in southwest Europe or northwest Africa.

Richard's Pipits on the Point are frequently only seen briefly in flight, drawing attention to themselves by their distinctive, far-carrying call. This species favours rank grassland and the Point therefore offers poor feeding opportunities.

Tawny Pipit
Anthus campestris campestris
Rowan notes the first for the Point secured by Frank Richards on 15th September 1910. White lists a further seven records between 1955 and the end of the 1970s.

Birds have occurred at both migration seasons, though with slightly more in autumn, extreme dates in spring being 26th April and 12th June, with most in mid-May. Autumn records have fallen between 12th August and 30th October but most have been in September. All post-war records are as follows:-

2 on 23rd August 1955, with one of these or another on 24th.
6th September 1956.
9th June 1964.
12th August 1973.
25th August 1976.
30th October 1976.
13th May 1981.
30th September 1985.
1st September 1987.
12th June 1988.
16th – 26th May 1989.
26th – 27th April 1992.
18th September 1992.
26th September 1992.
6th September 1998.
14th May 2000.
16th – 17th May 2003.

Despite no longer being considered a national rarity, Tawny Pipits are now increasingly rare in Britain and the Point's track record for this species is a good one. In contrast with the previous species, birds often linger in the sandy and stony areas, which closely resemble the species' semi-desert breeding grounds. Tawny Pipits have a large southern European and Central Asian range and, although the spring birds are likely to be Mediterranean 'overshoots', some, especially later, autumn birds may be from further afield.

Olive-backed Pipit
Anthus hodgsoni yunnanensis
There are two records of this tree-loving Siberian vagrant, whose normal winter quarters lie in southeast Asia. Both were on typical dates for British occurrences:-

2nd October 1987, in the Sandhills. This was the fourth record for Norfolk.

18th October 1990, heard calling in fog over the Hood before being seen well in the salt-marsh and on the shingle bank at the Long Hills. This bird arrived as part of a huge arrival of thrushes which also featured two Arctic Redpolls.

The almost complete lack of trees on the Point will probably prevent this species from ever becoming more regular.

Tree Pipit
Anthus trivialis trivialis

Rowan lists the Tree Pipit as fairly regular, though never abundant, in September while White notes a particularly high count of 60 in from the sea on 6th September 1960.

Tree Pipits are recorded at both migration seasons, though less frequently in spring. Birds at this season are generally recorded in late April and May, usually as singles, though seven were present on 13th May 1988.

An exceptional record concerns a singing male which took up territory in *Suaeda* clumps just west of Cley Coastguards in May 2004, right at the very edge of our recording area. Remarkably, this bird reappeared for a period in April 2005.

Autumn passage may feature the occasional bird from the third week of August but is concentrated in early and mid-September, typically involving only one to three birds in a day. Higher numbers are, however, occasionally seen, for example 25 on 2nd September 1958, 10 on 18th September 1995 and 20 between 9th and 13th September 2002. October records are rare and an exceptionally late bird occurred on 8th November 2003.

At both seasons birds are invariably found singly and are typically elusive and silent in deep *Suaeda* or long grass.

The preponderance of autumn records is the opposite of occurrence patterns at the Irish Sea observatories where British breeders in spring are largely responsible for the records. By contrast, most Tree Pipits recorded on the Point will be continental in origin. The species has an extensive range, covering most of Europe and a broad swathe across central Russia, with wintering grounds in Africa.

Meadow Pipit song-flighting. (*James McCallum*)

Meadow Pipit
Anthus pratensis

Rowan notes the Meadow Pipit as a resident, nesting in considerable numbers and also seen all year round in large numbers. Its nests are recorded as being found most frequently on the more solid moss-covered parts of the dunes, usually in the open but once in an empty golden syrup tin.

White reiterates this status and adds that Meadow Pipits are also regular passage migrants and probably winter visitors in small numbers. White considered that breeding numbers were rising. For example, 23 pairs in 1953 had risen to 60 pairs by 1967 and numbers in the 1990s were generally also around 60 pairs, with 67 pairs counted in a 1999 census. A record 119 pairs was counted in 2004 – one of the highest concentrations in Norfolk. The species is a dominant feature of the dunes in spring and summer.

Meadow Pipits are common spring migrants, with small parties regularly encountered on westward passage in March and April. These movements involve birds returning from wintering grounds in France, Spain and northwest Africa. Significant numbers are occasionally involved, for example 150 on 16th April 1988 and 250 on 2nd April 2000.

Birds with strikingly uniform pale orange underparts and reduced underpart streaking were seen on 14th March 1993 and 15th March 2004 – a noteworthy near-coincidence of dates. Both these birds showed characters sometimes associated with an 'Atlantic' form *whistleri*, but some uncertainty seems to surround the appearance, distribution and even validity of this form and Meadow Pipit is probably best treated as monotypic. Photographs of the 2004 bird, together with a discussion of birds with this appearance, are in *Birding World* 18:169-172.

Meadow Pipits are also frequent autumn migrants, with the largest numbers occurring in the second half of September, typically forming large, mobile flocks in the Sandhills. Recent high counts have included 200 on 20th September 2002 and 250 on 25th September 2003. Although many such birds may be British breeders, birds from Iceland, the Faeroes and Norway are probably also involved, though the relative proportions are not known.

Red-throated Pipit

Anthus cervinus

Regular watching in spring since the mid-1980s has revealed the Red-throated Pipit to be one of Blakeney Point's most regularly-occurring rarities which could soon overtake Greenish Warbler as the commonest rarity overall. There are now 14 accepted records of this attractive species, 13 of which fell in spring between 3rd and 31st May. In spring, the Point has become one of the best places in Britain to see this species. Warm southeasterly winds in May displace birds west of their central European route from African wintering grounds to Scandinavia.

Unlike many British records, a very small percentage are 'fly-overs', most giving splendid views on the ground. This must be because the habitat is to their liking, with the shingle, short grass and low *Suaeda* clumps perhaps resembling their Scandinavian and Arctic Russian tundra breeding habitat, even encouraging some birds to burst into song. In this respect it is interesting to note that all those seen on the ground have been in such habitat west of the Hood, with the only two 'fly-overs' being those in the less suitable Marrams.

This species can be hard to sex but extremely bright birds with extensive fully-saturated red on the supercilium, throat and upper breast are recorded here as 'male types' and dull birds with weak and restricted red as 'female-types'. Those heard singing are recorded as definite males whilst one of the birds in spring 1992 which completely lacked red is recorded as a definite female. Birds seen too poorly are not assigned to either sex. All records are listed:-

Male on 15th – 16th May 1988, singing around the chalets (photographed). This bird occurred on the same day as the Point's first Thrush Nightingale.
Male-type on 16th May 1988 (accepted by BBRC as different), also around the chalets, with either this bird or the previous present until 17th.
Male-type on 13th – 16th May 1989, seen arriving over the shingle ridge near the Long Hills

however, occur from July to September when the Harbour muds and tidal fringes of the spits abound with juveniles, with counts of up to a couple of hundred birds recorded at this time. Many of these will be locally-bred but to what extent birds from elsewhere in Britain are involved is not known. Contrary to Rowan's experience the species is now only encountered in ones or twos after mid-autumn.

White Wagtail
Motacilla (alba) alba
Rowan does not list this taxon but Pinchen's diaries record one on 6th May 1922. White notes that it may be seen occasionally.

White Wagtail is an annual early spring migrant between late March and early May in small numbers, but as many *alba* wagtails are 'fly-overs' they may be under-recorded. Some birds are, however, occasionally seen on the ground, for example a group of ten on 21st April 2000. These birds are migrants returning to Icelandic and Faeroese breeding grounds.

Although their occurrence in autumn is possible, the combination of poor 'fly-over' views of *alba* wagtails, identification difficulties at this season and the dominance until mid-autumn of Pied Wagtails has rendered their status effectively unknown.

Waxwing (Bohemian Waxwing)
Bombycilla garrulus garrulus
Pashley notes a bird shot by a Mr. Mortimer on 31st October 1900. Rowan notes:-

'In those years when the Waxwing arrives in large numbers on the British coasts a few are usually observed. A specimen secured in October 1903 was one of several.'

We are not aware of further published records until late October and early November 1988 when one or more are noted in the *Norfolk Bird Report*. Two are also noted for December of that year but no details are given.

The only other recent records are as follows:-

21st January 1996, arriving from the sea at the Watch House with 5 Fieldfares.
19th October 2004, flying south down Yankee Ridge.
7 on 27th October 2004, flying south over Pinchen's Creek.
28th October 2004, arriving from the sea at the Long Hills.

All these birds passed straight through – an indication of the absence of suitable habitat for this berry specialist. The winter of 1995/96 saw a large irruption of this species into Britain from breeding grounds in Scandinavia and Russia whilst October 2004 saw further large arrivals coinciding with a record irruption into Britain of Northern Bullfinches.

Wren (Winter Wren)
Troglodytes troglodytes indigenus (British Wren)
Troglodytes troglodytes troglodytes (European Wren)
Rowan describes the Wren as occasional in September and October. White notes them as passage migrants in small numbers, with most occurrences between February and March and again in September and October.

Wrens are now most prominent as autumn migrants in the *Suaeda*, usually first seen in August and peaking in October when some notable counts have occurred, for example 31 on 22nd

October 2002.

The occasional bird is seen in spring and summer and breeding had long been suspected until in 2002 a pair was proved to have bred near the Watch House.

Although any breeding birds are doubtless of the British form *indigenus*, the origin (and therefore form) of the other Wrens recorded on the Point is not known, though the slightly paler continental nominate form is thought likely to predominate in autumn.

Dunnock (Hedge Accentor, Hedge Sparrow)

Prunella modularis occidentalis
Prunella modularis modularis (Continental Dunnock)

Rowan describes the Dunnock as frequent on passage in September and October. White notes it as a breeder, with birds seen at any time of year.

The Dunnock first bred in 1961 and by 1966 there were two pairs. This had risen to four pairs by 1967, two in the Lupins and two near the Laboratory. By the early 1980s there were between four and six pairs annually. Dunnocks have continued to increase with an estimate of 15 pairs by 1993, though this was down to eight pairs in 2004. These are no doubt all of the British form *occidentalis*.

Every autumn, however, sees evidence of arriving continental birds of the slightly paler nominate form, with high-flying calling flocks not infrequently encountered. Numbers in September and October can be significant with, for example, 30 recorded in the large 'fall' of 16th October 1988. The occurrence of continental Dunnocks was first recorded by Riviere who notes birds of this form shot on the Point on 17th October 1919 and 25th September 1931.

There is occasional evidence of a return passage of these birds in spring, though such occurrences are largely masked by the presence of breeding birds. A more significant arrival, however, took place on 28th March 2005 when over 30 were recorded during a 'fall' of Blackbirds and other northbound migrants. This movement coincided with larger than normal numbers of Dunnocks recorded elsewhere in coastal north Norfolk and eastern England.

Robin (European Robin)

Erithacus rubecula melophilus (British Robin)
Erithacus rubecula rubecula (Continental Robin)

White notes the British Robin as 'occasional throughout the year, commonest in August and September'. The Continental Robin (from Europe and northwest Russia) is recorded as 'regular' by Rowan and 'abundant' in September and October by White.

Whilst separation of the two forms is possible in the field given excellent views, the poor views usually obtained on the Point generally prevent critical examination. However, the vast majority of Robins occurring on the Point are doubtless *rubecula*, and British *melophilus* is likely to be quite rare. Rowan's assertion that the British form is commonest in August and September does not reflect their current status, which shows no such occurrence peak.

Occasional records in the first half of the spring, and rarely into May, presumably refer to departing continental *rubecula* or displaced migrants from the near-continent. The species does not become regular again until autumn when immigrant continental *rubecula* appear from mid-September. Numbers in September are generally small, with counts of ten on 13th September 1993 and eight on 20th September 2000 both noteworthy. A high count of 100+ on 25th September 2001 was therefore particularly unusual.

Peak numbers always occur in October, usually in the first week of the month, and very large 'falls' have been noted. High counts include:-

'Hundreds' on 1st October 1951, during that year's famous 'Robin Rush'.
500 on 23rd October 1955 (listed incorrectly as 23rd November in Taylor *et al.* 1999).
100 on 3rd October 1964.
200+ on 4th October 1973.
200 on 18th October 1990.
375 on 1st October 1998.
300+ on 2nd October 1998.
500 on 3rd October 1998.

On days with such large movements birds are often seen arriving throughout the day, still flying in from the sea as darkness falls. The 1951 'Robin Rush' is documented in *Wild Bird Protection in Norfolk* 1951, whilst a full account of the 1998 'fall' appears in the *Norfolk Bird Report* for that year.

Late birds are recorded in small numbers into November.

Robins have never been recorded breeding on the Point, so a very recently-fledged juvenile (therefore clearly *melophilus*) on 8th June 2003 must have dispersed from the 'mainland'.

Robins on the Point are notorious skulkers and readily evade observation in the *Suaeda* and dune grass, on occasion even hiding in Rabbit holes. It is quite possible to see tens in a day without once glimpsing a red breast!

Thrush Nightingale (Sprosser)

Luscinia luscinia

This rare visitor is the eastern counterpart of the Common Nightingale, breeding in southern Scandinavia, eastern Europe and western Russia and wintering in east Africa. Accepted records are as follows:-

Male on 15th – 18th May 1988, in the Marrams, seen largely in flight, though it responded well by singing back to a tape. This was the third for Norfolk, arriving the same day as the Point's first Red-throated Pipit.
Male on 16th – 17th May 2003, in the Sandhills, occasionally in song on 17th. The bird was seen briefly on the ground but the vast majority of views were in flight. It arrived the same day as a Pallid Harrier and a Tawny Pipit.

A further individual occurred on 7th June 1992 in the Long Hills. This was a very dull nightingale seen well and close in flight but not well enough to be submittted to BBRC. It arrived with a Grey-headed Wagtail and a Red-backed Shrike and was identical in appearance to the other records listed.

All these birds have been extremely skulking and difficult to see in the *Suaeda*. It is worth noting that all the spring Common Nightingales have appeared in late April and the first half of May, with Thrush Nightingales only recorded after the middle of May. This is a typical set of dates for this species which has extended its range in northwest Europe and is therefore increasingly recorded in Britain.

Common Nightingale (Nightingale)

Luscinia megarhynchos megarhynchos

The first for the Point was one brought to Pashley on 30th September 1899, while Rowan records that it had been 'taken, I believe, more than once, and observed in September'. White gives subsequent records as 16th May 1962, 'September 1968' and 20th August 1977.

Other records traced are:-

5th September 1965.
25th August 1968.
17th – 18th November 1984.
5th May 1985.
1st May 1989.
23rd April 1994.
1st – 2nd September 1994.
8th August 1997.
10th May 1998.
23rd April 1999, in song.
2nd May 2004.

In addition, a bird on 24th September 1957 is listed in the *Norfolk Bird Report* for that year for 'Blakeney' but is referred to as having occurred on Blakeney Point in Taylor *et al.* (1999).

Given that the species breeds nearby, it is surprisingly rare as a migrant. Spring occurrences coincide with the late April and early May arrival dates of local breeding birds, but autumn birds are more likely to be continental in origin. It is particularly interesting to speculate on the origin of the exceptionally late bird on the Hood on 17th – 18th November 1984, the latest record for Norfolk, at a time when Nightingales should already be south of the Sahara. This bird was not seen well enough to establish its racial identity and there is therefore at least a theoretical possibility that it might have been of the eastern form *hafizi*, of which the tiny number of British records have all been in late autumn.

Bluethroat

Luscinia svecica svecica (Red-spotted Bluethroat)

The Bluethroat is a formerly regular migrant in September, often in some numbers, now rare and erratic in occurrence and as likely to be seen in spring as in autumn. The vast majority of, if not all, spring and autumn birds are from the Scandinavian population of the form *svecica*. This form winters in sub-Saharan Africa, Arabia, Pakistan and northwest India. Later birds, however, may conceivably be from further afield and involve other forms which would be indistinguishable in the field, such as Russian *volgae* or *pallidogularis*. White lists one of the white-spotted form *cyanecula* as present around the Laboratory on 10th September 1963, but this record is not included in the *Norfolk Bird Report* for that year. Nor is it included in the list of Norfolk records of this form in Taylor *et al.* (1999), all of which are typically early spring birds. Given this record's absence from the wider literature it is perhaps best discounted.

Bluethroats on Blakeney Point were first discovered by Fred and George Power. Their notes for 12th September 1884 (Power, 1885) record the following:-

'September 12th. Wind E., turning to N. by noon, and becoming very gusty… The day was passed at the sandhills, and a most prolific haunt they proved. Bluethroats were present in extraordinary numbers, for we reckoned those seen at from eighty to one hundred… The Bluethroats we secured were immature, and males preponderated quite in the proportion of six to one. Of the eight skinned and examined by myself, only one was certainly a female; of the rest, five were males, leaving two doubtful (being badly shot), but believed to be male and female. There can, I think, be little doubt, but that these all belonged to the Arctic variety (*C. suecica*), although one only had the red spot well marked. Of the rest, four out of five possessed blue on the breast to some extent, and placed together, presented a pleasing variety of plumages.'

Their efforts continued the following day:-

'An examination of the Bluethroats, and their companions, occupied us a large part of the day. We found all in greatly diminished numbers, although the Bluethroats numbered perhaps four dozen.'

Prior to this remarkable 'fall' only a handful of Bluethroats had ever been recorded in Britain and only one in Norfolk. Subsequently, Bluethroats attracted much attention from the gunners, each striving to bag a bird with more blue than his rivals. Pashley took particular pains to document their occurrences between 1888 and 1924, with Bluethroats recorded in 20 of these years. Peak numbers occurred as follows:-

1889 – 11.
1892 - 'A great flight of Bluethroats – I had nine brought in.'
1901 – 25.
1906 – 11.
1908 – 12.
1910 – 11.
1913 - 'This was a great Bluethroat year…the bushes were said to be full of Redstarts and Bluethroats.'

The all-time autumn total is impossible to calculate but must be over 350 birds. All but one autumn records fall between 25th August and 11th October, and almost all are in September. An extremely late bird was, however, present on 20th November 1900, the latest date for the county.
Peak autumn day counts since 1950 are:-

5 on 2nd October 1951.
6 on 10th – 17th September 1952.
Up to 7 daily on 10th – 18th September 1956.
Up to 6 on 2nd – 11th September 1958.
8 on 20th September 1960.
Approximately 12 between 2nd and 5th September 1965, with around 18 between the Point and Salthouse.

Since the mid-1960s autumn Bluethroats have been in steady decline and since the 1970s the only autumn records are:-

17th September 1988.
12th September 1989.
16th – 18th September 1993.
2nd September 1994.
3rd October 1998.
20th September 2000.
19th September 2001.
25th September 2001.

It is worth noting that Bluethroat is now rarer in autumn than both Siberian Stonechat and Greenish Warbler! Few autumn Bluethroats would now escape undetected and yet their occurrence is sporadic at best. Why this should be so is unclear though Sahel droughts have been suggested as a possible factor. The species is still a regular scarce migrant in autumn in some other parts of Britain, notably Shetland.

In contrast to the above, a new pattern of spring occurrences has emerged. The first of these was trapped in 1954 but no more were recorded until the 1970s, since when well over 50 have been seen, over half of them occurring in the remarkable arrivals of May 1985 and May 1987 - events which have, unfortunately, not been repeated.

Spring records fall between 6th May and 3rd June. All records, some of which involve singing birds, are listed below:-

1st – 2nd June 1954, trapped and ringed on 2nd. Its photograph appears in the 1954 *Norfolk Bird Report*.
1+ in May 1970.
26th May 1975.
22nd May 1978.
20th – 21st May 1984.
Daily 10th – 21st May 1985, with a maximum of 14 on 14th and two further birds on 24th, with one until 25th.
3 on 22nd May 1987, rising to 11 on 23rd, with six remaining to 24th and one to 26th.
3 on 16th May 1988, with one until 17th.
3rd June 1989.
14th May 1990, rising to three on 15th.
20th May 1991.
21st May 1993.
3 on 20th May 1994, rising to four on 21st – 22nd, with further birds on 24th and 26th.
23rd May 1995.
24th – 25th May 1995.
6th – 7th May 1996.
7th May 1996.
19th May 1996.

It must be remembered, however, that the Point was poorly watched in spring until recent times, so it is possible that occurrences at this season may not be an entirely modern phenomenon. It is interesting to speculate on whether spring occurrences will continue to be a feature as, at the time of writing (May 2005), none have been seen for nine years.

For the sake of completeness it may be worth noting that White records three birds in breeding plumage in the last week of April 1970. There are, however, no late April records of Bluethroat from Blakeney Point, or, indeed, from the whole of Norfolk, referred to elsewhere in the literature. The 1970 *Norfolk Bird Report* records the first bird that year on the more usual date of 9th May. This series of records is likely, therefore, to be an error and it is not included in the analysis above. White also refers to birds in the springs of 1974 and 1975 with the comment that in those years 'there were more spring records than autumn ones'. This is, however, also incorrect. The bird in 1974 was actually at Cley and, although there was a spring bird on the Point in 1975 (on 26th May), there were two birds in the autumn of that year.

The Bluethroat is such a historically significant Blakeney Point bird that to conclude it is fitting to enjoy Richard Richardson's eloquent comments on the species, contained in the draft of a never-published work on the birds of the Cley area (although extracts were reproduced in Taylor, 2002):-

'To most birdwatchers Blakeney Point and its almost legendary Bluethroats are synonymous. Ever since the skin-collecting Power brothers 'discovered' the Point in the 1880s, and became the first to tap its wealth of rarities, interested people have made pilgrimages there hoping to catch a glimpse of the spry and elusive little bird with the black and chestnut tail. More often than not the tail is all they do see as the bird reluctantly breaks cover beneath their feet and with fast low flight and an adroit twist drops suddenly back into the suaeda.

If one is patient, however, and waits quietly by the dunes or out on the flats some way from the edge of the bushes, the hungry Bluethroat will emerge into the daylight from its secret, shell-paved corridors under the tangled stems and hop like a Robin on the sand, nervously flicking its tail and keeping a lustrous eye alert for any hint of danger, always ready to scuttle back into concealment on its spindly legs.'

Black Redstart
Phoenicurus ochruros gibraltariensis

Rowan notes the Black Redstart as irregular but by no means rare, chiefly in October, with White recording it as a regular spring and autumn migrant in small numbers. These rather brief status summaries provide little evidence of the expansion of this species in northwest Europe during the twentieth century but occurrences on the Point are probably now more frequent than previously.

Birds have occurred in spring as early as mid-March (though Rowan notes that he saw one in January 1913) but more typically occur from late March through April until early May and are associated with arrivals of other migrants, such as Northern Wheatear or Firecrest, in incursions of mild air. Birds doubtless originate from the near-continent and records are normally of single birds, though an exceptional 12 were present on 18th April 1989. Sightings are rare after the second week of May but occasional birds occur later in the month and even into June, with particularly late birds recorded on 15th – 17th June 1997 and 27th June 2001.

It is interesting to speculate on the origin and destination of these late migrants as Black Redstarts would normally be breeding at this time.

Birds have also occurred occasionally in July and August, as follows:-

14th August 1946.
1st August 1994.
17th August 1995.
13th August 1997.
14th July to 1st August 2002.
2 – 3 birds on 1st July 2003, with two to at least 2nd.

Autumn immigrants from the near-continent, typically between one and four individuals in a day, occur from the second week of October, with passage normally over by the end of the month. However, Pinchen's diaries contain a reference to a bird on 2nd September 1926 - a date which would now be exceptional. An unprecedented autumn total of 10 occurred on 19th – 20th October 1987. Records are rare in November, though a high total of six occurred on 5th November 1994, with three on 7th – 8th November 1998. Northern and central European Black Redstarts are short-distance migrants, wintering largely around the Mediterranean and their autumn arrivals are often closely correlated with southeasterly winds.

Birds at both seasons are normally found at the Watch House, around the Lifeboat House or perched on the chalet roofs and are usually shy and wary.

Common Redstart. (*James McCallum*)

Common Redstart (Redstart)
Phoenicurus phoenicurus phoenicurus

Rowan and White record the species as regular in varying numbers in September and October, some years quite plentiful in September, also occasional in March and early April.

It is still a common migrant though numbers vary greatly from year to year. Redstarts are now regularly recorded in spring from the last week of April and throughout May, with occasional birds recorded into June, the latest being on 11th June 1988. It is rare to encounter more than one or two birds in a day at this season though ten were present on 14th – 15th May 1985 and an exceptional 25 on 11th May 1993. Rowan's reference to occasional birds in March and early April seems highly doubtful and raises the possibility of confusion with the previous species.

The Redstart is most common as an autumn migrant from Scandinavia on passage to wintering grounds in Africa north of the equator, occasionally abundant in 'fall' conditions, though scarce in some years with unsuitable weather patterns. For example, in 2003 only around half a dozen were recorded during the whole autumn.

Birds can occur from the second week of August, but peak numbers are always in the first three weeks of September when it can be the dominant species in 'falls'. October records are decidedly scarce and the latest birds recorded are singles on 30th October 2004 and, latest of all, 6th November 1984.

Pashley noted 'thousands' on 21st September 1892 and recounts the following:-

> 'On the night of 20th the wind flew round easterly and blew such a hurricane that the oldest man in Sheringham had never experienced such a gale. The following morning the bushes were full of birds. Thousands of Redstarts'.

Subsequent large arrivals include the following:-

100 on 21st September 1957.
150 on 4th September 1958.
200+ on 3rd September 1965, part of the 'great fall'.
'Hundreds' on 17th September 1968.
130 on 14th September 1993.
400 on 18th September 1995.

The 'fall' of Redstarts in 1995 was the largest in living memory. Birds appeared suddenly around midday and by evening over 5,000 had been counted around the coast of Norfolk. Even when present in such numbers, however, Redstarts can be hard to see well on the Point, with often only flashes of orange tails visible against the dark *Suaeda*.

A bird with a pale secondary panel, and therefore considered to show characters of an intergrade with the southwest Asian form *samamisicus*, was recorded on 14th September 2002.

Ringing effort at the Point in the 1960s yielded the following recoveries:-

Ringed Blakeney Point 12th May 1965, recovered Vilches, Spain 6th October 1967.
Ringed Blakeney Point 7th October 1966, recovered Pademe, Portugal 30th September 1967.

These recoveries neatly illustrate the southwesterly trajectory of birds from Scandinavia through Iberia on passage to wintering grounds in sub-Saharan Africa.

Whinchat. (*James McCallum*)

Whinchat
Saxicola rubetra

Rowan describes the Whinchat as regular in September and early October, less frequent in April. No mention is made of May occurrences and, presumably as a consequence, White quotes a record of one seen by himself on 12th May 1967.

Whinchat is now regular in spring, though in small numbers, records falling between the third week of April and the beginning of June. The earliest record is one on 21st April 2001 and peak counts are of 10 on 13th May 1988 and 15 on 11th May 1993. The latest spring bird occurred on 2nd June 1991.

The species is far commoner in autumn as a migrant from Scandinavia (and perhaps western Russia), normally featuring prominently in early-mid autumn 'falls'. The first birds appear in early August, with most seen in September, and the last birds have normally departed for African wintering grounds by the month's end. Peak counts are:-

60 on 12th September 1989.

50 on 17th – 19th September 1992, with 60 on 18th.

30 on 9th – 10th September 2002.

Whinchats can be sociable on passage and are often encountered in loose flocks on the fringes of the *Suaeda* or in the open areas.

European Stonechat (Common Stonechat)
Saxicola rubicola hibernans
Saxicola rubicola rubicola (Continental Stonechat)

The Stonechat complex is perhaps best separated into three species – European Stonechat (breeding in western and southern Europe), Siberian Stonechat (breeding throughout northern Asia) and African Stonechat *Saxicola torquata* (breeding in southern Africa). It should be noted, however, that, pending further review, the BOURC list refers to European Stonechat as *Saxicola torquatus* (previously *Saxicola torquata* but recently amended in the interests of grammatical accuracy).

The origin of the European Stonechats reaching Blakeney Point is not clear and may involve both British *hibernans* (the form which also occurs in Ireland, western Brittany and western Iberia) and continental nominate birds. However, *hibernans* is not a well-differentiated form and its continued separation from *rubicola* may not be justified.

Rowan and White describe the species as occurring most years in September and October, occasionally through the winter and in the early spring.

This is broadly the case today. Spring migrants, with a daily maximum of four recorded, occur largely during late February and March, with April records rarer. There are only two records of singles in May and a particularly late bird on 4th June 2000. It is interesting to speculate on the origin and destination of these later birds.

The only summer records concern a recently-fledged juvenile in the Lupins on 12th – 13th August 2000 and a bird on 16th August 1986.

Stonechats are mainly a late autumn migrant on the Point, albeit in very small numbers. The first typically occur in the second half of September though one was shot on 2nd September 1904 (see Siberian Stonechat below) and one was present on 1st – 2nd September 1991. Most are seen in October, with a day maximum of four on 1st October 2003, and a few are seen into November, the latest record being of two on 12th November 1994. These autumn birds are presumably continental in origin.

Siberian Stonechat (Eastern Stonechat)

Saxicola maurus maurus

The taxonomic treatment of this species is outlined above. It should be noted, however, that, pending further review, the BOURC list includes the taxon within the above species as *Saxicola torquatus maurus* (previously *Saxicola torquata maura* but recently amended in the interests of grammatical accuracy).

A record of a male 'Indian Stonechat *Saxicola indica*' secured by S.F. Arnold on 2nd September 1904 was described by Rowan as the only record for England. Pashley notes it as having been received from Arnold and refers to it as the only British specimen. He goes on to say that Howard Saunders had seen this bird in his (Pashley's) shop and thought it to be a melanistic variety of Stonechat but that, having compared it with skins in the National Museum, he had realised his mistake. The record is given further authority by Riviere in his introduction to Pashley's work. The record was included in Witherby *et al.* (1940) on the strength of Saunders's examination.

The bird is included in Rowan's list of birds recorded from the Point while Arnold's notes describe it as obtained at 'Morston or Point'. However, later authors describe its location somewhat differently - Richardson (1962) refers to it as having been shot between Blakeney and Morston, and Seago (1977) refers to its location as Morston. Its precise location is therefore unclear.

White placed the record in square brackets as it did not appear on the British List and he considered it an escape from captivity. The form *indica* is indeed not on the British List but this terminology was in use at the time as a synonym for the Siberian form *maura* (now *maurus*), already on the British List. White's assertion and his resultant suggestion of a captive origin therefore seem misplaced.

The specimen was initially held at the Eastbourne College Museum but was acquired by the Castle Museum, Norwich in 1966. It was, however, examined by Derek Goodwin in the mid-1970s (at the request of Iain Robertson as part of a review of the identification and European occurrence of Siberian Stonechats subsequently published in *British Birds*) and considered probably to be an old male European Stonechat. It was recommended for removal from the British List, thereby promoting an occurrence on the Isle of May on 10th October 1913 as the first for Britain. The 1904 specimen was re-examined in the preparation of this book and confirmed as a male European Stonechat.

The first genuine Siberian Stonechat for the Point did not occur until 1984. It is now regular though rare, occurring almost entirely in autumn but with one record in spring. All autumn records fall between 9th September and 24th October and all occurred between 1984 and 1995, with none since. All have been pale individuals showing characters closest to the *maurus* end of the *maurus/stejnegeri* cline and therefore originating from European Russia and western Siberia. All accepted records are as follows:-

5th October 1984, on Yankee Ridge.

12th – 13th October 1986, on Near Point and subsequently in the Lupins.

First-winter male and first-winter female on 29th – 30th September 1991, one remaining to 4th October, in the Long Hills (both photographed, the male shown in Plate 29). These birds were found within a few yards of a Red-throated Pipit.

First-winter female on 21st October 1991, at the Hood.

24th October 1994.

Male, probably adult, on 9th – 13th September 1995, at the Watch House (photographed).

First-summer male on 21st – 23rd May 1997, at the Long Hills.

Further records of apparently unsubmitted individuals are as follows:-

12th September 1984.
3 additional birds on 29th September 1991, with one present till 30th.
4th October 1992 near the Plantation.

The upsurge in records between the mid-1980s and the mid-1990s reflects an extension of the breeding range into northwest Russia, with breeding also recorded as close as Finland during this time. The sudden end to this run of records on the Point (also reflected nationally) is therefore surprising. This species was rapidly challenging Red-throated Pipit, Subalpine Warbler and Greenish Warbler to be the commonest rarity recorded on the Point but whether this series of records will be resumed now remains to be seen.

Isabelline Wheatear
Oenanthe isabellina
An extremely tame first-winter bird was present on 1st October 2000 at the Watch House. This was the second record for Norfolk, though another has already occurred and others will doubtless follow.

A full account of the occurrence of this Middle Eastern and Central Asian species, wintering in Africa and the Middle East, appears in the *Norfolk Bird Report* for 2000.

Northern Wheatear (Wheatear)
Oenanthe oenanthe oenanthe (Common Wheatear)
Oenanthe oenanthe leucorhoa (Greenland Wheatear)
Rowan notes that two or three pairs of Wheatears nest most years, with a pair invariably to be found in the vicinity of the *'Yankee'*. White states that it was last known to breed on the Point in 1936 and that it certainly had not bred since the 1939-1945 war, although birds were always present during the summer. In 1999 a pair was holding territory in a Rabbit burrow in late May, with the male in song, and a female held territory in a Rabbit burrow on Near Point for about eight days in May 2003.

The Wheatear is now essentially only a spring and autumn migrant and can be common at either season.

Spring birds normally arrive in the second half of March, though three were present on 11th March 1989, and passage builds rapidly to peak in late April and early May. Peak counts have been 70 on 13th May 1985, 60 on 26th April and 4th May 1992 50 on 25th April 1995 and 75 on 30th April 2005. Spring Wheatears often band loosely together at a favoured location, for example the Watch House or the base of Yankee Ridge, with other apparently identical sites deserted. Passage declines rapidly from mid-May, with only scattered individuals recorded in late spring, and June sightings are rare. Early spring males appear small and pale and typical of British-breeding *oenanthe*, but from the third week in April larger, browner males of the Greenland and Iceland (and even Canadian) form *leucorhoa* predominate.

The occasional very young-looking juvenile appears in mid to late July (though there is no suggestion that these are locally-bred) and numbers build slowly during August, with a peak for that month of 35 recorded on 23rd August 1997. The largest numbers, however, occur in September, peak numbers having been recorded as follows:-

100+ on 21st – 22nd September 1957.
150 on 4th September 1958.

ca. 450 between the Point and Salthouse on 3rd – 4th September 1965, part of the 'great fall'.
200 on 14th September 1993.
80 - 100 on 22nd September 1994.
200 on 18th September 1995.
100 on 23rd September 1998.

Such peak numbers coincide with 'falls' of Scandinavian migrants and are therefore likely to involve largely continental *oenanthe*, though occasional birds showing characters of *leucorhoa* can also be encountered in autumn even though they have a more westerly route at this season.

Numbers drop sharply in October, with only ones and twos recorded after mid-month, though four were seen in the large 'fall' of 16th October 1988. November birds have occurred in five years, the latest being two on 11th November 2002 and one on 15th November 1984.

Pied Wheatear

Oenanthe pleschanka

A first-winter female, the fourth for Norfolk, was present near the Watch House in the late afternoon of 16th October 1988, the day of a large arrival of thrushes which also featured a Radde's Warbler.

Although Pied Wheatears breed as close as the European Black Sea coast, the bulk of the population is in Central Asia and this is the most likely source area for this bird, particularly given the date of its arrival and its travelling companions. The species winters in northeast and east Africa and southwest Arabia.

Desert Wheatear

Oenanthe deserti deserti/atrogularis (Levant/Eastern Desert Wheatear)

There are four records of this species, all typically in late autumn.

Pashley records the shooting by M.A. Catling of an adult male on 31st October 1907 – the first for Norfolk and only the second for England. This individual formed part of the Connop collection at Rollesby Hall and is now in the City of Birmingham Museum.

It is described by Rowan as being of the western (north African) form *homochroa* but no further details are given to substantiate this. Given the history of limited northward vagrancy by such largely sedentary north African passerines, however, Rowan's conclusion seems open to doubt. Desert Wheatears are now expected late autumn vagrants to Britain and invariably occur in circumstances overwhelmingly suggestive of an eastern origin, arriving frequently at the same time and in the same weather conditions as, for example, Dusky Warblers from Siberia. Such records doubtless involve one or other of the more migratory eastern (Middle Eastern and Central Asian) forms *deserti/atrogularis*. The forms are perhaps synonymous but Central Asian birds have the longest migration to winter quarters lying between Arabia and northwest India – a pattern typical of other vagrant Asian passerines in Britain.

Subsequent records are as follows:-

First-winter male on 14th – 17th October 1978, along the inner edge of the shingle ridge at the Marrams. A photograph of this bird is in the *Norfolk Bird Report* for that year.
First-winter male on 6th November 1994, just west of Cley Coastguards, having previously been at Salthouse earlier in the day and at Weybourne on 5th. A photograph of this bird is in the *Norfolk Bird Report* for that year.
Female, probably first-winter, on the outer beach at the base of the far spits on 9th – 10th November 2003 (Plate 23). This bird was rather grey-toned above with deep buff on the

breast and therefore showed characters strongly associated with an eastern origin. Its photograph is also in *Birding World* 16: 451. This bird is incorrectly described as a male in the BBRC report for 2003 (*British Birds* 97: 599).

Ring Ouzel
Turdus torquatus torquatus

Rowan notes Ring Ouzels as occasional on passage in September and October, rare in spring. White records that Ted Eales flushed three on Yankee Ridge in January 1964, but this seems inherently unlikely and no reference to this record can be found elsewhere.

Ring Ouzel is now a mid-spring and late autumn migrant in small and variable numbers, being obvious in some years but almost absent in others, typically wild and flighty at both seasons.

Spring birds traditionally occur between the second week of April and the middle of May, normally in ones or twos, though 1989 saw a particularly strong passage with a truly exceptional 16 on 13th April and seven on 23rd April. An early bird was seen on 17th March 1974 and unusually late birds occurred on 26th – 29th May 1993 and 2nd June 1979. This pattern strongly suggests that these are continental birds as British-breeding Ring Ouzels usually arrive much earlier, in March and early April, peaking at this time at the Irish Sea bird observatories.

In autumn, birds occur from the first week of September but most arrive later in the month and into October. Counts of up to five are occasionally recorded, and seven were seen on 12th September 1968, but particularly large numbers have occurred as follows:-

20-30 on 3rd October 1951.
20 on 18th October 1990 (listed incorrectly in Gantlett (1995) as 1991).
15 on 10th October 1991.
21 on 29th September 1993.

The latest record involves five birds on 27th October 1989 and there are no known November sightings. The *Norfolk Bird Report* for 1958, however, contains a reference to a bird at 'Blakeney' on 1st December 1958 which is referred to in Taylor *et al.* (1999) as having occurred on Blakeney Point. It may therefore also have been within our area.

Ring Ouzels generally occur in conditions conducive to arrivals from the continent, clearly indicating their origin at this season. Northern European Ring Ouzels winter in southern Spain and the Moroccan Atlas mountains.

Blackbird (Common Blackbird)
Turdus merula merula

Rowan lists the species but records no details. White notes it as a passage migrant, especially in the autumn, sometimes in large numbers. It is also noted as an occasional winterer, with two or three birds present in the winter of 1955/56.

A small spring passage of birds, either returning from Britain to Scandinavia or displaced from the near-continent, is occasionally noted in March and April, though numbers are normally very low, with recent counts of 40 on 8th April 1984 and 30 on 19th March 2005 being notable. The 1946 issue of *Wild Bird Protection in Norfolk* does, however, refer to the *Suaeda* bushes being 'full of them' on 1st March of that year. Late March 2005 also saw a much more significant 'fall' over 26th – 28th, with over 100 present on each day and a maximum of 130 on 27th. Significant numbers of Redwings, Fieldfares and other northbound migrants were also present at this time.

In 1966 a male was present during most of the summer and in 1967 a pair was present. They frequented the Lupins near the Lifeboat House but although no evidence of nesting was obtained at the time, two very young Blackbirds, thought incapable of having travelled far, were caught and ringed shortly afterwards. The first nest was found in 1971 from which three chicks fledged. Blackbirds then bred annually in the 1970s with two nests in 1974 and 1976 and a record three in 1975. In 1979 no nest was found but breeding was suspected on Yankee Ridge. Breeding must have ceased sometime shortly after this for there has been no evidence of breeding for some years.

The first autumn immigrants from Scandinavia appear in the third week of September and numbers increase through October. Largest numbers often occur in the first half of November, with 100-300 in a day recorded on many occasions. Blackbird influxes are a particularly evocative feature of this time of year, with loose parties gathering at the tips of the spits before launching themselves off towards the mainland with insistent '*seep*' calls. A large arrival took place on 16th October 1988 but the largest number recorded was over 1,000 as part of the massive thrush 'avalanche' of 18th October 1990. A huge Blackbird arrival also took place on 5th November 1961 with 'many thousands' seen at Cley but there do not appear to be any specific accounts from the Point on this date. Late migrants may continue arriving into December.

Migrants often succumb to Merlins and Sparrowhawks and bundles of black or brown feathers are a regular sight on the spits in late autumn.

Winter thrushes. (*James McCallum*)

Fieldfare

Turdus pilaris

Rowan notes the species as occurring between October and April, occasionally in September and May. Fieldfares are noted as more frequent in spring than Redwings. White notes birds arriving from as early as 29th July in 1968.

In early spring Fieldfares are occasionally seen on return passage from Britain to Scandinavia or displaced across the North Sea. Numbers are generally small though an exceptional 400 were seen on 26th March 2005 along with high numbers of Blackbirds, Redwings and other northbound migrants. They are rare after the end of April, the only recent late spring records being singles on 8th May 1954, 15th May 1988, 11th June 1988 and 10th May 2004.

The first autumn immigrants are now often seen in easterly conditions in the second half of August or the first week of September, though particularly early birds occurred on 30th July 1991 and 7th August 1999. Singles are the norm at this time of year but an exceptional 20+ occurred on 22nd August 1971. A lull then typically occurs before the vanguard of winter immigrants arrives in late September. Main arrivals, typically of up to a few hundred birds in a day, take place in October with birds mainly passing over high, mixed in with Redwings. The largest numbers recorded were 'thousands' on 16th October 1988 and 'thousands', all on the ground, in the thrush 'avalanche' of 18th October 1990. Ringing has shown that Fieldfares wintering in southeast England originate largely from Sweden and Finland.

Occasional birds may occur in winter, particularly in hard weather, and many were picked up dead in the 'big freeze' of January 1963.

Song Thrush

Turdus philomelos clarkei (British Song Thrush)
Turdus philomelos philomelos (Continental Song Thrush)
Rowan notes that single individuals may be seen at any time of year. White also notes it as a passage migrant, especially in September and October.

The occasional Song Thrush, rarely more than five in a day, is noted in spring through until the second week of June. Autumn singles have been noted as early as 1st September but the first real arrivals take place in mid-September and numbers peak between then and the third week of October, earlier than Redwings. Numbers rarely exceed 100 in a day but larger arrivals have occurred as follows:-

200 on 28th September 1993.
700 on 1st October 1998.
800+ on 18th October 1990.
2,820 in off the sea on 8th October 2002, a truly exceptional count.

Significant later movements include 50 on 27th October 2004 and, later still, 50 on 7th November 2002.

British Song Thrushes are either largely sedentary or move southwest to France or Spain, and their precise status on the Point is not clear. Those occurring on the Point are likely to be largely of the greyer continental nominate form and many no doubt originate in the Netherlands. Two ringing recoveries of Blakeney Point-ringed Song Thrushes have been reported:-

Ringed Blakeney Point 6th October 1966, recovered Logrono, Spain 6th January 1967.
Ringed Blakeney Point 16th October 1960, recovered Gironde, France December 1961.

Both these recoveries confirm that continental immigrants also continue southwest after an autumn arrival on the Point. Whereas British Song Thrushes have suffered a major decline in recent years, there has been little evidence on the Point of any decrease in the number of autumn immigrants.

Redwing
Turdus iliacus iliacus

As with the Fieldfare, Rowan notes the species as occurring between October and April, occasionally in September and May. White records Redwings as passage migrants, especially in September and October and occasionally as a winter visitor.

Early spring sees a few birds returning across the North Sea or displaced from the near-continent, usually in March and more rarely in April. They are generally scarce at this season but 240 were seen on 26th March 2005 as part of a significant 'fall' of Blackbirds, Fieldfares and other northbound migrants. Exceptionally late spring records concern birds on 20th – 21st May 1984 and 2nd June 1979.

Autumn immigrants from Scandinavia and northern Russia can occur very rarely at the end of August, with singles seen on 26th August 1968 and 30th August 1974. However, arrivals occur typically from the third week in September, hot on the heels of the first Song Thrushes. Peak numbers, typically up to a few hundred birds in a day, occur in October, but larger numbers have included 'thousands' on 16th October 1988 and 3,000+ on the ground in the thrush 'avalanche' of 18th October 1990. Birds are usually heard high overhead as they pass over with Fieldfares. Sometimes, however, they will swoop down to land momentarily before continuing south across the Harbour.

Incoming thrushes, particularly Redwings, are often singled out by Merlins and desperate chases over the sea are a common sight in late autumn. Occasional birds may also occur in winter, particularly in hard weather.

Redwings recorded at the Point are presumably exclusively of the nominate continental form. Icelandic *coburni* winter largely in Scotland and Ireland and there are no ringing recoveries of this form from England.

A Redwing ringed on Blakeney Point on 5th October 1966 was recovered at Grasse, France on 10th November 1967.

Mistle Thrush
Turdus viscivorus viscivorus

Rowan states that single individuals may occasionally be seen at any time of the year, an assertion repeated by White.

Mistle Thrushes are now barely annual on the Point, with records largely falling neatly into the spring and autumn periods. In spring birds have occurred between the third week of March and the first week of June, whilst autumn records fall between the end of September and the second week of November, with most in mid-October. Singles are the norm though three occurred on 5th April 1987 and 16th October 1988.

British Mistle Thrushes are largely sedentary but some are capable of longer movements. However, it is likely that continental birds account for at least some of those recorded on the Point. Those seen in October, for example, often coincide with arrivals of Redwings and Fieldfares.

Pallas's Grasshopper Warbler
Locustella certhiola subsp.

A first-winter bird found in the morning of 22nd September 2001 in the Marrams and present until 24th September was the second record for Norfolk and only the third for England and caused by far the biggest 'twitch' ever to have occurred on Blakeney Point. Of the 24 previous British records, almost all have been on Shetland, with the vast majority on Fair Isle, so this bird provided the first opportunity for many to see this species in Britain. Although typically skulking, it was nevertheless possible to obtain occasional views of the bird on the ground. As a result, the best photographs ever taken of a vagrant Pallas's Grasshopper Warbler were obtained and have been widely published (Plate 19).

The bird was the highlight of a week which also produced large numbers of migrants, including both Yellow-browed and Radde's Warblers. On 22nd September winds at Blakeney Point were light northwesterly behind a slow-moving low pressure area centred over Denmark which had brought torrential rain to the western Baltic. The possibility exists, however, that the bird arrived before 22nd as conditions had been favourable since 18th.

Thanks to the excellent quality of the photographs it is possible to attempt to assign this bird to form. The Blakeney Point bird appeared to differ in a number of respects from some of the birds seen in recent years in Shetland which have most closely resembled the northern Siberian form *rubescens* - a dark, swarthy form with strongly rufous tones and very heavily-lined mantle. The Blakeney Point bird did not normally appear quite so dark or rufous and was rather more reminiscent in tone of Grasshopper Warbler. It therefore showed some characters associated with the rather variable (and perhaps poorly-differentiated) southern Siberian form *sparsimstriata* (Southern Pallas's Grasshopper Warbler) but its precise origin will never be known. The species winters in northeast India and southeast Asia.

Articles on this bird's occurrence with photographs appear in the *Norfolk Bird Report* for 2001, *Birding World* 14: 382-384 and the *Norfolk Bird Club Bulletin* No. 46. Further photographs appear in *British Birds* 94: 557 and 95: 509.

Grasshopper Warbler (Common Grasshopper Warbler)

Locustella naevia naevia
Rowan and White list the species as fairly regular in September.

Grasshopper Warblers are now scarce, almost annual, autumn migrants from northern Europe, on passage to poorly-known African wintering grounds, with only very rarely more than one in a day and only up to a maximum of five in a season, sometimes none at all. Records fall between 10th August and 22nd October but most are in September. The species is presumably under-recorded, however, as they are only seen when directly flushed. Despite an assertion in Golley (1997) that 'there is no firm evidence to support any of the recent Grasshopper Warbler sightings', a number of such birds have been seen well enough to allow a positive identification as Grasshopper Warbler and fully eliminate the possibility of a vagrant Lanceolated Warbler.

Spring birds are rare, with only a few records in the second half of April and the first week of May. These spring birds are usually detected only by song and may represent returning British breeders. Birds used to sing regularly along the south bank of the Glaven Channel just west of Cley Coastguards but records here have been fewer in recent years.

Aquatic Warbler

Acrocephalus paludicola
The first for the Point and for Norfolk was a bird shot by T.E. Gunn in the Sandhills on 8th September 1896. A male Aquatic Warbler, undated, from the Sandhills and received from the Gunn collection is in the Castle Museum, Norwich, and is presumably this bird. A further bird from the Gunn collection, a male secured from 'low scrub' (therefore possibly the Point) on 9th September 1902, is also in the Castle Museum but is not referred to elsewhere.

Rowan lists the 1896 bird and three subsequent records as follows:-

21st September 1903.
25th September 1911.
16th September 1913.

Pashley refers to 'two taken prior to my records' and lists a further five individuals, some or all of which are also likely to have been secured on the Point:-

15th September 1904.
23rd October 1912.
2 on 4th September 1924.
15th September 1924.

White traced eight records between 1896 and 1956, all in September except for one trapped and ringed on the Hood on 6th August 1954, the earliest county record.

The true total prior to 1960 is therefore impossible to judge accurately. This eastern European and western Russian breeder winters in west Africa though its precise range at this latter season is poorly-known. The species has declined significantly since the 1960s and this is reflected in its increasing rarity on the Point. All post-1960 records are listed below:-

4th September 1965.
21st September 1969.
5th – 6th September 1975.
14th August 1976.
22nd August 1976.
30th August 1976.
26th September 1976.
13th August 1985, seen arriving from the sea.

Sedge Warbler
Acrocephalus schoenobaenus
Rowan describes the Sedge Warbler as rare, occurring only in September. White describes it as a passage migrant, usually in September, but also recorded in May.

Sedge Warblers are now best described as scarce, with only a few recorded each year. They are surprisingly rare given that they are such a common breeder at Cley. Records fall mainly in September, with a day maximum of five on 19th September 1995, though an early bird was seen on 31st July 2004 and a late individual was present on 11th October 2002.

Birds occur occasionally in spring, sometimes singing from the *Suaeda*, and a juvenile, presumably locally-bred, was present on 8th July 2003. Most Sedge Warblers recorded on the Point are, however, probably from the large north European (or even western Russian) range on passage to and from their African wintering grounds.

Marsh Warbler
Acrocephalus palustris
The only record concerns a male shot on 10th October 1923 in the Sandhills and donated by Riviere to the Castle Museum, Norwich where it still resides in the 'British Bird Gallery' public display area (*British Birds* 17: 26). This bird was identified by Harry Witherby and Norman Ticehurst and was the first record for Norfolk.

The specimen was examined during the preparation of this book and found to be intermediate in measurements between Marsh and Reed Warblers in respect of wing length (69mm), the position of the notch on the second primary (10mm from tip) and the notch/wing ratio (0.15).

It does, however, fall conclusively within the range for Marsh Warbler given by Svensson (1992) according to the 'Walinder Method' (bill length to skull minus the product of bill width at the nostrils and tarsus width). In the case of this bird the measurements are 14mm – (2mm x 3.5mm) = 7. Furthermore the visible primary projection equals the length of the exposed tertials and the overall tone of the bird looks pale and olive-toned with no rufous hue, even on the rump.

Marsh Warblers breed in eastern Europe and western Russia and winter in southeast Africa. Given the recent pattern of increasing late spring occurrences in Norfolk, this species is now perhaps best sought on the Point in June.

Reed Warbler (Eurasian Reed Warbler)

Acrocephalus scirpaceus scirpaceus

Rowan lists the species as occasional in September, while White states that it can occur in May and cites a record in May 1956.

Reed Warblers are now scarce though regular annual migrants, always in tiny numbers and usually seen poorly in the *Suaeda*.

Spring birds occur from the first week of May but records are concentrated in late May and early June, the latest being on 8th June 1991. All records involve singles apart from two on 2nd – 3rd June 2000. Late spring birds are often in song.

The earliest autumn record is of one on 10th August 2004 but almost all other records fall between the first week of September and the third week of October. Records normally involve singles but five were present on 3rd September 1994 and 21st September 1996. Surprisingly, there are two November records – 4th November 2002 and, latest of all, 12th November 1983.

Although a common breeder at Cley, most Reed Warblers occurring on the Point are probably from central Europe (or even western Russia), displaced from their route to central African wintering grounds.

Icterine Warbler

Hippolais icterina

This central European and western Russian species, wintering in southern Africa, has long been recognised as a regular visitor to the Point with an all-time total of over 130 records. Rowan lists the earliest records as follows:-

5th September 1899, shot by Arnold on the Hood.
18th September 1903.
12th September 1907.

Rowan also notes the species as obtained by Power and Gurney, stating that at least five of the then nine Norfolk records were from the Point.

It is now a scarce but regular, almost annual, migrant in August and September, very occasionally in small numbers.

Autumn records fall between 4th August and 3rd October, mostly involving one or two individuals in a day, but autumn 1977 saw an unprecedented series of records with around 22 recorded during the season and the following peak day-counts recorded:-

8 on 7th August.
5 on 14th – 15th August.
8 on 19th August.

Other productive autumns have been 1968, with eight individuals, and 1984, with seven recorded during the season, whilst in more recent times three were recorded on 10th August 2004.

There have now been 16 spring Icterine Warblers, all since 1984, arrival dates falling between 12th May and 8th June but with most occurring in the last week of May and the first week in June. All spring records are listed below:-

23rd May 1984.
12th May 1988.
8th – 11th June 1988.
14th May 1992.
3 on 27th – 28th May 1992.
2 on 30th May 1992.
7th – 8th June 1992.
2 on 27th May 1993, with one until 28th.
5th – 6th June 1993.
20th – 21st May 1994.
Male on 6th June 1997, in song.
6th June 2002.

This increase in spring is possibly partly attributable to a recent range extension in northwest Europe, but also coincides with more regular watching at this season.

Blackcap
Sylvia atricapilla atricapilla
Rowan notes Blackcaps as regular in September in small numbers. White notes them as occurring at both seasons, contradicting a statement by Riviere (1930) that the species does not occur at the Norfolk coast in spring, and quotes records in April 1948 and 1955.

Blackcaps are now scarce but regular in spring between mid-April and early June and day totals have reached as high as six (on 22nd April 2000). A Blackcap ringed on the Point on 28th April 1969 was recovered at Burford, Oxfordshire on 26th June 1969, showing that British birds may be involved in spring arrivals.

They are, however, much more common as continental immigrants in mid to late autumn, sometimes arriving in numbers. Peak counts include 60 on 6th October 1982 and 35 on 29th September 1991. A particularly late bird occurred on 4th November 1993. Such numbers in autumn appear to be a recent trend as October Blackcaps were regarded as scarce as recently as the 1950s. This reflects the recent increase in wintering Blackcaps in Britain which ringing else-where has shown largely comprise birds from the Netherlands and Germany.

Blackcaps can be extremely skulking on the Point, with autumn birds often favouring the bramble clumps in the Lupins and the Plantation.

Garden Warbler
Sylvia borin borin
Rowan describes Garden Warblers as regular in September in small numbers, though also recorded in spring. White notes them occurring in August and September and less commonly in spring.

Garden Warblers are still scarce in spring, usually occurring in May but only in small numbers and with stragglers recorded into the second week of June. A notable count of ten was recorded on 15th May 1990 and four were seen as late as 11th June 1988.

The species is commoner in autumn and can feature prominently in late August and September 'falls', though numbers have been lower in recent years. Peak counts include:-

70 on 3rd September 1958.

100 on 1st September 1963.

450 - 500 between the Point and Salthouse on 3rd – 4th September 1965, in the 'great fall'.

80 on 26th August 1987.

30 on 15th September 1994.

40 on 18th September 1995, the day of the huge Common Redstart 'fall'.

A few have been recorded in late October and a particularly late bird was recorded on 6th November 1984. The vast majority of Garden Warblers on the Point are doubtless continental, originating from those breeding in central and northern Europe and wintering in Africa. It is, however, possible that the slightly larger and paler eastern European and Russian form *woodwardi* also occurs.

Barred Warbler and Garden Warblers. (*James McCallum*)

Barred Warbler

Sylvia nisoria nisoria

The first for Norfolk, and only the third for Britain, was shot by Fred Power on 4th September 1884. His notes (Power, 1885) contain the following:-

'September 4th. Wind N.E. and strong. Very wet; strong wind and stinging rain throughout… Many small migrants at the sandhills, principally Garden Warblers, Redstarts and Wheatears; but also two Wrynecks and some Greater Whitethroats. One immature Pied Flycatcher shot and another seen. On this day, the Barred Warbler was obtained. It was solitary; in colour and flight not unlike a Spotted Flycatcher, and made no note. It is a female, and bird of the year… This was exhibited, together with another immature bird obtained at Spurn, in Yorkshire, at the end of August, by Mr. Dresser, to the Zoological Society, November 4th. The species is moreover new to the Norfolk list.'

Although Rowan does not mention this record he notes that most of the ten Norfolk records come from Cley and Blakeney Point and that it appeared to be getting more frequent. All examples taken (in 1902, 1908, 1910, 1912 and 1913) were secured in September.

White notes that Barred Warblers are rare autumn migrants, mostly in September but sometimes in late August and occasionally in October, occurring annually in small numbers.

A total of around 120 Barred Warblers has now been recorded on the Point. Records fall between 8th August (in 1968 and 1977) and 25th October (in 1956), with most in the last week of August and the first half of September. The maximum recorded in a day is five on 21st August 1971. There are no spring records.

There are only four October records, as follows:-

25th October 1956.
9th October 1968.
13th October 1979.
14th – 15th October 2003.

The last of these birds was a particularly pale and pure grey individual which arrived as part of a large influx of Pallas's Warblers into the county. It may therefore have been of the poorly-differentiated form *merzbacheri* from Central Asia and southern Siberia.

The regularity with which Barred Warblers are seen on the Point is perhaps surprising given the species' strongly southeasterly migration track from its nearest eastern European breeding grounds to winter haunts in east Africa.

Richard Richardson's unpublished notes give a flavour of encounters with this species:-

'On Blakeney Point it feeds quietly among the *Suaeda* bushes, ragwort and tree lupins, keeping well hidden as a rule though sometimes climbing up to balance heavily on a higher spray as it looks around before taking wing.'

Lesser Whitethroat

Sylvia curruca curruca
Sylvia curruca blythi (Siberian Lesser Whitethroat)
Rowan lists the Lesser Whitethroat but gives no details while White describes the species as a passage migrant, mostly in the autumn but occasionally in the spring.

Lesser Whitethroats are now regular in spring in small numbers between late April and late May, most occurring in early May. The peak count is of 20 on 11th May 1988 (listed incorrectly as 20th in Taylor *et al.* 1999).

Autumn records fall between early August and late October, with most occurring in September. An unusually high number occurred in 1993, when 40 were seen in mid-September. The latest record is of one on 25th October 1991.

Although a British breeder, the species' range lies largely to the east, extending as far as Siberia and Central Asia. British birds have a strongly southeasterly migration track around the eastern end of the Mediterranean to wintering grounds in northeast Africa.

White lists records of the Siberian form *blythi* on 26th August 1954 (trapped and identified on wing formula) and in the Septembers of 1956, 1959 and 1961. It should be noted, however, that *blythi* is marginally distinguishable and therefore a questionably valid taxon.

Asian Desert Warbler (Eastern Desert Warbler)

Sylvia nana

A singing male took up territory on the Hood from 27th May to 1st June 1993. The day of its arrival was one of torrential rain which also produced two Icterine Warblers and a Common Rosefinch. This first for Norfolk was also the first spring record for Britain of this Central Asian desert species (though a second spring bird has subsequently been recorded in East Yorkshire). Asian Desert Warblers winter in Arabia, Iran, Pakistan and northwest India.

During its stay it was often in full song and even started nest-building in what must have passed as acceptable semi-desert breeding habitat. This is not entirely unprecedented, for a singing male built two nests on the Baltic coast of Schleswig-Holstein, Germany between 21st June and 7th July 1981.

The bird was well-photographed during its stay (Plate 28) and articles on its occurrence together with photographs appear in the *Norfolk Bird Report* for 1993, *Birding World* 6: 182-183 and the *Norfolk Bird Club Bulletin* No. 5. A further photograph is in Taylor *et al.* (1999).

Common Whitethroat (Whitethroat)

Sylvia communis communis

Sylvia communis icterops (Eastern Whitethroat)

Rowan describes the Whitethroat as regular in September in small numbers. White records it as regular in August and September, occasionally in the spring.

Whitethroats can now be encountered at either season. In spring they occur from the third week of April with stragglers into the second week of June. Numbers are always small and anything over five in a day in spring would be notable. An exceptional 15 occurred on 24th April 2000 and a notable count for so late in the season was of four on 11th June 1988. Despite an assertion in Golley (1997) that the Whitethroat is a common breeder, the species has never bred on the Point.

In autumn they occur between mid-August and early October, but largely in September, again in small numbers only. Notable counts include 30 on 5th – 6th September 1958, 15 in mid-September 1993 and 15 on 24th September 2000. There are relatively few British recoveries of Whitethroats ringed elsewhere in northern Europe, further underlining their status as a scarce continental immigrant.

Whitethroats breed throughout Europe and western and central Russia, wintering in Africa. In eastern Europe and Russia the species is represented by the form *volgensis*, a form which could potentially reach the Point. A male in sub-song in the Lupins on 30th April 2003 showed characters of the darker and rustier southeastern form *icterops* from Turkey and southwest Asia. An account of this bird can be found in the *Norfolk Bird Club Bulletin* No. 54.

Dartford Warbler

Sylvia undata dartfordiensis

There are only two records of this species:-

> Female on 17th – 19th May 1986, visiting the Lupins, the Plantation and Yankee Ridge. A photograph of this bird, only the third county record, appears in the *Norfolk Bird Report*s for 1986 and 1992.
>
> Female on 28th March 2005, initially near the Watch House and subsequently in the Marrams.

Dartford Warblers breed in southernmost Britain, western France, around the western Mediterranean and in northwest Africa. With increasing numbers now present in coastal Suffolk, further occurrences on the Point seem likely.

Subalpine Warbler
Sylvia cantillans cantillans (Western Subalpine Warbler)
Sylvia cantillans albistriata (Eastern Subalpine Warbler)
Birds showing characters of both these forms of this rare visitor have occurred on Blakeney Point. The western form (in which males show extensive pink underparts) breeds largely in Iberia, southern France and Italy and the eastern form (in which males show darker and more restricted pink tones) breeds in the Balkans, Greece and western Turkey. Both forms winter in Africa north of the equator.

There have been 11 accepted records as follows, with the likely form identified where known:-

First-winter male on 29th September 1955, ringed and photographed at the Hood and still present on 30th. This was the second record for Norfolk and England (*British Birds* 49: 86).
First-summer male on 22nd – 23rd May 1960 (ringed on 22nd), near the Laboratory. On 22nd it shared the Point with a Woodchat Shrike.
Male '*cantillans*-type' on 8th – 11th May 1988, at the Watch House.
Male '*albistriata*-type' on 20th – 22nd May 1990, at the Marrams.
Male on 21st May 1994, at the Marrams.
Male '*cantillans*-type' on 7th May 1995, at the Marrams.
Male '*cantillans*-type' on 23rd May 1995, on Yankee Ridge – the same day as two Red-throated Pipits.
Female on 24th May 1995, in the Sandhills.
Female on 17th May 1997, at the Marrams (photographed).
Male '*cantillans*-type' on 24th – 25th May 2001, in the Lupins and later on Near Point.
Male '*cantillans*-type' on 21st May 2002, singing in the Lupins and later in the Plantation – the same day as a Red-footed Falcon and a Red-throated Pipit.

In a neat mirroring of the increase in records of Red-throated Pipit since 1988, Subalpine Warblers have also become, since that same spring, a regular feature in May. It is now one of only four national rarities to have amassed more than ten records on the Point.

Birds typically occur as 'overshoots' in warm southeasterly conditions and presumably find the *Suaeda* somewhat reminiscent of their favoured Mediterranean scrub.

Greenish Warbler
Phylloscopus trochiloides viridanus
Although the Greenish Warbler is a national rarity in Britain, the Point is one of the most regular sites in Norfolk (and indeed in the whole country) for this species. This is in many ways the 'classic' Blakeney Point rarity with at least 16 now recorded – it is certainly the Point's most frequently-recorded rare bird, with otherwise only Red-throated Pipit, Siberian Stonechat and Subalpine Warbler having amassed more than ten records each. Records have become noticeably more frequent since the 1970s, reflecting a continued westward expansion of this species into countries bordering the Baltic. All birds have been of this western form *viridanus* which breeds eastwards from the Baltic to western Siberia and Central Asia.

The autumn records demonstrate clearly the typical mid to late August and early September occurrence pattern, with all records falling between 12th August and 6th September. This reflects the species' very early departure from the breeding grounds towards winter quarters in the Indian subcontinent. All recent autumn individuals have been particularly bright and fresh-plumaged and records at this season are doubtless all of first-winter birds. Autumn Greenish Warblers are noteworthy for their habit of occurring in anticyclonic weather not particularly conducive to 'falls' of continental migrants. They usually occur in bright clear conditions, often accompanied by only a tiny handful of Willow Warblers or Pied Flycatchers.

The Point has also attracted two spring individuals, much rarer in Britain and, coincidentally, both recorded on the same date (though in different years). The westward expansion of Greenish Warblers into the Baltic is erratic, with much larger numbers occurring in years when high temperatures coincide with their late May and early June arrival. The late May date of the two spring records is therefore typical and it is no coincidence that 1992 was a notably hot spring which also brought a number of other 'overshooting' birds from the same region. Nor is it surprising that both of these spring birds were singing males.

All accepted records are as follows:-

6th September 1951 in the Plantation – the first for Norfolk (*British Birds* 45: 413-414).
21st – 23rd August 1971.
27th – 28th August 1972.
1st – 3rd September 1972.
14th August 1976, in the Plantation.
13th August 1977, on the Hood.
25th – 30th August 1987, at the Marrams (photographed), occurring at the same time as a Great Snipe.
27th – 28th August 1987.
25th August 1990, on the Hood.
1st September 1991, in the Plantation.
Male on 30th May 1992, singing on the Hood.
5th – 7th September 1992, on the Hood.
2nd September 1995, at the Marrams.
Male on 30th May 1998, singing in the Long Hills.
26th August 2000, in the Lupins (Plate 26). Its picture also appears in the *Norfolk Bird Report* for 2000.
14th – 17th August 2004, in the Plantation. Photographs of this bird appear in *Birding World* 17: 323 and 17: 521.

A further individual on 12th – 15th August 1977 at the Long Hills appears never to have been submitted to BBRC. In addition Gantlett (1995) lists a third individual in August 1987 and Golley (1997) notes a bird on 15th August 1996 but no trace of these records can be found either amongst records accepted by BBRC or in the *Norfolk Bird Report*.

With Greenish Warblers now recorded breeding sporadically as close as northern Germany and even the Netherlands, continued appearances by this delightful *Phylloscopus* seem assured.

Arctic Warbler
Phylloscopus borealis borealis
The first 'Eversmann's Warbler' for England was shot by Arnold at the Marrams on 4th September 1922 and is quoted in Seago (1977) and Taylor *et al.* (1999) as being held at the Castle Museum, Norwich. Unfortunately, the specimen could not be found by the Museum when searched for during the preparation of this book. It was correctly listed by Riviere (1930) as the first for England but is incorrectly described as the first for Britain in Taylor *et al.* (1999) as there are earlier records from Sule Skerry Lighthouse, Orkney on 5th September 1902 and Fair Isle, Shetland on 28th

September 1908.

The typical pattern of September occurrences is well-illustrated, with the exception of the 1968 record which might warrant review to ensure that the possibility of Greenish Warbler has been eliminated.

All records are listed:-

4th September 1922, shot by Arnold at the Marrams.

21st September 1951, 'in the *Suaeda* bushes' (*British Birds* 45: 415-416).

24th – 31st August 1968, at the Long Hills (this is listed erroneously by White as 'September' in his 1969 list but is corrected in the 1981 edition). Interestingly, the record does not appear in Gantlett (1995) (see comment above).

8th September 1978, at the Long Hills.

1st – 2nd September 1993, at the Marrams. This bird was seen to depart inland on the morning of 2nd. It was extremely approachable and was well-photographed (Plate 25). Its picture also appears in the *Norfolk Bird Report* for 1993 and in *Birding World* 6: 354.

Despite breeding as close as northern Norway (with a breeding range extending right across northern Russia and even into Alaska), it is not surprising that Arctic Warblers remain rare. They have a remarkable migration to wintering grounds in the far south of southeast Asia, for much of which their heading is due east, taking them directly away from Britain.

Pallas's Leaf Warbler (Pallas's Warbler)

Phylloscopus proregulus

There are 12 records of this, a perennial favourite Siberian gem, all falling between 15th October and 10th November.

The first for Norfolk and for Britain was shot on 31st October 1896. Dresser (1897) recounts the following:-

'One of the most interesting additions that has of late been made to the avifauna of the British Islands is certainly that of Pallas's Willow Warbler (*Phylloscopus proregulus*), a single example of which was shot at Cley-next-the-Sea, Norfolk, on the 31st October 1896 by Mr. Ramm who forwarded it to Mr. Thomas Southwell, and informed the gentleman that he "found it amongst the long grass on the bank or sea-wall, not far from the sea at Cley, a locality which has produced many rare migrants, and at first took it for a Goldcrest, but on approaching to within two or three yards, the bird being very tame, he thought he recognised a Yellow-browed Warbler, a species he had seen before, and therefore secured it." Mr. Southwell identified it correctly as Pallas's Willow Warbler, but forwarded it to me for confirmation, and at his request I exhibited it at a meeting of the Zoological Society on the 1st December last. On comparing the bird with those in my collection from Siberia and the Himalayas it agrees most closely with a fully adult bird from Siberia; and I may here state that it is an adult female in very fresh plumage and is quite as bright in tinge of colour as any Siberian specimen I have seen.'

According to Bishop (1996), Arnold had neglected to obtain the bird, believing it to be nothing out of the ordinary, only for it to be diligently pursued by Ramm's dog 'Duchess' and secured by Ramm himself. Other accounts cite Pinchen as the unfortunate companion (Wallace, 2004). An entertaining account of this event by Clifford Borrer is contained in the 16th September 1955 issue of *The Shooting Times & Country Magazine*, recently reprinted (*Birding World* 13: 126-127).

The bird was subsequently sold to Ernest Connop for either £40 or £50 (accounts vary) and passed into his collection at Rollesby Hall before being sold to W.R. Lysaght of Chepstow who in turn donated it to the City of Birmingham Museum, where it now resides. This transaction gives a clear idea of the amount of money at stake on such occasions - £50 in 1896 would today be worth almost £4,000!

The bird is described by Borrer as having been 'in a great tuft of grass' and 'in a corner of the sea-bank' adjacent to an old railway carriage then on Cley beach. Rowan describes it as having been shot 'against the Railway Hut' which formed the edge of his recording area and he therefore includes it in his list of Blakeney Point birds. Although the precise location is not known to the authors, the record is included here on the basis of its inclusion by Rowan.

In addition to being the first for Britain, this was only the third Pallas's Warbler to be recorded in Europe, the first having been secured on Heligoland, Germany on 6th October 1845, with a further bird observed there on 29th October 1875. Dresser's ageing of the Blakeney Point bird as an adult seems to modern eyes somewhat surprising as the overwhelming majority of Pallas's Warblers (and indeed all vagrants) are now known to be young birds.

Eighty-eight years were to pass before the next Pallas's Warbler was seen on the Point but it has since become regular though still rare, reflecting a huge increase in records not only in the county but also nationally since the early 1980s.

All subsequent records are as follows:-

10th November 1984, in the Lupins.
21st October 1985.
4th – 5th November 1987, in the Lupins.
21st – 22nd October 1988, just west of Cley Coastguards.
15th – 16th October 1989, at the Watch House (Plate 27). Its photograph also appears in the *Norfolk Bird Report*s for 1989 and 1992.
25th October 1991, in the Plantation.
10th November 1994, at the Watch House.
16th – 17th October 1999, at the Watch House.
14th October 2003, by the Laboratory.
15th October 2003, at the base of Near Point (a different bird from that of 14th, not as stated in the 2003 *Norfolk Bird Report*).
22nd October 2003, in the Marrams.

As with the following species, Pallas's Warblers seem disproportionately scarce at the Point compared with occurrences elsewhere in the county, doubtless a reflection of the poor feeding opportunities in late autumn. Pallas's Warblers breed in Siberia and winter in southeast Asia. The duller Himalayan birds referred to by Dresser are now 'split' as Simla Leaf Warbler *Phylloscopus chloronotus*.

Yellow-browed Warbler

Phylloscopus inornatus

Rowan describes the species as a rare passage migrant in mid-September and October.

This tiny visitor from the Siberian taiga, wintering in southeast Asia, is still a rare migrant, with 30 records to date. All but one are dated between 16th September and 12th October, with a notably late bird on 3rd – 4th November 1984.

Pashley details the following:-

'1st October 1894 - The first Yellow-browed Warbler for Norfolk was taken on this date. This bird was shot with a 10-bore gun and very large shot. Its head was nearly severed and the rump and intestines almost entirely shot away so the sex could not be determined. The man who shot it fired off his battered old muzzle loader at the first bird he saw rather than take it home loaded.'

Subsequent records in the first half of the twentieth century are as follows:-

29th October 1907.
2 on 23rd September 1908.
2nd October 1908.
16th September 1910.

Since the 1960s the species has occurred more regularly as follows:-

21st – 23rd September 1962.	1st October 1985.
9th – 10th October 1965.	11th October 1985.
24th – 25th September 1971.	2 on 5th October 1986.
1st October 1971.	2nd October 1988.
24th – 25th September 1973.	12th October 1990.
1st October 1973.	10th October 1991.
20th September 1977.	8th October 1993.
1st October 1979.	25th September 1994.
6th October 1982.	1st October 2000.
16th – 17th September 1984.	22nd September 2001.
4th – 5th October 1984.	25th September 2001.
3rd – 4th November 1984.	30th September 2004.

Records from the Point neatly mirror the increase in the county as a whole. Records became more regular from the 1960s, with a new level of occurrences set in 1984. Although some of this increase is no doubt genuine, increased observations have also presumably played a part as Yellow-browed Warblers were regularly recorded by Gätke on Heligoland, Germany in the late nineteenth century and many must have reached Britain at this time.

However, given the numbers of Yellow-browed Warblers now reaching Norfolk, the species is surprisingly scarce on the Point. This is most likely to be due to the absence of trees and associated food – for such an arboreal specialist the Point must seem a particularly unattractive place. Some evidence for this is provided by the bird of 12th October 1990 which was seen flying in over the grassy sward at the Watch House before passing the observer within a few feet and flying directly off over the Harbour towards Blakeney.

Radde's Warbler
Phylloscopus schwarzi
A first-winter male of this charismatic Siberian warbler was found and trapped by R. Harris and Barry Spence at the Hood on 3rd October 1961 (Plate 20). This was the first record for Norfolk and only the second for Britain, following the first at North Coates, Lincolnshire on 1st October 1898. A full article on this occurrence is published in *British Birds* 55: 166-168, together with a photograph. Further photographs are held in the Richard Richardson archive. The *Norfolk Bird Report* for 1961 contains the following:-

'The 3rd was probably our most exciting day of the year. It most certainly produced the rarest bird, for shortly after ringing an Icterine Warbler among the tree lupins on Blakeney Point a strange, large, dark olive leaf warbler was mist-netted in the suaeda bushes at the Hood which proved to be a first winter male Radde's Bush Warbler.'

The bird was taken back to Cley and kept in Richard Richardson's aviary in order to be inspected by H.G. Alexander and Kenneth Williamson, the latter travelling overnight to see it, thereby becoming the first person to 'twitch' this species in Britain! After examination it was ringed, photographed and released back at the Hood on 4th October and was last seen there on 5th.

Considering the subsequent regularity of this species' occurrence in Norfolk, its further appearances on the Point have been surprisingly few. There are only three further records:-

16th October 1988, in the Sandhills, a day of a massive thrush arrival which also featured a Pied Wheatear.
30th September 2000, on Near Point, coinciding with a record arrival of this species in England, including no fewer than eight at Spurn Point, East Yorkshire on this and the following day.
25th – 26th September 2001, on Yankee Ridge, often perching on the 'Yankee' itself.

The September dates of the 2000 and 2001 birds are not typical of the normal occurrence pattern in Britain of Radde's Warbler, which peaks in the second week of October, but reflect a series of particularly early arrivals nationwide in both years. The species' normal wintering grounds lie in southeast Asia.

Dusky Warbler
Phylloscopus fuscatus fuscatus
There have been five accepted records of this increasingly-recorded but frustratingly elusive Siberian rarity:-

18th October 1975, between the Hood and the Long Hills. This bird is listed incorrectly by White as having been present for several days prior to 18th.
3rd – 4th October 1987, trapped (but not ringed as no ringer was present) at the Watch House.
12th November 1989, in the Marrams (photographed). This bird is listed in Gantlett (1995) as present until 15th.
16th October 2000, between the Hood and the Long Hills, subsequently moving into the Long Hills themselves. A Siberian Chiffchaff occurred on the same day.
20th October 2004, by the Laboratory, occurring at the same time as three Pallid Swifts.

The bird in 2000 wandered readily out into the saltmarsh, reflecting the species' liking for damp waterside vegetation, a habitat in which many birds winter in southeast Asia.

Western/Eastern Bonelli's Warbler
Phylloscopus bonelli/P. orientalis
The only record is of a bird on the Hood on 14th May 1988, accepted by BBRC as a 'Bonelli's Warbler' prior to the recent BOURC 'split' into Western and Eastern Bonelli's Warblers. Following a review of such records by BBRC, this bird remains in the official record as 'Bonelli's Warbler sp.' in the absence of any notes on its call. A review of all Norfolk's Bonelli's Warbler

records is contained in the *Norfolk Bird Club Bulletin* No. 27.

This bird's bright plumage tones, however, leave little room for doubt that it was the far commoner western species. At least one photograph of this bird exists which shows well its bright green-toned upperparts and yellow-green fringes to the remiges, white underparts, bland face-pattern and pale-looking bill – all strong pointers to *bonelli*.

Western Bonelli's Warbler breeds in central and southwest Europe and northwest Africa, wintering in Africa north of the equator.

Wood Warbler
Phylloscopus sibilatrix

Rowan knew of only one record, a bird obtained near the Watch House by J.H. Gurney but for which no date is given. Pashley, however, records at least five as having been brought in 'from the bushes' in the 1890s, regarding them as scarce and noteworthy.

White records Wood Warblers as occasional passage migrants, usually in August or September, though with one record in May.

There have been 46 records since 1955. Seventeen were in spring, all singles falling between 26th April and 26th May, with most in the first half of May. A rare grey morph individual was seen and heard singing on 11th May 2002.

Autumn records fall between 9th August and 26th September, normally involving singles, but two have been recorded on four occasions and three were present on 21st – 22nd September 1957. A bird on 15th August 1976 entered the Lifeboat House to catch flies.

Spring records have become more frequent since the 1980s, with autumn occurrences correspondingly rarer. It is not known why this should be the case though increasing coverage in spring is no doubt a partial explanation. As with many migrant passerines, it is likely that the majority of Wood Warblers seen on the Point (and all those in autumn) are continental in origin, in this case from central Europe (or even western Russia) on passage to and from wintering grounds in tropical west Africa.

Common Chiffchaff (Chiffchaff)
Phylloscopus collybita collybita
Phylloscopus collybita abietinus (Scandinavian Chiffchaff)

Rowan records Chiffchaffs as fairly regular in September and irregular in October, although much rarer than Willow Warbler. White describes them as passage migrants in small numbers, more frequent in autumn than in spring.

Chiffchaff is a regular early spring migrant in small numbers, typically occurring between mid-March and early May, by which time their place has been increasingly taken by Willow Warblers. Peak numbers in spring include seven on 26th March 1989 and nine on 23rd April 1999. These early birds are likely to be mainly British *collybita* returning from winter quarters in southern Europe or Africa. Chiffchaffs are scarce after early May but in most years the occasional bird is recorded at the end of the month or even in early June, presumably bound for northern Europe.

Autumn migrants occur mainly in September and October, though an early bird was seen on 10th August 1994 and the very occasional Chiffchaff is seen until mid-November. Numbers are generally small, with peaks of only 12 on 5th October 1998, eight on 16th October 1988 and eight on 25th – 26th September 2001. Early October 1998 saw a major influx of Chiffchaffs into north Norfolk with, for example, 100 in Holkham Meals on 5th. The relatively small numbers on the Point at this time merely serve to illustrate its unattractiveness to arboreal *Phylloscopi* in late autumn.

Autumn birds are all likely to be continental immigrants from northern Europe and western

Russia and therefore largely *abietinus*, although many such birds are effectively indistinguishable from *collybita*. Some, however, including those in the influx of late September 2001, are more clearly *abietinus*, showing 'colder', paler grey tones above and whiter underparts.

Siberian Chiffchaff

Phylloscopus (collybita) tristis
This dull, northeastern form of the Chiffchaff breeds across northern Russia, reaching as far west as the Pechora River, and winters in the Indian subcontinent. Birds from the west of this range, sometimes referred to as *fulvescens*, resemble *abietinus* Chiffchaffs but show drab crowns and mantles lacking green and they also lack yellow in the face and underparts. More eastern birds show browner plumage and increasing buff clouding in the face and flanks. However, both types share the same songs and calls which are strikingly different from those of the familiar Chiffchaffs of Europe. Although traditionally 'lumped' with Chiffchaff, Siberian Chiffchaffs are generally identifiable in the field and are therefore treated separately here. They are rare migrants to the Point, rarer than, for example, Pallas's Warbler.

All records are as follows:-

27th October 1987.
24th October 1990.
10th November 1990.
11th May 1993.
16th October 2000, the same day as a Dusky Warbler.
11th – 12th October 2004 (Plate 22).

All most closely resembled birds from the western populations with the exception of the bird in 2000 which showed characters associated with a more eastern origin. The coincidence of this bird's arrival with a Dusky Warbler is therefore noteworthy.

Willow Warbler

Phylloscopus trochilus trochilus
Phylloscopus trochilus acredula (Northern Willow Warbler)
Rowan states that Willow Warblers are fairly regular in September, often in considerable numbers, and irregular in October. White describes them as a passage migrant in spring and autumn. White also notes that birds of the form *acredula* were noted in May 1954 and September 1961.

Willow Warblers have a huge range extending from Ireland across the whole of northern Europe and Russia to the shores of the Bering Sea, wintering in the southern half of Africa. They are common migrants in both spring and autumn, though numbers vary considerably between years. The earliest record is of one on 4th April 1993 but peak numbers occur in the last week of April and the first half of May, the most notable counts being 25 on 19th May 1996, 26 on 26th April 2000, 30 on 30th April and an exceptional 50 on 2nd May 1995. Large numbers must, however, also have been occurring in spring 1969 for Cant's notes refer to 116 Willow Warblers being ringed in the nine days up to 5th May of that year. The occasional late bird is seen into early June. Some spring birds appear particularly 'cold' and grey, lacking all yellow in the plumage, and may warrant being referred to the northern and eastern form *acredula*, breeding from Norway and northern Sweden east to the Yenisey River.

The first autumn migrants occur from the last week of July, with moderate numbers appearing in any late August 'falls', the peak numbers at this time of year being 150 on 22nd August 1963 and 100 on 21st August 1977. Larger numbers, however, generally occur in September, for example:-

200 on 3rd – 4th September 1958.
100 on 14th September 1993.
200 on 18th September 1995, the day of the huge Common Redstart 'fall'.

This September peak is in marked contrast to the earlier August peak passage of departing British breeders recorded at the Irish Sea bird observatories and further illustrates the continental origin of most passerine migrants recorded on the Point. Most autumn Willow Warblers are doubtless *acredula* but racial identification of individual birds in the field is generally unsafe.

Numbers drop rapidly after the first week of October and birds become rare by mid-month. Late Willow Warblers have occurred on 1st November 1974, 27th - 30th October 1991 and, latest of all, 3rd November 1994.

Goldcrests. (*James McCallum*)

Goldcrest
Regulus regulus regulus

Rowan and White record Goldcrests as regular passage migrants in September and October. Particularly noteworthy was 29th October 1948 when flocks estimated in hundreds took cover in the bushes. An account in Gaze (1946) gives a flavour of these occasions:-

> 'I remember one lovely September day when hundreds upon hundreds of tiny golden-crested wrens dropped in exhausted, little bigger than humblebees. They flooded the tearoom eagerly, seeking the tiny flies on the window-panes. Too tired and hungry to be shy, they would alight upon one's finger tips'.

Today Goldcrests are common autumn immigrants from the continent between early September and mid-November, usually associated with winds from an easterly quarter. The numbers vary from year to year according to the prevailing weather conditions. Autumn arrivals can be spectacular, sometimes coinciding with 'falls' of Robins and, towards the end of October, big immigrations of Goldcrests are worth checking for any accompanying Pallas's Warbler. Notable recent 'falls' include:-

'Several hundred' on 29th October 1983.

200-300 on 16th October 1988.

200+ on 19th October 1990.

200 in the first week of October 1998.

200 on 22nd October 2001.

In spring they are scarce though regular, appearing mainly in March and April as returning migrants from Britain to Scandinavia or displaced from the near-continent. However, Cant's notes refer to a 'large fall' of the species on 15th April 1967 and, more recently, at least 20 were counted on 8th April 1984.

Goldcrests on the Point are usually encountered in the *Suaeda*, often gathering together in small, loose groups and giving away their presence by insistent calling. On days with large 'falls' they can be spotted arriving over the shingle ridge well into the afternoon.

The tiny size and apparent frailty of Goldcrests give few clues to the long distances they travel between their Scandinavian, northern European and western Russian breeding grounds and more southerly wintering locations. They are one of the lightest species in the world to make regular sea crossings.

Firecrest
Regulus ignicapilla ignicapilla

This delightful species is a scarce spring and autumn migrant. Rowan reports only a single undated record of one taken by Ramm near the Watch House. This is probably the bird recorded by Pashley as taken on the beach on 6th November 1913 – the first specimen he had seen in the flesh.

The next record concerns a bird on 21st October 1951, not noted by White who does, however, list three further spring records and seven in the autumn before 1975. A further record on 22nd April 1968 is similarly not listed by White.

Since 1975 around 25 birds have occurred in spring, with records falling between 18th March and 12th May, and at least 25 in autumn, predominantly in October, with records falling between 6th September and 27th October.

Normally only one or two birds are seen in a day. Higher counts include five on 17th April 1983, four on 15th April 1984, three on 26th October 1985, three on 13th October 2004 and an exceptional 11 on 12th October 2002 during a record influx of Firecrests into the county. At either season birds are often associated with southeasterly winds and arrivals regularly coincide with those of Black Redstarts, clearly indicating their origin on the near-continent. A male on 27th April 2001 was in full song.

The increase in the number of Firecrests recorded on the Point neatly mirrors the expansion of their range in northwest Europe since the 1960s. Firecrests are scarcer on the Point, and in north Norfolk, than in the east of the county and counties further south, doubtless a reflection of the species' southeasterly origin.

Spotted Flycatcher
Muscicapa striata striata

Rowan notes the Spotted Flycatcher as irregular in September, whilst White records the species as a regular passage migrant in small numbers. Never an abundant migrant, there appears to be evidence of a decline since the early 1960s and currently it is scarce at both migration seasons.

Spotted Flycatcher is one of the latest summer visitors to arrive on its European and Russian breeding grounds and tiny arrivals of migrants in late May and early June often feature a high percentage of this species. The earliest spring record is of a bird on 8th May and the latest on 8th

June. Typically only between one and five birds are present in a day in spring, but higher counts include 10 on 15th May 1990 and 11 on 30th May 1998.

Autumn birds are mostly seen in late August and September. Numbers are always small but an unprecedented 50 occurred in the large 'fall' of 4th September 1958. An exceptionally late bird occurred on 27th October 1991 - a day more noted for a record influx of Long-eared Owls. By this date Spotted Flycatchers should already be on their southern African wintering grounds.

At both seasons arrivals typically occur in easterly conditions, confirming that these are continental birds 'overshooting' in the spring and drifting westwards in the autumn.

Red-breasted Flycatcher
Ficedula parva

The Point has a long history of records of this attractive 'semi-rarity' – indeed the first for Norfolk was recorded here on 13th September 1890.

Pashley lists 13 further records before 1928, of which ten by 1917 represented half of all the Norfolk records. Rowan reports the species as rare in September and all birds as immatures apart from an adult male on 24th September 1908 – still the only confirmed autumn adult. This bird suffered the misfortune of being shot by Frank Richards whilst it was perched on the bulwarks of Pinchen's houseboat, the *'Britannia'*. Further birds occurred in the autumns of 1949 and 1953 and White notes that records have been annual at this season since 1955, mainly of single birds. Over 100 have now been recorded.

Two birds in a day have been recorded on seven occasions, but up to three were present on 4th – 10th October 1966, with three on 14th September 1975 and an exceptional five on 12th September 1989.

The earliest autumn records were on 21st August 1967 and 21st August 1971 and the latest on 12th November 1983, one of only two county records after the end of October. There are, however, only seven August records and the majority occur in September and early October. Later birds must now be worth examining critically for the possibility of Taiga Flycatcher *Ficedula albicilla*, its recently 'split' Siberian counterpart now added to the British List. Indeed it is interesting to speculate on whether this species might already have occurred.

There have been only six spring records, very close to the national average of six per cent of all occurrences. All records at this season are as follows:-

Female or first-summer male on 4th June 1979.
Female or first-summer male on 19th – 24th May 1985.
First-summer male on 17th – 18th May 1986, in song.
Female or first-summer male on 21st May 1994.
Female or first-summer male on 7th June 2003 (plate15).
First-summer male on 17th May 2004, in sub-song.

The literature is contradictory on the age and sex of some of these individuals. All have been 'non red-throated' and, as the ageing and sexing of such birds in spring is difficult, all are recorded here as 'female or first-summer male', with the exception of the birds in 1986 and 2004 which were heard to sing.

The all-time total number of sightings is surprisingly high for a species with an eastern European and Russian breeding range and a strongly southeasterly migration track in autumn to wintering grounds on the Indian subcontinent. Arrivals of Red-breasted Flycatchers are often associated with warm southeasterly winds in late September and early October, conditions which also regularly produce Yellow-browed Warblers on the north Norfolk coast.

Pied Flycatcher. (*James McCallum*)

Pied Flycatcher
Ficedula hypoleuca hypoleuca

Pied Flycatchers are 'classic' early autumn drift migrants from the continent and are a familiar feature of 'falls' in August and early September. Rowan notes the species as irregular but its current status as a regular autumn and rare spring migrant accords with White's assessment.

Numbers in autumn fluctuate from year to year according to the frequency of suitable easterly winds. Birds often arrive from the first week of August and occurrences continue into early October. An exceptionally early bird occurred on 21st July 1955 and the latest records concern singles on 16th October 1988 and 20th October 1994. Passage peaks in mid to late August and early September, though an exceptionally early large arrival involved 50 on 3rd August 1968.

Other high counts have been:-

50 on 2nd – 4th September 1958.
50 on 30th August to 1st September 1963.
60 on 22nd – 23rd August 1968.
75 on 15th August 1977.
50 on 19th August 1977.
50 on 30th August 1985.
60+ on 12th September 1989.
65 on 10th August 2004.

On such occasions their loud 'whit' call is a characteristic sound in the Plantation. Autumn birds originate predominantly from Scandinavia and northern Germany, though the breeding range extends into western Russia. With an autumn heading to the south or southwest, it is likely that no British-bred Pied Flycatchers occur on the Point at this season.

In the spring Pied Flycatchers are rare migrants, occurring less than annually between the end of April and the beginning of June. There are only five April records, the earliest of which was on 23rd April 1994, and three records in June, the latest being on 9th June 1988. The highest spring counts are of 20 on 3rd May 1956 and eight on 12th May 1993. Further influxes occurred in 1954, when up to three were recorded on six dates in May, and 1988, when a minimum of eight occurred, with a peak of five on 15th May.

Birds at this season also normally arrive in easterly conditions, confirming that these too are predominantly continental birds. Most British-breeding Pied Flycatchers arrive in April, somewhat earlier than most of those recorded on the Point which coincide with the slightly later arrivals in Scandinavia and central Europe.

Bearded Tit (Bearded Reedling)

Panurus biarmicus biarmicus

The species does not feature in Rowan's list but White lists three records - two on 5th October 1961, one on 21st August 1964 and one with Long-tailed Tits at the Hood on 6th October 1971. These correspond with the peak periods of immigration into Britain from the Netherlands in the mid-1960s and early 1970s. Only eight further sightings have been traced, all in the autumn and mostly involving high-flying flocks:-

5 on 22nd October 1983.
2 on 27th September 1986, in the *Suaeda*.
12 high southeast on 17th October 1987.
2 on 2nd October 1988.
8 west on 24th September 1998.
1 high east on 25th September 2001.
2 on 1st October 2002.
4 high southeast on 19th October 2004.

Short-distance irruptive flights in autumn are a feature of this species and ringing has revealed regular movements across East Anglia. It is likely that most recent records refer to birds of local origin.

Long-tailed Tit

Aegithalos caudatus rosaceus (British Long-tailed Tit)

Rowan and White describe Long-tailed Tits as occasional at various times of the year, with small parties of up to a dozen birds noted in the autumn and early winter of 1959. Since then there have been at least eight records of small flocks of between seven and 20 individuals, all falling between 2nd October and 4th November apart from an isolated spring record of two birds on 16th – 17th March 1991.

There is no information on the form involved in the early sightings but recent records have appeared to be of the rather dusky British form *rosaceus* as opposed to the slightly whiter European form *europaeus*. At least one of the parties occurred following violent southwesterly gales, further suggesting a local origin. Long-tailed Tits are particularly weak flyers and there are, as yet, no ringing recoveries in Britain of foreign-ringed birds, suggesting that immigration from the continent is very limited.

Coal Tit

Parus ater ater (Continental Coal Tit)

White notes that one or two were seen with many Blue Tits on 21st September 1957, with a further record of three on 19th September 1966. There are no other known records.

It is not stated in the literature whether these were of the British form *britannicus* or the grey-backed nominate European and Asian form. Given the association, however, with the irrupting Blue Tits of 1957 a continental origin can safely be inferred for these, if not all, the records.

Blue Tit

Parus caeruleus caeruleus (Continental Blue Tit)

Rowan's list does not include the Blue Tit but White records the species, though noting that it is not often seen. Tits have a strong aversion to crossing large stretches of water and as a consequence all are rare on the Point. Blue Tit is the species most regularly seen, but it is still rare.

Remarkable numbers, however, occurred in north Norfolk on 19th September 1957, with a large influx and westward movement noted at the Point on 21st and 22nd September, fewer on 8th and 13th October and again many on 2nd November of the same year. On 12th October, four Blue Tits were noted alighting on a yacht sailing in the Harbour. These movements coincided with one of their periodic irruptions from continental Europe, linked to high late summer population levels and a scarcity of winter food.

All subsequent records have also been in late autumn, falling between 20th September and 2nd December. Single birds were ringed in 1965 and 1966, with three birds in 1969. Three further birds were seen in October 1975, and between 1983 and 1992 Blue Tits were recorded annually, with a peak of up to 30 birds in 1985. Since 1992 only two records have been traced – a single on 2nd November 2002 and four (a party of three and a single) on 19th October 2004. It is possible that the improving climate and increasing availability of human-provided winter food on the continent is now reducing the frequency of Blue Tit irruptions into Britain.

The movements of 1957 were clearly continental in origin and the majority of other records may also be of continental birds as British Blue Tits (of the poorly-differentiated form *obscurus*) are known to be largely sedentary. Indeed whether British Blue Tits have occurred on the Point at all is open to speculation. Continental Blue Tits have an extensive range across northern and central Europe and western Russia.

Great Tit

Parus major major (Continental Great Tit)

Rowan notes Great Tits as occasional, seen at various times of the year. White records one or two on 21st September 1957 and one on 21st October of the same year. The only subsequent records are of singles on 8th April 1984 and 19th – 23rd March 2005. This latter bird, although a female, was heard to give brief bursts of song.

The 1957 records were part of that autumn's record tit irruption, caused by a beech crop failure in Europe, and were therefore clearly of the nominate continental form which breeds across central and northern Europe and Russia. In contrast to the highly sedentary British form *newtoni*, continental birds are partial migrants, with large movements occasionally noted in response to high population levels and limited winter food supplies. Females are invariably the greatest wanderers in such movements.

Both the 1984 and 2005 birds occurred in easterly conditions with small 'falls' of Blackbirds and Goldcrests, providing strong circumstantial evidence that they were displaced across the North Sea from the near-continent. The mid-late March and early April dates coincide with the typical return passage period through northern Europe. Interestingly, the 2005 bird was part of a wider influx of Great Tits which took place in coastal north Norfolk in mid-March of that year and photographs of this bird appear to show the thinner bill typical of continental birds.

Eurasian Nuthatch (Wood Nuthatch, Nuthatch)

Sitta europea subsp.

White notes the only record - one seen on 27th October 1899, although this record is not listed by Rowan. Pashley's diaries, however, record that this bird was 'got from the bushes' on this date by the Rev. Ashworth. It is not known whether it was thought to be of the largely sedentary British and central European form *caesia* or the more irruptive nominate Scandinavian, northern European and Russian form though, given the date, the latter may perhaps be more likely.

This species shares with Buff-breasted Sandpiper and Pallas's Sandgrouse the distinction of being unrecorded on the Point since the nineteenth century!

Eurasian Treecreeper (Treecreeper)

Certhia familiaris subsp.

Treecreeper is a very rare species on the Point with only three records. Pashley refers to one 'taken in the bushes' on 16th January 1897. On 28th – 29th September 1985 a single bird frequented the *Suaeda* at the Hood and the Long Hills and the most recent sighting is of a bird in the Lupins on 24th August 2001.

The origin of these birds is uncertain but the 1985 bird did coincide with a small arrival of continental migrants and may therefore have been of the nominate Scandinavian form (Northern Treecreeper). The other birds, by contrast, may have been local in origin and therefore of the largely sedentary British form *britannica*.

Golden Oriole (Eurasian Golden Oriole)

Oriolus oriolus oriolus

The only records are of a bird on 15th August 1977 and a female on 24th May 1994. This is a central European and western Asian species with wintering grounds in Africa and the Indian subcontinent.

Red-backed Shrike. (*James McCallum*)

Red-backed Shrike

Lanius collurio collurio

Rowan refers to casual summer visitors and occasional records in September. White describes the species as an irregular passage migrant in August and September, with most birds being juveniles. Pashley's diaries refer to Red-backed Shrikes 'fairly often occurring in the bushes during autumn migration'. Birds are now exclusively either autumn immigrants from southern Scandinavia, central Europe and Russia or, in recent times, 'overshooting' continental breeders in the spring. Rowan's note of summer occurrences reflects the fact that Red-backed Shrike was formerly a regular breeding bird in Norfolk, with, as recently as 1950, between 20 and 25 pairs breeding within three miles of Cley.

The precise number of autumn occurrences prior to the 1950s is not clear, but since 1950 around 50 have been recorded at this season, with records concentrated between late August and mid-September. The earliest autumn record since 1950 is of a bird on 7th August 1977, while a particularly late bird occurred on 12th – 13th October 1992 - the only October record.

Birds are usually recorded singly, though two birds have been seen on at least three occasions, up to four were recorded between 7th and 23rd August 1977 and three or four were noted on 15th August 1996. The regularity with which Red-backed Shrikes are seen on the Point is perhaps surprising given the species' strongly southeasterly migration track from its breeding grounds to winter haunts in southern Africa.

The first spring record was in 1970. Subsequently a further 18 birds have occurred at this season, all between 8th May and 16th June and all singles with the exception of two on 31st May 1984 and two on 10th May 2004. A majority of these spring birds have been pristine males. As with a number of species, however, this apparent increase may just reflect more intensive watching at this season in recent years as the Red-backed Shrike has been extinct as a British breeding bird since 1988 and continues to decline in the northwestern parts of its range.

Great Grey Shrike. (*James McCallum*)

Great Grey Shrike

Lanius excubitor excubitor

Rowan refers, somewhat euphemistically, to Ted Ramm being 'present at the death of three of these birds on the area', while White records the Great Grey Shrike as a rare autumn passage migrant, occurring less than annually and usually in October.

All 23 sightings since 1953 are in the period 1st to 25th October though there are earlier records on 16th September 1932 and 10th September 1952. These would be exceptionally early for Great Grey Shrikes today and might raise the possibility of a misidentification of Lesser Grey Shrike. However, it is probably more likely that Great Grey Shrikes simply occurred earlier in the autumn prior to the 1960s as did also, for example, Woodcock.

Almost all records are of singles with the exception of two on 13th October 1985 and a remarkable five birds on 23rd October 1955, each of which was defending its own feeding territory and preying on Robins and Goldcrests. Up to three single birds in early October 1998 were part of a major influx into the county, triggered perhaps by a year of high breeding success in Scandinavia and northern Russia and a dearth of small rodents.

Most birds only stay briefly, no doubt a reflection of the Point's poor feeding prospects, but those arriving with larger 'falls' of migrants have sometimes lingered to feed on exhausted small birds, with Goldcrests typically featuring high on the menu. A bird on 10th October 1975 was observed on active migration, flying west with Starlings and on another occasion a bird was noted arriving from the sea.

There are no spring records despite the occasional occurrence of Great Grey Shrikes elsewhere along the coast at this season.

Woodchat Shrike (Woodchat)

Lanius senator senator
There have been three records of this Mediterranean rarity as follows:-

Female on 20th – 22nd May 1960, on Yankee Ridge, often perching on the *'Yankee'* itself. On its last day it also shared the Point with a Subalpine Warbler.
Adult male on 22nd August 1966.
Female on 15th – 17th May 1992, initially in the Plantation but subsequently ranging widely in the Sandhills (photographed).

The birds in 1960 and 1992 are known with certainty to have been of the widespread nominate form, which shows the characteristic white primary patch, and the 1966 bird was presumably also of this form.

Woodchat Shrikes winter in Africa north of the equator and in spring are prone to 'overshooting' their southern European breeding grounds.

Eurasian Jay (Jay)

Garrulus glandarius glandarius (Continental Jay)
Jays are reluctant to fly across large stretches of water and are therefore, not surprisingly, very rare on the Point. There have been just two sightings - on 21st May 1997 and 29th September 2002.

The bird in September 2002 occurred during an irruption of continental Jays into north Norfolk. These invasions of the duller, less pink nominate form originate in Scandinavia or north-west Russia and are triggered by acorn crop failures. The bird in May 1997 passed east and may have been returning to the continent following an influx in October 1996. It is therefore likely that the largely sedentary British form *rufitergum* has not occurred on the Point despite being resident nearby.

Despite an earlier memorable invasion of continental Jays into Norfolk and the rest of the country in autumn 1983, no records can be traced from the Point.

Magpie (Black-billed Magpie)

Pica pica pica

This very sedentary species is, not surprisingly, very rare, with just eight records traced. White refers to a solitary bird spending the summer of 1978 on the Point and building three nests in spring 1979, but subsequently found dead. The only other known records are as follows:-

16th March 1991.
15th October 1994.
20th March 2002.
3rd April 2002.
12th April 2004.
2 on 14th April 2004.
2 on 19th October 2004.

An interesting pattern of early spring and mid-October occurrences is emerging.

Eurasian Jackdaw (Jackdaw)

Corvus monedula spermologus (Western Jackdaw)

Jackdaw is a surprisingly rare species on the Point given its abundance nearby. Rowan refers to 'a few every summer, mostly June and July, apparently on marauding expeditions'. White notes Jackdaws as seen very occasionally.

Jackdaws are still scarce, with records traced in only six years since 1990. Sightings are split evenly between spring (April and May) and autumn (August and October) and the peak count is of ten on 6th May 1999. Birds are usually passing over high and are not generally noted on the ground.

All modern records have presumably been of local birds rather than continental immigrants and therefore of the western European form *spermologus*.

Rook

Corvus frugilegus frugilegus

Rooks were formerly common on the Point. Rowan and Pashley both considered this species to be fairly regular in large numbers in autumn and Pinchen's diaries from the 1920s contain frequent references to numbers of migrant Rooks in October and the first half of November. Around the turn of the nineteenth century the species was also regarded as a significant predator on the tern colony.

Winter immigration has been much reduced in recent years, linked perhaps to a decline in the European population and the fact that Russian birds are now less prone to long-distance migrations. If immigrant Rooks are still occurring in eastern England there is no longer any evidence of it on the Point.

Rooks are now scarce, with only around 20 known records since 1989, involving at least 65 birds. Most records are in spring, falling between 11th March and 10th June, usually relating to small parties moving west along the coast.

There are only three known autumn records in recent years, between 28th September and 31st October, but these include the peak count of 10 on 12th October 1991.

Carrion Crow

Corvus corone corone

Pashley remarked in 1925 that he had never seen the species in the Cley area and Rowan only lists the Hooded Crow. By the 1960s, however, White refers to birds frequently seen on marauding expeditions in the breeding season – a reflection of this species' northward spread, both in Britain and on the continent. This corvid is now a regular species in very small numbers at all times of year. There is a small westerly passage in spring and coasting flocks sometimes include one or two Jackdaws or Rooks. These movements are most likely to be short-distance wanderings of local birds.

A Carrion x Hooded Crow hybrid flew west on 20th April 2004.

Hooded Crows. (*James McCallum*)

Hooded Crow

Corvus cornix cornix

The Hooded Crow's historical distribution pattern is a mirror image of that of the Carrion Crow. Hooded Crows were formerly regular winter visitors and passage migrants from Scandinavia or northern Russia. Pashley refers to hundreds in a flock arriving on 1st October 1897 and Pinchen's diairies from the 1920s make frequent reference to numbers of migrant 'grey crows' in October and the first half of November. These movements continued well into the twentieth century with, for example, birds seen passing through all day on 8th October 1946. A particularly late spring bird occurred on 19th May 1946, feeding on a dead Ringed Plover.

By the 1960s, however, the winter numbers had declined and the large movements were no more. White describes the species as 'now quite scarce, with only the odd one or two in mid-winter'.

Cant notes odd singles until the mid-1960s and three were seen on 2nd November 1966. These were followed by four birds on 1st May 1967 and further records at this season on 27th April 1968 and 27th April 1969. This reduction in the number of wintering birds is thought to be a consequence of displacement by expanding Carrion Crow populations on the continent and a change in migratory behaviour in Scandinavian birds, where a greater proportion now remains throughout the winter, perhaps assisted by winter food at rubbish tips.

Since the 1970s there have been only 13 occurrences, all of singles, with the exception of two on 26th March 1989. All but two recent records are from spring, between 26th March and 3rd June. Both autumn birds were in late October.

With the most recent record in April 1995 it is now ten years since this species has occurred on the Point.

A Carrion x Hooded Crow hybrid flew west on 20th April 2004.

Common Starling (Starling)

Sturnus vulgaris vulgaris

Rowan lists the Starling as a breeding species and recounts that there was usually a nest in the Lifeboat House. The species could be seen at all times of year, although it was never numerous and seldom seen in flocks of any size.

By the time of White's list the Starling had increased as a breeding species, with the Lifeboat House and Laboratory roofs the chosen nesting sites. In 1967 about five pairs nested, while in August and September of that year 50-75 residents roosted in the Plantation. Starlings still bred on the Lifeboat House in the 1980s but breeding has now ceased.

Even though Starlings no longer breed, noisy flocks of local birds, sometimes up to 1,000-strong, regularly visit the saltmarshes and *Suaeda* clumps in late summer and early autumn.

During the middle years of the twentieth century the Starling was certainly a very common late autumn immigrant, the 1950 issue of *Wild Bird Protection in Norfolk* referring to birds 'passing all day' on 18th, 19th and 23rd November of that year. Starlings are still regularly seen arriving from the sea in October and November and heading away inland, harbingers of the coming winter. Large numbers can also be seen coasting westwards. These movements can be spectacular, with numbers exceeding 5,000 on 7th November 1998 and 30th October 1999 and even larger counts of 8,000 on 21st October 2000 and 13,000+ on 10th October 2001.

Outside the summer and autumn, however, the Starling is now generally scarce on the Point, though March 2005 saw much larger numbers linked to a series of 'falls' of northbound thrushes, peaking at 3,500 passing west on 28th.

Ringing recoveries elsewhere have shown that different Starling populations move at different times. Birds from the Netherlands pass mainly in September and early October, with German and Scandinavian birds in mid-October whilst those in late October and November are predominantly from Poland, Finland and Russia.

Rose-coloured Starling (Rosy Starling)

Sturnus roseus

The only record of this irruptive southwest and Central Asian starling is of a juvenile in the Marrams on the surprisingly early date of 22nd August 1983. Late spring and summer adults account for the vast majority of Norfolk records of this species so the occurrence of an autumn juvenile is particularly noteworthy. Rose-coloured Starlings winter in the Indian subcontinent.

House Sparrow

Passer domesticus domesticus

House Sparrows have had a chequered history on the Point. Rowan records that they may appear occasionally at any time but that he had seen the species himself only once, in July 1912. White records that they can be seen throughout the year and refers to two pairs nesting successfully in 1961 in the Lifeboat House roof for the first time in many years.

By the 1980s there were two flourishing colonies, the second in the Laboratory roof, establishing the House Sparrow as a common breeding species. From this high point its status had changed by the 1990s to that of an occasional visitor.

A bird was present in March 1991 and from 1989 to 1993 a flock of up to 40 birds frequented the *Suaeda* for short periods each October and November but this habit soon ceased and today the House Sparrow is virtually unknown on the Point. The only recent traced record is of a male passing high to the west on 22nd April 2003.

Tree Sparrow (Eurasian Tree Sparrow)

Passer montanus montanus

Tree Sparrows have always been rare on the Point. Rowan notes that Ramm had shot one once in the *Suaeda*. White cites two further records – single birds trapped in 1966 and another in 1969. Cant's notes also refer to 'Tree Sparrows' on 8th May 1960 and 27th April 1968.

Since White's list there appear to have been eight records, all bar one of single birds, five sightings in April and May and three in autumn:-

19th May 1984.
2 on 13th October 1985.
29th April 1990.
26th August 1990.
27th April 1991.
6th September 1998.
8th April 2000.
6th – 7th May 2000.

The Tree Sparrow has a huge European and Asian range but populations in the west are largely sedentary. However, it is worth noting that all sightings on the Point are at migration periods and some birds may be continental in origin. The bird in 1998, for example, was present on the same day as a Tawny Pipit.

Despite its well-publicised decline as a British bird, the Tree Sparrow is now marginally more regular on the Point than the House Sparrow!

Common Chaffinch (Chaffinch)

Fringilla coelebs coelebs (Continental Chaffinch)

Rowan describes the Chaffinch as irregular, mostly occurring singly in the winter months. White notes the species as somewhat irregular as a passage migrant and possibly an occasional winter visitor. However, the 1946 issue of *Wild Bird Protection in Norfolk* refers to 'a great number of Chaffinches' on 2nd November 1946 and a flock of over 1,000 is noted by Cant as being present in late December 1968. White's status assessment therefore seems a little misplaced given this evidence of occasional abundance.

Such flocks, however, have not been witnessed in recent years and the Chaffinch is now largely a scarce and irregular 'fly-over' migrant in very small numbers between September and November.

Occasional birds can also be found feeding along the shingle bank. Ones and twos are the norm though ten occurred on 25th September 1990 and a (now) exceptional 85 on 12th October of the same year. The Chaffinch is rarer in spring, with only occasional birds, exceptionally up to around 20 in a day, recorded on return passage to Scandinavia or displaced from the near-continent, normally in March or April, though a late bird occurred on 28th May 2004.

In the autumn most northern European, Scandinavian and western Russian Chaffinches are diurnal migrants, moving southwest through the Netherlands into northern France. Some enter southeast England via the short Channel crossing, with only relatively few undertaking a longer flight across the North Sea. Chaffinches are nevertheless a reasonably common westward-coasting bird on the north Norfolk coast but the paucity of observations on the Point is presumably a result of birds preferring to take a more inland route on the south side of the Harbour.

This pattern of records indicates that the majority of birds are undoubtedly attributable to the slightly brighter nominate continental form rather than the essentially sedentary British form *gengleri* – indeed it is possible that the British form does not normally occur on the Point at all.

Brambling
Fringilla montifringilla
Rowan notes Bramblings as seen and taken at the end of September and during October in various years. White describes the species as an irregular passage migrant in varying numbers and a winter visitor in hard weather.

Autumn migration from Scandinavia and northern Russia to wintering areas in central and western Europe extends from mid-September to early November, peaking in mid-October. The highest counts include 40 on 16th October 1986, 60 on 18th October 1990 and 30 on 10th October 1991 but by far the largest autumn count was of 300+ on 16th October 1988, the day of a very large 'fall' of migrants. They are typically heard passing over singly or in small parties but on occasion they will land briefly in the *Suaeda*.

Perhaps surprisingly, Bramblings are far more regular on the Point than the closely-related Chaffinch. This is presumably attributable to their very different autumn migration strategies, as Bramblings fly directly across the North Sea at night, making landfall at the north Norfolk coast from a northerly or northeasterly direction.

In recent times only occasional birds have been noted in winter, typically in hard weather, but higher numbers were recorded in earlier years. The 1948 issue of *Wild Bird Protection in Norfolk* refers to 'flocks' being present from January to March that year and many were found dead in the 'big freeze' of January 1963. A totally unprecedented occurrence was a flock of 3,000 noted in the *Norfolk Bird Report* for December 1968. This remarkable number may, however, be an error as Cant's notes refer to at least 300 being present at the time.

Bramblings are rare on the Point in spring but Cant's notes refer to a 'fall of Robins, Bramblings and thrushes' on 9th April 1966 and Pinchen notes one on the remarkable date of 9th June 1922. Other more recent spring records involve a male in song in the Plantation on 17th April 2003 and one on 8th – 9th May 2004.

European Serin (Serin)
Serinus serinus
The only record of this tiny central and southern European finch concerns a singing male in the Lupins on 8th April 1996. The date is typical for British records of this species which regularly 'overshoots' its breeding grounds in spring, perhaps becoming caught up in flocks of Goldfinches returning to Britain from their wintering grounds in southern Europe and north Africa.

Greenfinch (European Greenfinch)

Carduelis chloris chloris

Rowan lists the species but provides no details, while White notes Greenfinches as occurring occasionally, usually only one or two individuals in the autumn and winter.

Greenfinches can now be seen in small numbers, mainly in autumn and winter, often feeding with Goldfinches and Linnets just west of Cley Coastguards. Greenfinches are partial migrants, small numbers arriving to winter in Britain from continental Europe, mainly from Norway, so the occasional birds seen arriving in the autumn are presumably genuine immigrants.

The highest autumn counts include 100+ on 10th November 1984 and 100+ on 20th September 1997.

Goldfinch (European Goldfinch)

Carduelis carduelis britannica

Rowan's list does not include this species and White only records Goldfinches as occasional.

Since then they appear to have become more regular and are now common migrants in spring when, between late March and mid-May, there are small westward movements with Linnets, with daily counts of over 100 noted. These are presumably British birds moving north from wintering grounds in southwest Europe or north Africa.

Small parties can also sometimes be encountered at other times of year feeding in weedy areas on the edge of the saltings, particularly on the thistles just west of Cley Coastguards. There is little evidence of autumn immigration from other parts of their European range, although a bird which flew in off the sea on 29th October 2004 may have been continental and therefore of the slightly larger and brighter nominate form.

Siskin (Eurasian Siskin)

Carduelis spinus

In Rowan's time Siskins were rare and he only records four taken by Frank Richards in the Sandhills in September 1901. These were the first migrants to have come to Pashley's notice.

White, however, records them as regular passage migrants in autumn, but less regular in spring – a reflection of their increase in Britain and northwest Europe during the twentieth century.

Currently Siskins are scarce migrants in the autumn and rare in the spring. Continental birds arrive on the east coast from early September, making a direct crossing of the North Sea from Scandinavia and Russia, on passage to winter quarters in southern or western Europe. The high-pitched flight calls are often the first indication of arriving birds and frequently they continue inland without alighting, though occasionally they pause briefly in the *Suaeda* or dunes. Numbers are never great but up to 40 birds have been counted in a day.

Linnet (Common Linnet)

Carduelis cannabina cannabina

Rowan notes Linnets as breeding in the *Suaeda* in small numbers. White records them as abundant at all times of the year, as breeders, passage migrants and winter visitors. In Rowan's day the population was around 25-30 pairs but 40 pairs were breeding in 1959 and by 1967 this had risen to 100 pairs. Numbers subsequently fell back again to 40-50 pairs by the early 1980s and 37 pairs bred in 2004. The Point therefore continues to host an important population of this declining farmland species.

Linnets are also still relatively common partial migrants. A proportion of the British breeding population winters in the Netherlands and returning birds are common diurnal migrants passing west in early spring along the north Norfolk coast. On the Point, however, these movements are smaller as some birds appear to choose a more inland diversion. However, daily counts of 200-300 birds have been regularly recorded in March and April. Late summer and autumn flocks roaming the *Suaeda* also frequently reach around 200 birds, though flocks are now generally smaller than in earlier years.

A Linnet ringed on the Point on 30th April 1968 was recovered at Chertsey, Surrey on 15th September of the same year, illustrating the autumn departure from the Point of what was probably a breeding bird. There is no evidence of autumn immigration from elsewhere in the Linnet's extensive European and western Russian range.

Twites and Shore Larks. (*James McCallum*)

Twite

Carduelis flavirostris pipilans (British Twite)
The Twite is a winter visitor and passage migrant which has experienced large fluctuations in numbers.

Rowan notes the species as an irregular winter visitor, but White notes 100 present in January 1958 and also records it as a passage migrant.

By the 1970s and early 1980s Twite were regular in winter, peaking at 400-500 in March 1983. Since then there has been a steady decline in the wintering flock, with birds now largely encountered as autumn migrants in October and November. Numbers of such birds reached up to 50 during the late 1980s and early 1990s but have subsequently declined further. Small numbers continued to be seen in winter on the inland edge of the Harbour through the 1990s but these flocks fall largely outside our area and there is no longer a regular wintering flock on the Point. In 2003, for example, the only Twite recorded were five flying east on 7th November. A useful status update is contained in the *Norfolk Bird Club Bulletin* No. 9. An exceptional spring record concerns two on 7th June 1986.

Ringing has shown that winter birds on the Norfolk coast originate from breeding grounds in the southern Pennines, where there has been a marked decline since the mid-1970s. It is not clear whether any birds from the Scottish or Norwegian populations (the latter of the paler form *flavirostris*) ever reach the Point.

Lesser Redpoll
Carduelis cabaret

Rowan notes that the Lesser Redpoll is said to have been seen two or three times but adds that there is some doubt as to the authenticity of these records. White records Lesser Redpolls as occasional in small numbers.

However, a spectacular autumn influx of redpolls occurred on 28th October 1963 when at least 500 were estimated between the Marrams and Cley Coastguards, with many remaining in the area into November. These birds are described in the *Norfolk Bird Report* for 1963 as follows:-

> 'appearing paler, sandier and smarter-looking than native Lesser Redpoll though differing little in size. The impression was of miniature editions of the Greenland race '*rostrata*' and this was further enhanced by the clear-cut blackish striping on flanks and rich, sandy buff throat and fore-breast'

Despite an assumption in Taylor *et al.* (1999) that these relate to Common Redpoll, the description sounds much closer to Lesser Redpoll. Nor is there any suggestion in the 1963 *Norfolk Bird Report* of an invasion of Common Redpolls elsewhere in the county that autumn and in the early months of 1964 the only record of Common Redpoll in the whole of Norfolk is of a flock of just five in February. Given the high population level of Lesser Redpolls at the time it seems much more likely that this was the species involved. Following a range expansion between the 1950s and the 1970s, Lesser Redpolls were at that time found commonly throughout northwest and central Europe and were described in the 1964 *Norfolk Bird Report* as 'as common in some areas as the Linnet'. Around this time Cant's notes also refer to 'many redpolls' on 14th October 1965, 100+ 'redpolls' on 4th October 1966 and 'many redpolls' on 8th October 1968, all of which are also likely to have been of this species. Further 'redpolls' are also noted for 27th April 1969.

The ongoing decline of the species in Britain and northwest Europe since the 1970s is also reflected on the Point, where there have been only 31 examples since the early 1980s. Small peaks occurred in 1989 and 1990 of eight and nine birds respectively and records have been split fairly evenly between spring and autumn. Spring records fall between 1st April and 10th June while those in autumn fall between 20th September and 7th November. Numbers are always small, the highest single day count being four on 19th October 1990.

A proportion of British-breeding Lesser Redpolls migrates southeast to the Netherlands and northern France in the autumn, and back in the spring. This is likely to account for the spring records on the Point though the autumn birds, notably of course those in the 1960s, are more likely to be of continental origin.

Common Redpoll (Mealy Redpoll)
Carduelis flammea flammea

Rowan and White refer to the species as seen in autumn in some years only, but in very small numbers.

This accords with their current status as a rare autumn visitor, usually seen in irruption years when food is short or the weather is particularly severe in their Scandinavian and northern Russian birch and pine forest haunts.

Although there was a large influx into the county in October 1972, no records can be traced from the Point. However, at least 13 birds have been seen since 1984, almost all in late autumn or winter. The only years with more than one bird were 1990 and 1995, precursors of the 1990/91 and 1995/96 invasions of both Common and Arctic Redpolls.

All known modern records are as follows:-

6th November 1984.
18th, 19th and 20th October 1990, coinciding with the arrival of three Arctic Redpolls.
3 on 12th January 1992.
1st – 2nd May 1995, with possibly two present on 2nd.
4th, 11th and 18th November 1995, the last of these consorting with an Arctic Redpoll.
8th November 1998.
21st October 2001.
23rd October 2003.
31st March 2005.

Arctic Redpoll
Carduelis hornemanni exilipes (Coues's Redpoll)
There are five accepted records of this attractive frosty northern finch:-

13th October 1975.
First-winter on 18th October 1990, at the Hood.
First-winter on 18th – 21st October 1990, in the Sandhills.
20th October 1990, at the Watch House.
18th November 1995, at the Marrams.

All these birds were the precursors of significant invasions of northern redpolls in the following winters, with Arctic Redpolls particularly prominent in 1990/91 and 1995/96. With increased knowledge of the identification of this species, more were identified in each of these years in Britain than ever before. The birds of 18th October 1990 were part of a massive arrival of thrushes grounded in thick fog – conditions which also produced an Olive-backed Pipit. Both of these buffy-faced first-winter Arctic Redpolls were astonishingly tame and allowed a particularly close approach, as is often the case with lone redpolls. The bird on 20th October 1990 was with a Linnet flock, while that of 18th November 1995 was accompanied by a Common Redpoll.

Arctic Redpolls of the form *exilipes* breed to the north of Common Redpoll in tundra habitat with dwarf willow or other shrub cover. The nearest birds are in Arctic Norway but the range extends across northern Russia and, as with Common Redpoll, also across Arctic Canada.

Two-barred Crossbill
Loxia leucoptera bifasciata
The only record of this occasionally irruptive Scandinavian and northern Russian crossbill is of a female or immature seen briefly in the *Suaeda* near the Watch House on 15th September 1969, before flying off. This was only the third record for Norfolk.

Common Crossbill (Crossbill)
Loxia curvirostra curvirostra
Rowan notes that the species had been taken at least once – on 2nd October 1909. Pashley's diaries, however, refer to a male taken in the bushes on 4th September 1894. Pinchen's diaries note a pair on 13th July 1927 and a further bird on 15th July of the same year. White describes the

species as rare and lists one bird killed on 5th September 1910 and 34 seen on 27th August 1966. Small parties of up to seven were subsequently seen until the end of October in this irruption year.

Recent records of this well-known irruptive species have been few, as follows:-

26th August 1990.
Female on 20th October 1990, at the Watch House.
9 on 27th August 2002, flying south over the Plantation.
Female on 12th September 2002, in an exhausted condition at the Watch House.

Both 1990 and 2002 were Crossbill irruption years, those in 1990 apparently originating from northern Russia, though Scandinavia represents the closest source area.

Common Rosefinch (Scarlet Rosefinch)

Carpodacus erythrinus erythrinus
Common Rosefinches are surprisingly rare on the Point even though they breed in growing numbers as close as Denmark and the Netherlands and occurrences elsewhere in Norfolk are slowly increasing. They remain particularly rare in comparison with their much more regular occurrence in Shetland, where small parties are sometimes encountered in September.

The first record, only the second for Norfolk, was of a juvenile which frequented the Plantation on 19th – 20th August 1973. At least five more have occurred:-

Up to 2 females or first-summer males on 5th – 6th June 1992, one on 5th being near the Watch House.
Female or first-summer male on 27th May 1993, in the Sandhills, arriving the same day as an Asian Desert Warbler.
First-summer male on 2nd June 1999, singing in the Lupins.
Female or first-summer male on 29th May 2003, in the Lupins.
Juvenile on 28th September 2003, in the Lupins.

All spring birds have been 'brown' individuals and, as the ageing and sexing of such birds in spring is difficult, all are recorded here as 'female or first-summer male', with the exception of the 1999 individual which was heard to sing.

The first spring record, in the hot spring of 1992, coincided with a record year in Britain for the species, when several pairs remained to breed elsewhere in the country. Such signs of expansion were not, however, sustained. Common Rosefinches breed from northeast Europe across Asia and winter in the Indian subcontinent.

Bullfinch

Pyrrhula pyrrhula pyrrhula (Northern Bullfinch)
The species was unrecorded on the Point until 2004 when the following individuals of the large, bright northern form were seen:-

Female on 17th October 2004, in the Lupins (Plate 24).
Male and female on 18th October 2004, in the Lupins and the Plantation.

These records formed part of an unprecedented irruption of this form into Britain, particularly Shetland, in October 2004. This invasion peaked in the third week of October, coinciding precisely with the records above. Northern Bullfinches breed throughout the taiga zone from Scandinavia east through Russia and are periodically irruptive in response to failures of winter berry crops, particularly those of Rowan, though their irruptions rarely reach Britain. It is worth noting that Waxwings, also irruptive berry specialists, were also recorded in October 2004 as part of a simultaneous invasion of that species.

The bird of 17th October was noticeably tame and fed actively on brambles and nettle seeds. The calls of these birds were striking - a loud, nasal trumpeting very different from the typical low, piping calls normally associated with both British and Scandinavian birds.

It is interesting to note that, despite being widespread on the 'mainland', the smaller, duller British form of Bullfinch (*pileata*) has never reached the Point.

Lapland Bunting (Lapland Longspur)
Calcarius lapponicus lapponicus

Rowan notes Lapland Buntings as irregular autumn migrants, fairly plentiful in some years. White notes them as passage migrants and winter visitors and records that during the exceptionally cold winter of 1963 Lapland and Snow Buntings were seen feeding on large lumps of copra washed up on the beach.

They are now scarce passage migrants, mainly in the autumn and only occasionally in the winter. The first autumn migrants, probably from Norway, typically appear in the second week of September (with the earliest on 8th September 1993), but number rarely more than three in a day, and records normally continue into November. However, 14 occurred at the end of September 1969 and an exceptional 40 were counted on 17th September 1993 as part of that autumn's large influx.

Spring birds are rare and only six records have been traced but the concentration of records in the second week of May is striking:-

14th – 17th May 1988.
14th May 1989.
13th May 1990.
3 on 23rd April 1995.
8th May 1999.
11th May 2003.

Lapland Buntings on the Point are typically only heard or seen in flight, often proving frustratingly difficult to see well on the ground. The species has a circumpolar distribution and, although most birds are undoubtedly Scandinavian in origin, the possibility of the occasional bird from the Greenland and Canadian population (of the slightly larger form *subcalcaratus*) cannot be eliminated.

Snow Bunting
Plectrophenax nivalis nivalis
Plectrophenax nivalis insulae (Icelandic Snow Bunting)

Snow Buntings have a long association with Blakeney Point. Despite their nomadic habits in winter they can usually be found somewhere along the Point at this season feeding in the dunes or on the shingle bank. There have, however, been periodic fluctuations in their numbers.

Rowan refers to the species being fairly regular between September and March in varying numbers. Writing in 1899, Pashley bemoaned the scarcity of Snow Buntings and notes that in former years:-

'I have seen flocks on the beach with at least 1,000 birds and have walked a few hundred yards and put up another and yet another large flock. I think the decreasing number

Their breeding status is therefore not entirely clear. White records the species as a breeder which may be seen throughout the year. He notes that breeding was first recorded in 1960 when a pair nested successfully in a clump of marram grass amongst the terns. By 1966 there were nine pairs. He may, however, be referring here specifically to the end of the Point for he goes on to say that most areas of *Suaeda* seem to contain a pair of these buntings.

Whatever the precise history, Reed Bunting is now a common breeding bird on the Point and a distinctive feature of the *Suaeda* at all seasons. In common with many seed-eating species, Reed Buntings have undergone a major decline in Norfolk since the mid-1970s, linked to changes in agricultural practices. At the Point, however, the population appears to have remained healthy with counts of 21 pairs in 2000 and 31 pairs in 2004. The breeding populations at coastal sites such as the Point therefore represent a significant proportion of Norfolk's breeding Reed Buntings.

This species is also an autumn immigrant to the Point from Scandinavia, usually in small numbers, but 40 were seen arriving singly from the sea on 16th October 1988 and an exceptional 200-300 were present on 18th October 1975. This latter record is, however, listed by White, surely in error, as involving 2,000-3,000 birds.

Around 50 birds are present in winter but occasionally up to about 100 have been counted, the maximum being 108 birds present in inter-tidal habitat in November and December 1997, demonstrating the area's importance as a wintering site as well as a breeding stronghold.

Black/Red-headed Bunting
Emberiza melanocephala/E. bruniceps
A first-winter bunting was present on 10th – 11th September 1989, initially on Yankee Ridge but then taking up residence on Middle Point, where it fed on the beach with Linnets. Although considered probably to be a Black-headed Bunting at the time, it has never to our knowledge been submitted to BBRC. This species needs to be distinguished with care in this plumage from Red-headed Bunting but literature published since 1989 confirms the significance of this bird's deep call, relatively large size and slightly warm-toned rump. It is therefore very likely that this was a Black-headed Bunting although it does not appear as such in the official record. Assuming it to have been this species, this would be the second record for Norfolk.

Black-headed Buntings breed in southeast Europe and southwest Asia and winter in the Indian subcontinent. Most British records are of 'overshooting' adults in late spring and summer so the occurrence of a first-winter bird in autumn is therefore particularly noteworthy.

Corn Bunting
Emberiza calandra calandra
This species is listed by Rowan and White as rare. This would be an accurate description of its status today, with only three modern records:-
    1971, but date not known.
    11th May 2001, in the Sandhills.
    17th May 2003, in the Sandhills.

It is interesting to note that the species was always rare even when significant numbers occurred on the 'mainland'. The well-publicised decline in the British population will no doubt ensure that this species remains a rare visitor to the Point. Corn Buntings have a wide central and southern European range but are largely sedentary.

Unproven Records

Sociable Lapwing (Sociable Plover)
Vanellus gregarius
Rowan records, without any qualification, that an immature of this Central Asian species was seen, though not secured, by Arnold and his party on 3rd September 1903.

Arnold's notes describe it as:-

> 'Sandy-brown on the breast with a head like a Dotterel's and a distinct light stripe over the eye… about the size of a Lapwing with black and white wings.'

Although this description sounds highly suggestive of the species, this record was 'square-bracketed' by White as the species was not at the time on the Norfolk list. Nor is the record listed in Taylor *et al.* (1999) so must at some stage have been deemed unacceptable. If genuine, this would be the first record for Norfolk.

Pectoral Sandpiper
Calidris melanotos
The occurrence of this Nearctic and Siberian species on the Point is not well documented.
Rowan notes that he 'believed one had been taken in some year prior to 1896', also noting that Arnold was 'convinced that one had been seen and heard by him and his party on 2nd September 1908'.

Western/Eastern Black-eared Wheatear
Oenanthe (hispanica) hispanica /O. (hispanica) melanoleuca
An adult male 'Black-eared Wheatear' is accepted for 'Cley' on 13th May 1975 and appears as such widely in the literature. However, Gantlett (1995) lists this record for Blakeney Point. Its precise location is unfortunately not known.

Lanceolated Warbler
Locustella lanceolata
Although no records of this notorious 'skulker' have yet been accepted for the Point, the species has been strongly suspected on several occasions by a number of observers. Such occasions include, but are not limited to, 28th September 1985 in the Marrams (though not accepted by BBRC), 29th September 1991 in the Marrams, with another near the Long Hills, and 18th September 2001 on Near Point.

Lanceolated Warblers breed in northern Russia and Siberia and winter in southeast Asia. The regularity with which they are recorded on Shetland suggests that they are well worth pursuing as a 'target species' on the Point.

Lesser Grey Shrike
Lanius minor
Intriguingly, Rowan notes that:-

> 'There are grounds for believing that the far rarer Lesser Grey Shrike *L. minor* was shot in the suaeda bushes many years ago by Ramm himself'.

However, no further details are revealed and this record is not referred to elsewhere in the literature.

Escapes

Black Swan
Cygnus atrataus
During the late 1990s and early 2000s up to three birds have regularly been present in the Harbour.

Ross's Goose
Anser rossii
An adult flew over the Point and disappeared towards Blakeney on 17th May 2003 and two adults flew over with a Greylag Goose on 24th September 2003. Both records relate to two feral individuals present at various locations on the inland side of the Harbour (notably Stiffkey Fen) throughout 2003.

Lesser White-fronted Goose
Anser erythropus
A very tame adult was once recorded on the outer beach but the date of this record has been lost.

Large Falcon
Falco sp.
An unidentified large falcon resembling a Lanner *Falco biarmicus* was seen on 21st October 1994 and another such bird was present in April and May 2004, sitting in the tern and Black-headed Gull colony and causing its temporary abandonment.

Chilean Flamingo
Phoenicopterus chilensis
A bird visited the Harbour from Cley in July 1967.

Demoiselle Crane
Anthropoides virgo
A bird seen on Wiveton Marshes in the summer of 1924 had been reported at the Point about the middle of April of that year.

Northern Mockingbird
Mimus polyglottos
A bird in worn plumage frequented the Point, particularly the area around the *'Yankee'*, on 20th – 28th August 1971, during which time it was filmed by Ted Eales and Dick Bagnall-Oakley.

Sparrow/Weaver sp.

Passer/Ploceus sp.

An unidentified bird consorted with House Sparrows at the Watch House on 20th October 1990.

Sudan Golden Sparrow

Auripasser luteus

An immature male was present on Yankee Ridge on 8th June 1996.

Red-billed Quelea

Quelea quelea

An adult accompanied Linnets in the Marrams on 24th June 2000.

Scientific Names of Non-bird Species Mentioned in the Text

Plants

Annual Sea-blite	*Suaeda maritima*
Birdsfoot Trefoil	*Lotus corniculatus*
Biting Stonecrop	*Sedum acre*
Black Pine	*Pinus nigra*
Bramble	*Rubus fruticosus*
Common Cord-grass	*Spartina anglica*
Common Dog Violet	*Viola riviniana*
Common Sea-lavender	*Limonium vulgare*
Curled Dock	*Rumex crispus*
Dewberry	*Rubus caesius*
Elder	*Sambucus nigra*
Glasswort	*Salicornia sp.*
Grey Hair-grass	*Corynepherus canescens*
Marram Grass	*Ammophila arenaria*
Matted Sea-lavender	*Limonium bellidifolium*
Orache sp.	*Atriplex sp.*
Rock Sea-lavender	*Limonium binervosum*
Rosebay Willowherb	*Epilobium angustifolium*
Rowan	*Sorbus aucuparia*
Sand Sedge	*Carex arenaria*
Sea Aster	*Aster tripolium*
Sea Beet	*Beta vulgaris*
Sea Bindweed	*Calystegia soldanella*
Sea Buckthorn	*Hippophae rhamnoides*
Sea Campion	*Silene vulgaris*
Sea-heath	*Frankenia laevis*
Sea Purslane	*Halimione portulacoides*
Sea Sandwort	*Honkenya peploides*
Sheep's Sorrel	*Rumex acetosella*
Shrubby Sea-Blite	*Suaeda vera*
Silver Birch	*Betula pendula*
Sycamore	*Acer pseudoplatanus*
Tamarisk	*Tamarix gallica*

Thrift	*Armeria maritima*
Tree Lupin	*Lupinus arboreus*
White Poplar	*Populus alba*
Willow sp.	*Salix sp.*
Yellow Horned-poppy	*Glaucium flavum*
Yucca	*Yucca recurvifolia*

Butterflies

Brown Argus	*Aricia agestis*
Camberwell Beauty	*Nymphalis antiopa*
Common Blue	*Polyommatus icarus*
Gatekeeper	*Pyronia tithonus*
Grayling	*Hipparchia semele*
Painted Lady	*Vanessa cardui*
Small Copper	*Lycaena phlaeas*
Wall Brown	*Lasiommata megera*

Mammals

Atlantic Grey Seal	*Halichoerus grypus*
Brown Hare	*Lepus europaeus*
Common Rat	*Rattus norvegicus*
Common Seal	*Phoca vitulina*
Harp Seal	*Phoca groenlandica*
Otter	*Lutra lutra*
Rabbit	*Oryctolagus cuniculus*
Red Fox	*Vulpes vulpes*
Stoat	*Mustela erminea*

Bibliography

Acklam, G.H. *et al.* 1956. Subalpine Warbler in Norfolk. *British Birds* 49: 86.

Alder, L.P. 1952. Eversmann's Warbler in Norfolk. *British Birds* 45: 415 – 416.

Allison, H. and Morley, J.P. 1989. *Blakeney Point and Scolt Head Island*. National Trust.

Alström, P. and Mild, K. 2003. *Pipits & Wagtails of Europe, Asia and North America*. Christopher Helm.

Bishop, B. and B. 1996. *Cley Marsh and its Birds*. The Boydell Press.

Bloomfield, A. 2003. Some Lost Records of Roseate Terns. *Norfolk Bird Club Bulletin* 50: 31-32.

Borrer, C. 1955. Article in *The Shooting Times & Country Magazine*, September 16th 1955, reprinted in *Birding World* 13 (3): 126-127.

Brown, A. 1994. Twite - what Twite? The Results of the NBC 1994 Mid-Winter Twite Count. *Norfolk Bird Club Bulletin* 9: 12-13.

Browne, P.W.P. and Hitchon, A. 1952. Greenish Warbler in Norfolk. *British Birds* 45: 413 – 414.

Burton, J.F. 1995. *Birds & Climate Change*. Christopher Helm.

Coward, T.A. 1923. The Birds of Blakeney Point: a Visit in the Breeding Season. *Transactions of the Norfolk and Norwich Naturalists' Society*, 11 (4), 344-359.

Cramp, S. 1960. The Irruption of Tits in Autumn 1957. *British Birds* 53: 49-77.

Cramp, S (ed.) 1977-1994. *The Handbook of the Birds of Europe, The Middle East and North Africa: The Birds of the Western Palearctic*. Vol. 1-9. Oxford University Press.

Daukes, A.H. 1952. Exceptional Migratory Rush at Cley. *Wild Bird Protection in Norfolk* 1951: 22-23.

David and Gosselin. 2002. *Bull*. BOC 122: 14-49, 257-282.

Davis, P. 1966. The Great Immigration of Early September 1965. *British Birds* 59: 353-376.

Dresser, H.E. 1897. Notes on Pallas's Willow Warbler and some other rare European warblers. *Transactions of the Norfolk and Norwich Naturalists' Society*, 6 (3), 280-290.

Dunmore, G.E. 1998. Eastern and Western Bonelli's Warblers – the Norfolk Situation. *Norfolk Bird Club Bulletin* 27: 4-5.

Dunmore, G.E. (ed.) *Norfolk Bird and Mammal Reports 1998-2003*.

Durman, R. 1976 (ed.). *Bird Observatories in Britain and Ireland*. T. & A.D. Poyser Ltd.

Eales, W.J. 1986. *Countryman's Memoirs – A Warden's Life on Blakeney Point*. Published privately.

Elkins, N. 1983. *Weather and Bird Behaviour*. T. & A.D. Poyser Ltd.

Fisher, A. and Flood, R. 2004. A Scopoli's Shearwater off the Isles of Scilly. *Birding World* 17: 334-336.

Gantlett, S.J.M. 1987. Lesser Crested Tern: new to Norfolk. *Norfolk Bird and Mammal Report* 1986: 412-413.

Gantlett, S.J.M. 1987. The Great Snipe at Blakeney Point. *Twitching* 1: 218-219.

Gantlett, S.J.M. *et al.* The Oriental Pratincole in Norfolk. *Norfolk Bird and Mammal Report* 1993: 131.

Gantlett, S.J.M. 1995. *The Birds of Cley*. 5th edn. Published privately.

Gätke, H. 1895. *Heligoland as an Ornithological Observatory*. Edinburgh University Press.

Gaze, R. 1947. *Bird Sanctuary*. Faber and Faber Ltd.

Gilbert, R. 1996. Predation on Blakeney Point's Tern Colonies. *Norfolk Bird Club Bulletin* 18: 14-16.

Gillings, S. and Beaven, P. 2004. Wintering Farmland Birds: Results from Mass-participation Surveys. *British Birds* 97: 118-129.

Golley, M. 1993. Desert Warbler at Blakeney Point. *Norfolk Bird Club Bulletin* 5: 7-8.

Golley, M. 1994. Desert Warbler – a first for Norfolk. *Norfolk Bird and Mammal Report* 1993: 132.

Golley, M. 1997. *The Cley Year – A Birder's Guide*. Hill House Press Ltd.

Grussu, M. and Biondi, M. 2004. Record Numbers of Wintering Richard's Pipits in the Western Palearctic. *British Birds* 97: 194-195.

Gutierrez, R. 2003. The Balearic Shearwater: apparently heading for extinction. *Birding World* 16: 260-263.

Hazell, J.A. 1987. White-billed Diver: A Bird New to Norfolk. *Norfolk Bird and Mammal Report* 1986: 419-420.

Hough, J.R. 1992. Snowy Owl Plumages. *Birding World* 5: 96-97.

Joyner, S.C. 1988. Predicting Autumn Highlights on the North Norfolk Coast. *Norfolk Bird and Mammal Report* 1988: 262-272.

Joyner, S.C. 2001. The Pallas's Grasshopper Warbler in Norfolk. *Birding World* 14: 382-384.

Joyner, S.C. 2002. Pallas's Grasshopper Warbler at Blakeney Point – the second for Norfolk. *Norfolk Bird and Mammal Report* 2001: 283-284.

Joyner, S.C. 2002. Norfolk's Second Pallas's Grasshopper Warbler. *Norfolk Bird Club Bulletin* 46: 6-8.

Martin, J, 2002. From the Rarities Committee's Files: Unusual Brent Geese in Norfolk and Hampshire. *British Birds* 95: 129-136.

McCallum, J. 2003. A Red-throated Diver Oil Disaster in North Norfolk. *Norfolk Bird Club Bulletin* 50: 17-19.

McCallum, J. 2003. A Memorable Spring Fall on Blakeney Point. *Norfolk Bird Club Bulletin* 51: 13-18.

McCallum, J. 2004. Two Potentially New Sub-species for the County in 2003. *Norfolk Bird Club Bulletin* 54: 12-17.

Mc Elwee, S. 1998. Fea's/Zino's Petrel in Norfolk. *Norfolk Bird and Mammal Report* 1997: 557.

McElwee, S. 1997. The Soft-plumaged Petrel in Norfolk. *Norfolk Bird Club Bulletin* 25: 8-11.

McNeil, D. 1993, Sandwich Terns on Blakeney Point. *Norfolk Bird Club Bulletin* 2: 9-13.

McNeil, D. 1993. Tern Research on Blakeney Point. *Norfolk Bird Club Bulletin* 5: 14-16.

McNeil, D. 1994. Tern Research on Blakeney Point 1993 – Summary and Conclusions. *Norfolk Bird Club Bulletin* 8: 15-17.

McNeil, D and Reed, J. 1993. Nesting Mediterranean Gulls: New to Norfolk. *Norfolk Bird and Mammal Report* 1992: 433-434.

Millington, R. 1995. Blakeney Point - Memorable Days. *Norfolk Bird Club Bulletin* 15: 10-13.

Millington, R. 1997. Separation of Black Brant, Dark-bellied Brent Goose and Pale-bellied Brent Goose. *Birding World* 10: 11-15.

Myers, E.T. 1985. Ross's Gull – Bird of the Year. *Norfolk Bird and Mammal Report* 1984: 96-97.

Palmer, P. 2000. *First for Britain and Ireland 1600-1999*. Arlequin Press.

Pashley, H.N. 1925, *Notes on the Birds of Cley, Norfolk*. H.F. & G. Witherby, London.

Pinchen, R.J. 1935. *Sea Swallows*.

Porter, R.F. 2005. 'Orange-breasted' Meadow Pipit - an identification pitfall. *Birding World* 18: 169-172.

Power, F.D. 1885. Ornithological Notes at Cley and Blakeney, September 3rd to 19th 1884. *Transactions of the Norfolk and Norwich Naturalists' Society*, 4 (1), 36-43.

Richardson, R.A. *et al*. 1962. Radde's Bush Warbler in Norfolk. *British Birds* 55: 166-168.

Richardson, R.A. 1962. *Checklist of the Birds of Cley and Neighbouring Norfolk Parishes*. Cley Bird Observatory.

Riviere, B.B. 1930. Madeiran Little Shearwater in Norfolk. *British Birds* 23: 41.

Riviere, B.B. 1930. *A History of the Birds of Norfolk*. H. F. & G. Witherby.

Robertson, I. S. 1977. Identification and European Status of Eastern Stonechats. *British Birds* 70: 237-245.

Rowan, W. 1915. The Blakeney Point Ternery. *British Birds* 8: 250-266.

Rowan, W. 1918. Annotated List of the Birds of Blakeney Point, Norfolk. *British Birds* 8: 11 and *Transactions of the Norfolk and Norwich Naturalists' Society*, 10 (3), 256-279.

Sangster, G. and Oreel, G. 1996. Trends in Systematics: Progress in Taxonomy of Taiga and Tundra Bean Geese. *Dutch Birding* 18: 310-316.

Seago, M.J. 1977. *Birds of Norfolk*. (2nd edn.) Jarrold.

Seago, M.J. (ed). *Norfolk Bird and Mammal Reports* 1953-1997.

Shirihai, H., Gargallo, G. and Helbig, A.J. 2001. *Sylvia Warblers – Identification, Taxonomy and Phylogeny of the Genus Sylvia*. Christopher Helm.

Steers, J.A. (ed.) 1934. *Scolt Head Island*. W. Heffer & Sons Ltd.

Stevenson, H. 1866-1890. *The Birds of Norfolk*. Vols 1-3. John van Voorst and Gurney & Jackson, London.

Stoddart, A.M. 1990. Yellow-browed Warblers in Norfolk. *Norfolk Bird and Mammal Report* 1989: 420-423.

Stoddart, A.M. 1991. The October 1990 Fall. *Norfolk Bird and Mammal Report* 1990: 115-116.

Stoddart, A.M. and Eldridge, M.I. 1992. Snowy Owl in Norfolk. *Norfolk Bird and Mammal Report* 1991: 267.

Stoddart, A.M. 2001. Isabelline Wheatear at Blakeney Point – the second record for *Norfolk. Norfolk Bird and Mammal Report* 2000: 285-287.

Stoddart, A.M. 2004. Autumn 2003 in Norfolk. *Norfolk Bird Club Bulletin* 54: 17-22.

Svensson, L. 1992. *Identification Guide to European Passerines*. Published privately.

Taylor, M. *et al.* 1999. *The Birds of Norfolk*. Pica Press.

Taylor, M. 2002. *Guardian Spirit of the East Bank*. Wren Publishing.

Thevenot, M. *et al.* 2003. *The Birds of Morocco*. British Ornithologists' Union and British Ornithologists' Club.

Urquhart, E. 2002. *Stonechats – A Guide to the Genus Saxicola*. Christopher Helm.

Van Franeker, J. A. 2004. Fulmar Wreck in the Southern North Sea: Preliminary Findings. *British Birds* 97: 247-249.

Varney, P. 1988. Slender-billed Gulls – new to Norfolk. *Norfolk Bird and Mammal Report* 1987: 101-102.

Wallace, D.I.M. 2004. *Beguiled by Birds*. Christopher Helm.

Watson, K.M. 1921. The Tern Colony on Blakeney Point. Transactions of the *Norfolk and Norwich Naturalists' Society* 11 (2), 168-179.

Wernham, C.V., Toms, M.P., Marchant, J.H., Clark, J.A., Siriwardena, G.M. & Baillie, S.R. (eds). 2002. *The Migration Atlas: movements of the birds of Britain and Ireland*. T.& A.D. Poyser Ltd.

White, D.J.B. 1967. *An Annotated List of the Flowering Plants and Ferns on Blakeney Point, Norfolk*. National Trust.

White, D.J.B. 1969. *An Annotated Checklist of the Birds of Blakeney Point, Norfolk*. National Trust.

White, D.J.B. 1981. *An Annotated Checklist of the Birds of Blakeney Point, Norfolk*. National Trust.

Witherby, H.F. 1909. Two Norfolk Levantine Shearwaters. *British Birds* 2:313.

Witherby, H.F. *et al.* 1938 – 1941. *The Handbook of British Birds*. H.F. and G. Witherby Ltd.

Wright, T. and Young-Powell, M. 1999. The Classic Robin Fall of Early October 1998. *Norfolk Bird and Mammal Report* 1998: 300-303.

Wild Bird Protection in Norfolk - Issues to 1952.

Index of Bird Species

Numbers in **bold** refer to main species texts in the Systematic List.